THE LOST ARK

THE LOST ARK

NEW AND REDISCOVERED ANIMALS OF THE TWENTIETH CENTURY

Dr Karl Shuker

with a foreword by Gerald Durrell

HarperCollins*Publishers*

HarperCollins*Publishers*
London Glasgow Sydney Auckland
Toronto Johannesburg

To the Harry Johnstons, Richard Meinertzhagens, Hans Schomburgks, James Chapins, Marjorie Courtenay-Latimers, Geoffrey Orbells, Kitti Thonglongyas, Ralph Wetzels, Robert Ballards, Alain Delcourts, and Salim Alis of the future, and to all of those spectacular new and rediscovered animals that they will assuredly find; but most especially to Dr Reinhardt Møbjerg Kristensen, to whom the entire zoological world owes an immense debt of gratitude for bringing to attention a totally new phylum of animals, the loriciferans.

The author has sought permission for the use of all illustrations known by him to be still in copyright. Any omission brought to his attention will be rectified in future editions of this book.

The author asserts the moral right to be identified as the author of this work.

First published 1993

ISBN 0-00-219943-2
© 1993 Karl Shuker
Printed and bound by Butler and Tanner Ltd., Frome, Somerset

CONTENTS

FOREWORD

It was Cuvier, at the beginning of the 19th century, who made the rather pretentious and unwise statement that all large creatures on the planet had now been discovered and described. Since his day, of course, a host of creatures, ranging from pygmy hogs to white rhinos, Komodo dragons to coelacanths, have turned up to confound him. Usually, the local people were aware of the animal, but it was not known to European science. The pygmies, for example, knew all about the okapi long before Johnston 'discovered' it. In many cases, it is lack of observation that keeps a creature a secret from science for so long.

I remember being on a live animal collecting trip in Cameroon, and I had the fruits of my labours – some 250 specimens of 14 different species – housed in a large marquee on the river bank. The local District Officer asked if he might come and see them, so I welcomed him with warm beer and showed him round. He was absolutely dumbfounded. He told me that he had worked for 25 years in West Africa and had never seen any of these creatures. Where, he asked, had I found them? I told him that I had caught a good number of them in the tiny strip of forest at the end of his garden. I think he thought I was making fun of him, for our relationship remained somewhat cool from that moment onwards.

However, I was rather neatly hoist with my own petard for, on that particular expedition, I quartered miles of forest searching for the nesting site of the rare Bald Rock Crow (*Picathartes oreas*) with no success. Returning a year later, I made my base camp in the same village and the hunters told me with pride that they had found the nest site of the rare bird I wanted so badly. To my embarrassment and chagrin, they led me to a rock face approximately 200 yards from where, the year previously, I had made my base camp. *Picathartes* builds swallow-like mud nests and I could see this nest site was an old one. So while I had been blundering about the forest looking for the 'elusive' bird, it had been happily nesting almost in my tent.

I cannot understand why scientists on the whole look scornfully at the idea of some large unknown animal lurking in a lake or in the sea or on land. They don't believe it until they have a specimen – preferably dead – in their hands. I believe everything is possible and those of you who read and relish this book as I have done will see why. With delighted anticipation, I await the discovery of a sea serpent or, better still, an Abominable Snowman, and, if he proves too close to us in appearance for comfort, what do we do with him? Put him in a cage or send him to university?

This fascinating, encouraging book should be part of every naturalist's library to give them hope that one day they themselves may make a wonderful discovery of a new species.

Gerald Durrell
September 1992

ACKNOWLEDGMENTS

It would not have been possible to prepare a book of this scope without the willing interest and assistance of a great many persons, societies, and organisations. In particular, I wish to offer my most sincere and grateful thanks to the following:

In Great Britain: Dr Nick Arnold, *Avicultural Magazine*, Colin Bath, Endymion Beer, Trevor Beer, BIOSIS, Birdland (Bourton-on-the-Water), *Birmingham Evening Mail*, Birmingham Public Libraries, Janet and Colin Bord, Lena and Paul Bottriell, Michael Bright, Bristol Zoo Garden, British Library, British Museum (Natural History), Nick Brown, G.H.H. Bryan, Yoko and Owen Burnham, Chester Zoological Gardens, D.N. Clark-Lowes, Prof. John L. Cloudsley-Thompson, Dr Nigel Collar, Dr N. Mark Collins, the late Tim Dinsdale, Drayton Manor Park & Zoo, Dudley Public Libraries, John Edwards, Nick G. Ellerton, Excalibur Books, Fauna and Flora Preservation Society, Howie Firth, Reginald Fish, *Folklore Frontiers*, Fortean Picture Library, *Fortean Times*, Glasgow Zoo, Geoffrey R. Greed, Gina Guarnieri, Harrap Publishing Group, Dr Peter Henderson, David Heppell, R.R. Hepple, Dr John Edwards Hill, Richard Hill, Amanda Hillier, the late Mary Harvey Horswell, Gordon Howes, Jean and Keith Howman, International Congress for Bird Preservation, Dr Jonathan Kingdon, Michael Lyster, Midnight Books, Dr Desmond Morris, Nature Photographers Ltd, *New Scientist*, Richard J.P. O'Grady, Edward Orbell, Orkney Science Festival 1992, Paignton Zoological & Botanical Gardens, Paul Pearce-Kelly, Michael Playfair, Prof. David Pye, Bob Rickard, Roy Robinson, Craig Robson, Sandwell Public Libraries, Lady Philippa Scott, Paul Screeton, Mary D. Shuker, Paul Sieveking, Simmons Bookshop (Wednesbury, W. Mids.), Kenneth G.V. Smith, Dr Eve Southward and Prof. Alan J. Southward, Dr Paul Sterry, Michael K. Swales, Dr Ian R. Swingland, *The Times*, Gertrude Timmins, University of Birmingham, University of Leeds, Walsall Public Libraries, Wednesbury Typewriter Service Ltd (Wednesbury, W. Mids.), Jan Williams, *Wolverhampton Express and Star*, Wolverhampton Public Libraries, the late Gerald L. Wood, World Conservation Monitoring Center, World Pheasant Association, Dr Nathalie Yonow, Zoological Society of London.

Overseas: Dr Victor Albert (U.S.A.), American Museum of Natural History (U.S.A.), Dr Alan N. Baker (New Zealand), Dr Aaron M. Bauer (U.S.A.), Berlin Zoological Gardens (Germany), Dr Ian Best (Bahrain), Dr Wolfgang Böhme (Germany), Bronx Zoo (U.S.A.), Geert Brovad (Denmark), Mark Chorvinsky (U.S.A.), Janice Clark (U.S.A.), Loren Coleman (U.S.A.), Department of Conservation (New Zealand), Department of Conservation & Environment, Victoria (Australia), Dr Chris R. Dickman (Australia), Prof. John M. Edmond (U.S.A.), Elsevier Science Publishers B.V. (Netherlands), Dr Don D. Farst (U.S.A.), *Fate* (U.S.A.), Dr Richard Faust (Germany), Dr Jacques Forest (France), Matthias Forst (Germany), Dr Hans Frädrich (Germany), Frankfurt Zoological Gardens (Germany), Phyllis Galde (U.S.A.), Gladys Porter Zoo (U.S.A.), Dr Dennis Gordon (New Zealand), J. Richard Greenwell (U.S.A.), Prof. Karl G. Grell (Germany), Bob Hay (Australia), Dr Robert R. Hessler (U.S.A.), Dr Bernard Heuvelmans (France), Dr Shoichi Hollie (Japan), *Honolulu Advertiser* (U.S.A), *Honolulu Star-Bulletin* (U.S.A.),

Prof. G. Imadate (Japan), Prof. Yoshinori Imaizumi (Japan), International Society of Cryptozoology (U.S.A.), J.L.B. Smith Institute of Ichthyology (South Africa), Dr C.M. King (New Zealand), Jürg Klages (Switzerland), Dr Reinhardt Møbjerg Kristensen (Denmark), Dr Anne LaBastille (U.S.A.), Marcel Lecoufle (France), Gerard van Leusden (Netherlands), Dr Roy P. Mackal (U.S.A.), Dr Bernhard Meier (Germany), James I. Menzies (Papua New Guinea), Dr Christopher Mercer (Papua New Guinea), Dr Adam C. Messer (Japan), Dr Ralph E. Molnar (Australia), National Museum of Natural History (U.S.A.), Nature Production (Japan), New York Zoological Society (U.S.A.), Prof. Jørgen G. Nielsen (Denmark), Dr John P. O'Neill (U.S.A.), Dr Pierre Pfeffer (France), Dr Jordi Sabater Pi (Spain), Dr Chris Raxworthy (U.S.A.), Michel Raynal (France), Dr David C. Rentz (Australia), Dr Clyde Roper (U.S.A.), Royal Society of New Zealand (New Zealand), Lorraine Russell (New Zealand), Yohei Sakamoto (Japan), Ron Scarlett (New Zealand), SIR Publishing (New Zealand), Malcolm Smith (Australia), Society For the Investigation of the Unexplained (U.S.A.), Dr David Stein (U.S.A.), *Strange Magazine* (U.S.A.), Dr Thomas Teyke (Germany), Lars Thomas (Denmark), Prof. Michael J. Tyler (Australia), University of Michigan Press (U.S.A.), Wanganui Regional Museum (New Zealand), Robert M. Warneke (Australia), Bob Warth (U.S.A.), Albert G. Wells (Australia), Rudy Wicker (Germany), Wildlife Photos W.A. (Australia), World Wide Fund for Nature International (Switzerland), Dr Jill Yager (U.S.A.), Prof. Yin Wen-Ying (People's Republic of China), and Prof. Zhou Kaiya (People's Republic of China).

Lastly, I would like to offer my especial thanks to Gerald Durrell, to whom I am greatly indebted for his delightful foreword; and to Myles Archibald and Elizabeth Stubbs, of Collins*NaturalHistory* at HarperCollins*Publishers*, for their belief in this book, as well as for their invaluable assistance in relation to all aspects of its preparation for publication.

INTRODUCTION
Creatures from the Lost Ark

Nothing is rich but the inexhaustible wealth of Nature. She shows us only surfaces, but she is a million fathoms deep.

RALPH WALDO EMERSON – 'RESOURCES' IN LETTERS AND SOCIAL AIMS

The phrase 'lost ark', when applied to animals, may well conjure up images of creatures that no longer share our world – extinct animals, ranging from dodos to dinosaurs, whose lifeless remains, whether recent or fossilised, are all that we have left to remind us of their former existence. There is, however, a second, much less familiar lost ark, from which the subjects of this current book have originated – creatures which are very much alive, but that have only recently been discovered or rediscovered.

They are all visually spectacular, zoologically significant, or both. Yet, surprisingly, every one of them has successfully eluded scientific discovery until the 20th century, or was confidently written off by science as extinct until rediscovered in the last nine decades. In many cases, these animals were well known to our ancestors, to 'primitive' native tribes, and even to western laymen, but had been dismissed by zoologists as fantasy or folklore. While other species sharing their habitats had become known and duly catalogued, these more elusive or inaccessible species had instead experienced a bizarre exile from zoological reality – alive yet anonymous, real yet unrecognised, a veritable ark of animals effectively lost to scientific study for untold years.

This is not a new phenomenon. The lowland gorilla *Gorilla gorilla gorilla* was familiar to tribes sharing its African forests, but its existence was not accepted by zoologists until 1847. Baird's tapir *Tapirus bairdii*, Mesoamerica's largest mammal, is hunted by the local people, but was unknown to science until 1865. The golden snub-nosed monkey *Rhinopithecus roxellanae* (brought to zoological attention as a living species in 1870), the gerenuk or giraffe antelope *Litocranius walleri* (1878), and Grévy's zebra *Equus grevyi* (1882) had hitherto been known to science only from ancient, sometimes exaggerated depictions (and had thus been discounted as either extinct or non-existent). Hence there seemed no reason why this progression from scientific obscurity to rubber-stamped acknowledgement should not continue throughout the 20th century, and in fact, that is precisely what has happened. But very few people actually realise this. Why?

It is ironic that while man's knowledge of worlds beyond our planet is ever increasing, considerable expanses of his own, on land and under the water, are still virtually unexplored and unknown. One sad outcome of this is that much of the wildlife inhabiting these regions remains mysterious and sparsely documented. Regrettably, however, this tragic situation is largely unrecognised (or ignored) by most people – scientists and laymen alike – who find it difficult to believe that in this ultra-scientific age there could be portions of our world that have never been thoroughly charted, and which could therefore harbour some major new animals still awaiting discovery. Instead, at least as far as they are concerned, the days when such creatures were added to the zoological catalogue ended decisively with the scientific unveiling of the okapi in 1901 – and they consider the rediscovery of supposedly extinct animals to be as likely as the alchemic conversion of iron into gold.

Some, it is true, admit that the capture in 1938 of a living coelacanth – a peculiar lobe-finned fish belonging to an archaic group hitherto believed extinct for more than 60 million years – was indeed something of a surprise. However, they reassure themselves that this was doubtlessly a lone exception, a nonconformist novelty in an age when the mere concept of finding major new animals or encountering reputedly extinct ones is widely considered to be anachronistic – an antiquated, unrealistic dream of eccentrics, young children, and others who ought to know better.

The perpetuation of this narrow-minded and naive attitude even in such scientifically enlightened years as the 1990s is due in no small way to a gap in the vast spectrum of modern-day wildlife books. There are – and quite rightly so – many works recording the tragic plight of endangered animals and those species which have vanished. However, there is not a single volume devoted to the more optimistic side of this coin – the histories of those zoologically important and often striking new animal species that continue to be uncovered year after year, and of the equally impressive quantity of supposedly extinct species that defy all expectations by reappearing after many years (sometimes centuries) of 'official' non-existence.

As someone with a lifelong interest in such creatures and an extensive archive of relevant material, I have grown increasingly surprised as the years have passed by with no sign of such an omission in the literature ever being rectified. Consequently, I decided to attempt this myself, and I therefore present this book as the first to be devoted solely to the 20th century's treasure trove of new and rediscovered multicellular animals (thus excluding only the protozoans, i.e. single-celled animals).

Readers may wonder why I chose to produce it now, rather than perhaps in 1999. The principal reasons for this are not only that the preparation of such a book is already long overdue, but also that in these days of ever-decreasing natural wildernesses, there is so much that could be lost before its very existence is even realised.

The wholesale destruction of tropical rainforests, together with the obscene pollution of the oceans and freshwater ecosystems, have alerted us to some frightening truths about the likely outcomes of such desecration. Among these is the disturbing awareness that our world could lose unique, irreplaceable species of plant and animal that could yield vital additions to modern medicine's stock of life-saving drugs and antidotes; and there may be other equally irrevocable consequences that we are unable even to comprehend at present – with so incomplete a knowledge of global biodiversity, how can we?

Thanks to the illogical and blinkered attitude to the subject of new and supposedly extinct animals that has existed throughout this century, it is all too likely that many important species have already been allowed to slip into extinction without ever becoming known to science; and that certain 'officially' extinct species which may in reality have persisted in small numbers within remote, rarely-visited localities have at last truly died out through lack of serious investigation or interest in the possibility of their survival.

Why, therefore, should these trends be allowed to continue unchallenged until 1999? If my book can in the very smallest way inspire an interest in seeking these animals, and in so doing offer an additional reason for the conservation of wildlife habitats of every type throughout the world, then the best date for its publication is today, not tomorrow, or next year, or in a decade's time.

So great is the variety of those mystery beasts whose alleged existence is supported by reliable eyewitness accounts, photographs and sometimes even a specimen or two, that in 1982 a scientific organisation was established for the specific purpose of investigating such cases. Known as the International Society of Cryptozoology (ISC), its directors, officers, and members include some of the world's foremost zoological authorities – experts who have come to recognise that it is not the pursuit of such creatures which is antiquated, but rather the refusal of scientists to examine their credentials in an objective manner. Since the ISC's establishment, some of its members have been instrumental in revealing a number of remarkable new and rediscovered animals, as will be disclosed in this book. Clearly then, there is good reason for believing that cryptozoology – literally translated as 'the study of hidden life' – has much to recommend it.

Of course, most new and rediscovered animals of the 20th century have been small, inconspicuous forms – insects, rodents, tiny lizards, fishes, bats, songbirds, etc, or ones barely distinct from others already recorded. To document every animal listed since 1899 would require a volume of voluminous proportions. Moreover, as so many of those contained inside it would be of little general interest (especially when even the greatest cryptozoological sceptics have never denied the fact that many creatures in this category of undistinguished, unsurprising animals await formal detection), no useful purpose would be served in preparing such a volume.

Instead, I have concentrated upon this century's more spectacular discoveries and rediscoveries – unexpected creatures that defied the well-established belief that there were few if any notable zoological novelties still to be revealed. Accordingly, the animals that I have selected for inclusion within this book fall into at least one of the following categories:

1) They are relatively large, visually impressive creatures – or allegedly extinct forms that had been the subject of extensive searches in the past – whose concealment into the 20th century is therefore quite remarkable.
2) They are small in size, but are nonetheless of great scientific significance by comprising animals dramatically different from any previously documented.
3) They are not particularly important in a strictly scientific sense, but their

histories or some feature of their appearance or lifestyle are so extraordinary that they thoroughly deserve inclusion within any book devoted to twentieth century zoological finds.

Finally, all that remains to be discussed within this introduction are some matters concerning the scientific documentation and naming of new species – intrinsic aspects of animal discovery and discrimination, which adhere to certain strict rules and conventions that require a little elucidation before progressing further (see also the Appendix for an explanatory account of animal classification).

Description and naming of new species

The species is the fundamental 'unit' of taxonomy (the scientific classification of living organisms); and although it has been defined in a number of different ways (so that there is still some dispute regarding its precise definition), a species is considered by most authorities to comprise one or more populations of organisms whose members can freely interbreed with one another to yield fit, fertile offspring (see also the Appendix).

The discovery of a creature that seems to represent a new species is followed by a standard series of procedures in science. First of all, at least one specimen is collected, preferably a few more (including one of each sex and a juvenile) if such collection does not endanger the species' survival. Nowadays, there is a very laudable tendency for researchers to seek already-dead specimens for this purpose, rather than killing living ones. Occasionally a simple sample of blood extracted from a living specimen has proven sufficient – as in the case of Somalia's Bulo Burti boubou shrike *Laniarius liberatus*, formally recognised as a valid species in 1991 on the basis of DNA analysis carried out with some dried blood, present on a few feathers shed by a living specimen during a spell in captivity before being released unharmed back into the wild.

These specimens are then closely compared with those already-known species to which they seem most closely related – a meticulous process involving detailed comparisons of external morphology, internal anatomy, and also (particularly in recent times) various genetic and biochemical characters if possible. If the researchers carrying out such comparisons are satisfied that the new creature's representative specimens do indeed differ in taxonomically important ways from all ostensibly similar, currently-known species, then its status as a new species is accepted by them.

Its existence must then be officially reported to the scientific world and its distinguishing features fully documented. This is achieved by preparing a detailed *description* of the new species for publication in a scientific journal. Whenever possible, this description is based principally upon just one of the specimens collected; the specimen selected for this purpose is normally one that appears to be a typical representative of that species, and is (preferably) complete and undamaged. This specimen is designated as the new species' *type specimen* or *holotype* (and the precise locality in which it was collected is referred to as that species' *type locality*). If there is need to refer to other specimens (e.g. to include mention of any differences between sexes, and between adults and juveniles, or if the species exhibits notable variation in external colouration, overall size, and so forth), these specimens are designated as this species' *paratypes*.

In view of the great scientific value of type specimens and paratypes, they are carefully preserved afterwards within the collection of a natural history museum or some other scientific institution. As a consequence, if at some stage in the future some specimens are collected of a creature that may belong to that species, but whose identity is currently undetermined, researchers can compare its specimens with the earlier-described species' type and paratypes in an attempt to ascertain their creature's identity.

When a new species is formally described, it must also be given, as part of that description, its own scientific name – a unique, two-part (binomial) name that distinguishes it from all other species, and which is generally of Latin or Greek origin (or both). For example, the wolf's scientific name is *Canis lupus*; the name *lupus* is its specific or trivial name, and *Canis* is its generic name or genus. A new species' scientific name can provide clues concerning that species' closest relatives, because it will often share their generic name (see the Appendix for further details) – but sometimes a species may be sufficiently different even from those to which it is evidently most closely related for a completely new genus to be required for it. More rarely, a new species may be so distinct from all other species that it warrants its own taxonomic family, more rarely still its own taxonomic order, and even more rarely its own class. During the past 93 years, very many thousands of new animal species have been described (of which the vast majority have been insects), but only three have each been sufficiently different from all others to warrant the erection of an entirely new phylum – the taxonomic category at the very pinnacle of the hierarchy of animal classification.

Sometimes, later studies of a species will reveal that its original classification was incorrect; as a result, its scientific name may need to be changed. Equally, there are occasions when a new species is formally described by more than one researcher or group of researchers, wholly independently of each other; in this situation, the description that is published first has precedence over all others, so that the scientific name included within it for the new species is the one that becomes accepted.

Also worthy of note is that for a variety of different reasons, the year in which a new species is first discovered is not always the same as the one in which it is officially described – the latter sometimes does not occur for a few years after the species' discovery. For example, the megamouth shark was discovered in 1976 but was not described until 1983, on account of the immensely detailed study that was required to yield a definitive description of such a huge and radically separate species as this one. In the case of the ningaui marsupial mice, although the first species was discovered in the 1950s its distinctiveness was not recognised for many years; and it was not formally described until 1975.

Bibliography

I have supplied an extensive bibliography containing all of the principal sources consulted during the book's preparation. Whenever possible, these have included, for each newly-discovered species, the full reference to the published scientific paper or book in which it was formally described and named following its discovery. These works are distinguished by an asterisk (*) prefix. These very important references have never been brought together before within a single publication, thereby rendering this book's bibliography unique, and an essential addition to a work concerned with the finding of new species. Also included in the bibliography are the full references to papers, articles, and other publications that announced the rediscovery of those species once thought to be extinct.

Despite the universal adoption of the metric system by modern-day science, during my extensive correspondence while preparing this book I was intrigued to learn that most people still visualise the size of animals more easily when they are expressed in Imperial units. For that reason therefore, I have retained this system wherever possible.

Finally: among this book's illustrations are several rare archive items, comprising some of the earliest photographs in existence of certain species documented here.

Preparing this volume has given me a great sense of pleasure and an unexpected degree of optimism. My hope is that this book's readers will share this experience , and, as I do, look to the future in anticipation of the many equally exciting animals that are undoubtedly still waiting to step forth from the lost ark. As the American writer John Burroughs once said:

There is always a new page to be turned in natural history if one is sufficiently on the alert.

The International Society of Cryptozoology

Anyone who is interested in the possibility that there are a number of notable animal species still awaiting discovery or rediscovery should consider membership of the International Society of Cryptozoology (ISC) – the world's first scientific society devoted to this subject. The Society annually publishes four informal newsletters containing detailed accounts of the latest cryptozoological happenings worldwide, and also one volume of its formal scientific journal, *Cryptozoology*; all of these publications are free to ISC members. For further information, please contact: Mr J. Richard Greenwell, The Secretariat, The International Society of Cryptozoology, P.O. Box 43070, Tucson, Arizona 85733, U.S.A.

The Society for Cryptozoology and Anomalies of Nature (SCAN)

SCAN is an important new, non-profit-making society providing a forum for open-minded and rational appraisal of unexplained natural phenomena – including mystery animals and plants, earth energies, leys and standing stones, frog rains, crop circles, dowsing, bio forms, ball lightning, and much more. The Society's quarterly newsletter, *SCAN News*, contains a diverse selection of articles, reports and updates, and is free to members. For further information and membership enquiries please contact: Jan Williams, 72 Leek Road, Congleton, Cheshire CW12 3HU, England.

Ufiti (Loren Coleman)

MAMMALS

From Okapi to Onza – and Beyond

One can have no idea today of the romance surrounding the discovery of the Okapi, nor of the excitement caused in natural history circles, first by the vague reports of its presence, and later by its actual finding.

DR MAURICE BURTON – THE STORY OF ANIMAL LIFE, VOL. II

This issue features what may be the most significant cryptozoological find since the Society was founded 4 years ago; that is, the acquisition of a complete specimen of an Onza, the legendary Mexican cat which may have been overlooked by zoology because of its resemblance in coloration and size to the puma.

J. RICHARD GREENWELL – INTERNATIONAL SOCIETY OF CRYPTOZOOLOGY NEWSLETTER (SPRING 1986)

Although the okapi is certainly the most famous mammalian discovery of this century, it is joined by a host of other distinguished arrivals and revivals – including a giant ape of the mountains, one of zoology's biggest pygmies, the world's favourite wild animal and the seas' most mysterious whale, a foxy-furred goat-antelope first made known to science as a carpet, a mélange of supposedly extinct marsupials, a porcine recluse resurrected from the Ice Ages, a minuscule bat no bigger than a bumblebee, a Mexican pseudo-cheetah called the onza, the Queen of Sheba's gazelle, and much more.

Cotton's white rhinoceros

Following the discovery of Grévy's zebra *Equus grevyi* in 1882 and a last flourish of new antelopes in the early 1890s, zoologists confidently asserted that no further large animals remained unknown to science in Africa. How wrong they were was demonstrated dramatically when, within the space of just a few years, the Dark Continent unfurled a series of spectacular new mammals, one after another, to astonish the scientific world.[1-3]

Science was unaware of the white rhinoceros's existence in Central Africa until 1900. (Owen Burnham)

The first of these was truly extraordinary – a completely new subspecies of white rhinoceros, the world's third largest species of land mammal. Zoologists traditionally believed that the white rhino was restricted to areas of southern Africa located south of the Zambezi, including Botswana, Mozambique, and Zululand, but in 1900 Major Powell-Cotton bagged several specimens more than 2000 miles further north – on the Upper Nile, bordering the Sudan, Zaire, and Uganda. Also in 1900, and from that same locality, Captain A.St.H. Gibbons brought back a white rhino skull. Not surprisingly, zoologists were amazed to learn that entire populations of such an enormous mammal were existing undocumented by science, but this was swiftly remedied by mammalogist Oldfield Thomas's *Nature* report of 18 October 1900. And in 1908, Dr Richard Lydekker named the beast *Ceratotherium simum cottoni*, thereby differentiating it from its slightly hairier, southern counterpart.[1-3] (Intriguingly, unconfirmed encounters with Central African white rhinos were also reported by Dr John Gregory and Count Samuel Teleki in the 1880-90s.[1])

Okapi – the Congo's incongruous short-necked giraffe

Although, as this book demonstrates, it is inaccurate to refer to the okapi as the last major zoological discovery (as so many people do), there is assuredly justification for calling it this century's greatest – because in so many, very varied ways it is unique, and wholly unmistakable, embodying a bewildering plethora of morphological and historical paradoxy. With a richly-hued coat more comparable to the gleaming plumage of some jungle bird than to the pelage of a mammal, adorned with vivid zebra-like stripes, and equipped with an inordinately long blue tongue more at home in the mouth of a chameleon, this exotic-looking creature has always been a living contradiction in terms – first believed to be a cloven-hoofed zebra, then proving to be a short-necked giraffe.

It all began in 1890 when, in his book *In Darkest Africa*, the explorer Sir Henry Morton Stanley briefly mentioned a strange, supposedly ass-like beast familiar to the Wambutti pygmies inhabiting the dense, little-known Ituri Forest – nowadays housed within Zaire (formerly the Belgian Congo), but at that time contained within Uganda's borders. According to Stanley:[4]

The Wambutti know a donkey and call it 'atti'. They say that they sometimes catch them in pits. What they find to eat is a wonder. They eat leaves.

If the Wambutti did indeed know of a forest donkey, then they knew more than any western zoologist, because no specimen or remains of such a creature existed in any museum or scientific institution during that period. The anomalous *atti* attracted considerable interest, particularly from one of Stanley's friends, Sir Harry Johnston, the new Govenor of Uganda. Johnston was most anxious to follow up Stanley's information, but did not receive an opportunity to do so until 1899. This was when he succeeded in rescuing a band of Wambutti pygmies captured in the Ituri Forest by an unscrupulous German impresario, who planned to display them as 'ape-men' at the Paris Exhibition.[3,5-8]

The Wambutti were extremely grateful to Johnston, who entertained them at his home before sending them safely back to their forest, and were only too happy to answer his many questions regarding the mysterious *atti* or forest donkey. They did indeed know of such a creature, but disclosed that its name was not *atti* but *o'api* – the apostrophe being pronounced like the gasp-like Arabic 'k', to make it *'okapi'*.[3,5-8]

They described it as a shy creature, captured only by digging large camouflaged pits into which it would fall as it walked across the forest floor. Its body was dark grey or dun-coloured, with striped legs, and in overall form it resembled a large donkey or mule. Accordingly, Johnston felt sure that the okapi was a type of forest zebra, and, as such, was a completely new species awaiting formal description.[3,5-8]

In 1900 he set out on its trail, travelling into what was then the Congo Free State, and reaching the Belgian fort at Mbeni, whose officers he questioned thoroughly regarding the okapi's existence and whereabouts. To his delight, he learnt not only that they knew of this elusive creature, but also that they had frequently seen the bodies of specimens, brought back to the fort by native militia, who found its meat very tasty. Most exciting of all, the officers felt sure that a complete skin of an okapi was still at the fort. Sadly, however, after searching in vain, they discovered that it had recently been cut into strips to make waistbelts and head bands (bandoliers) – these latter being made from the striking striped portions of the skin.[5-7]

Although Johnston failed to obtain a complete skin, the officers were able to describe the okapi, and their description tallied with the account given the previous year by his pygmy friends. They also noted that its snout was markedly 'effilée' (long and drawn-out), and that its feet each bore more than one hoof. This latter feature was very significant, because whereas all modern-day horses, donkeys, and zebras only have one hoof on each foot, the extinct primitive horse *Hipparion* had three hooves per foot. Thus, Johnston decided to revise his view concerning the okapi's identity from a forest zebra to a surviving *Hipparion*. Suddenly the creature's scientific standing had increased greatly – it now seemed likely that this reclusive beast was a living fossil.[5-7]

The climax to Johnston's investigations at Mbeni came when its officers found and gave him two native bandoliers made from the striped sections of the skin. At last he had some physical proof of the okapi's existence and evidence of its distinctness, for the stripes' appearance and form were unlike those of any species known to science at that time.[5-7]

Johnston was clearly closing in on the okapi, but then missed a wonderful opportunity of meeting it face-to-face in its native homeland. On entering the Ituri Forest, he was shown some tracks that the natives insisted had been made by an okapi. To his disappointment, however, the tracks were of a cloven-hoofed mammal – one that had an even number of hooves on each foot rather than an odd number. Due to a preconceived notion that the okapi was a member of the horse family (and hence odd-toed), Johnston dismissed the natives' testimony, believing instead that the tracks had been made by some form of large forest antelope. And so the trail was never followed, and soon afterwards the expedition had to be abandoned on account of the inhospitable conditions within the forest's humid and fever-infested depths.[3,5-8]

On 21 August 1900, Johnston wrote to Dr Philip Sclater, Secretary of London's Zoological Society, informing him of his investigations to date and promising him the bandoliers. When they arrived, Sclater exhibited them at a meeting of the society on 18 December, and formally documented them in its *Proceedings* on 5 February 1901. Agreeing with Johnston's verdict that the okapi was an unknown species of horse, but preferring his original concept of a forest zebra to his later vision of a surviving *Hipparion*, Sclater named the new species *Equus? johnstoni*, cautiously adding the question mark after its genus, as he knew that it would be imprudent to adopt too dogmatic a stance regarding the identity of a creature known only from two slender strips of skin – a judgement that soon proved to be fully warranted.[7]

At much the same time as Sclater's report appeared, Johnston finally received all the material he needed to ascertain conclusively the okapi's true status. Karl Eriksson, a Swedish officer who had been the Commandant at Fort Mbeni, had succeeded in obtaining a complete okapi skin and two skulls, all of which were sent on to Johnston, now back at Entebbe, Uganda. Studying these priceless specimens carefully, Johnston prepared a detailed water-colour painting, which he dispatched with the skin and skulls in June 1901 to British Museum (Natural History) director Prof. Edwin Ray Lankester – along with his surprise conclusion as to what the okapi had proven to be.[5,9]

Against all expectations, it was neither a zebra nor a present-day *Hipparion*. Indeed, it was not an equid at all, but – just as the natives had insisted – a cloven-hoofed creature, thereby related to the cattle, deer, camels, pigs, and hippopotami, plus one other notable beast, the giraffe. And it was the giraffe that held the key to the okapi's identity – because the skulls showed unquestionably that the okapi was a specialised, forest-dwelling giraffe. Millions of years ago, there had been a wide variety of giraffe types. Some were tall and long-necked like today's giraffe; some were sturdy deer-like species (sivatheres) with spreading antler-like horns; and others smaller, short-necked forms very like the newly-discovered okapi. One of these last-mentioned, belonging to the genus *Helladotherium*, seemed especially similar.[5,9]

So, undeterred by his failure to resurrect *Hipparion*, Johnston saw a second chance to revive a fossil genus, by naming the okapi *Helladotherium tigrinum*, which he did in a letter to Lankester enclosed with the specimens and painting. The more knowledgable Lankester, however, recognised that the okapi was more closely related to the extinct short-necked giraffe genera *Palaeotragus* and *Samotherium*. Furthermore, he could see that certain features of its skull distinguished it even from these. So when he

formally described the okapi on 18 June 1901, Lankester created for it a new genus, *Okapia* and according to the rules of nomenclatural precedence its scientific name thus became *Okapia johnstoni*.[9]

The okapi proved to be a singularly striking animal – resembling an unlikely hybrid of giraffe, mule, antelope, and zebra, standing just under 5.5 ft at the shoulder (and marginally over 6 ft in total height, thanks to its slightly prolonged neck). It had a long tuft-tipped tail, and was clothed in a short, dark violet coat of a glistening velvet texture, vividly emblazoned with black and white stripes upon its rump and the upper portions of its limbs (especially the hind pair). Added to this was a pale ghostly face with a long muzzle accommodating its lengthy, leaf-tearing blue tongue, a pair of long ass-like ears, and (in the male) a pair of short horns.

News of this extraordinary animal's discovery made newspaper headlines throughout the world, which in turn inspired several, thankfully unsuccessful, attempts by western hunters to add an okapi or two to their trophy walls and cabinets. Eventually, however, the desire to become famous by shooting okapis was superseded by a comparable aim to achieve immortality by being the first to observe and photograph specimens in their native habitat, and especially to bring a *living* okapi back to the west. Between 1909 and 1915, an expedition sent to the Ituri by the New York Zoological Society, which included Dr James Chapin, uncovered a great deal about the okapi's docile, vegetarian lifestyle in its jungle demesne, and also captured two specimens. Sadly, however, both died shortly afterwards, but on 19 August 1919 a live okapi finally reached a western zoo, when a young specimen arrived at Belgium's Antwerp Zoo.[10-11]

Yet only 50 days after its Antwerp debut this first western okapi also died – a sad story that would be repeated with a succession of other captured okapis until Tele, a female specimen, arrived at Antwerp in 1928. Adjusting well to zoo life, she thrived there for the next 15 years, and her death in 1943 was due only to lack of sufficient food caused by World War II. America's first okapi, a male called Congo that arrived at the Bronx Zoo in autumn 1937, also lived for 15 years. By the 1950s, there were several okapis worldwide, and the species had begun to breed in captivity, with Britain's Bristol Zoo earning particular renown for accomplishing this difficult feat.[10-11]

Unlike so many discoveries that initially engendered international attention and interest but swiftly lost their wonder in the wake of newer finds, the okapi has never lost its romantic appeal as a truly unique animal, and as living proof that the age of animal discovery did not end with the close of the 19th century. For wildlife enthusiasts and scientists everywhere, it is the epitome of the unexpected and the unknown that still await disclosure within every aspect of nature. And in recognition of this, the okapi received a further accolade in 1982, when it was adopted as the official emblem of the International Society of Cryptozoology – a fitting tribute to the animal that remains the premier zoological discovery of the 20th century.

The five-horned giraffe and a giant genet

Sir Harry Johnston is principally remembered for the discovery of the okapi, but within weeks of this becoming news throughout the world, his name resurfaced in connection with the finding of a *second* new type of giraffe.

The true giraffe *Giraffa camelopardalis* exists in a number of different subspecies – some with two horns and some with three. Shortly after unveiling the okapi, Johnston travelled into the Ngishu Plateau of what was then the Uganda Protectorate, just south-east of Mount Elgon, and saw some unusually-marked giraffes whose males were further distinguished from all previously recorded forms by having *five* horns. In addition to the single median horn on the forehead and the pair sited just behind it (as in other giraffes), the males bore a second pair at the back of the skull. Greatly intrigued, Johnston obtained the skulls and head skins of two males and two females, which he sent to the British Museum.[12-13]

This latest new giraffe attracted the interest of Lord Walter Rothschild, who funded an expedition to bring back a complete specimen for the museum. This was eventually achieved, and the specimen duly mounted and displayed, revealing the new giraffe form to be a particularly handsome one, whose large brown blotches on the neck, body, and upper limbs each contained an attractive star-shaped motif; and whose slim lower limbs were pure white, in contrast to the darker shading characterising most of the other giraffe races. In recognition of Lord Rothschild's efforts the new subspecies was dubbed *G. c. rothschildi* – Rothschild's giraffe.[12-13]

And to complete Sir Harry Johnston's run of zoological success in 1901, this year also saw the description of a magnificent new species of genet, based upon a skin that he had obtained. Genets and civets belong to a family of cat-related carnivores known as viverrids, and, traditionally, there had never been any problem in distinguishing the various African genets from the African civet. Whereas the former were small, thin-bodied creatures with long, slender tails and readily-distinguished markings, the civet was much larger and bulkier, with a thicker, brush-like tail, and darker, less clearly-delineated markings. Johnston's new genet, however, made short work of disrupting this orderly classification, because although its anatomy undeniably allied it with the genets, outwardly it displayed a distinct resemblance to the civet – not just on account of its large, dense markings and very thick, rather bushy tail, but also by virtue of its enormous size. With a heavily-built body and a total length of 3.5 ft, it was almost twice the size of any other genet, thereby approaching the civet's own dimensions.[14]

Rothschild's giraffe – the males have five horns.

Unquestionably a new species, the giant genet was named *Genetta victoriae* by British Museum zoologist Oldfield Thomas, who believed that the type skin supplied by Johnston had been collected at Entebbe, on the shores of Lake Victoria. In fact, it had originated from the okapi's home, the Ituri Forest-Semliki River region (nowadays contained within Zaire's territory), but its species has since been recorded from western Uganda too, once again from dense lowland forests, though it remains little-known and rarely-spied.[14]

Mountain gorilla – giant ape of the volcanoes

Zoologists had scarcely recovered from the shock of the okapi's discovery when the Dark Continent unfurled another important new mammal. Prior to the 20th century, the gorilla (whose own existence was not officially recognised by science until the 1840s) was thought to be confined to the lowlands of west-central Africa. Yet as far back as 1860 the explorer John Speke had collected native reports of a huge monster, resembling a giant ape, which supposedly inhabited the lofty Virunga (Mufumbiro) Volcanoes range of mountains, constituting the borders of eastern Zaire, Rwanda, and Uganda. And in 1898, long-distance walker Ewart Grogan, passing through the Virungas, encountered the skeleton of an enormous ape. Unfortunately, he left it where he found it, but sufficient interest was aroused in scientific circles for others to take notice of further reports.[2-3,15]

By 1901, it seemed certain that an unknown form of gorilla did indeed exist in this mountain range – all that was needed for official verification was a specimen. And in October 1902, this vital requirement was supplied by Captain Oscar von Beringe,

Early photo of a mountain gorilla – dismissed as an ogre from native folklore until its scientific discovery in 1902.

from the Belgian Army, and his companion, Dr England, who bagged a couple of gorillas on the Virungas' Mount Sabinio, and sent their bodies on to Europe.[2-3,15]

By comparison with the western lowland form, the mountain-dwelling Virunga gorilla was larger and sturdier in overall build, with a broader chest and body, a jet-black (rather than a brownish-grey) coat with longer fur, and longer jaws with larger teeth, but relatively shorter arms. In 1902, Berlin Museum's director, Dr Paul Matschie, formally named the new subspecies *Gorilla gorilla beringei*, popularly known thereafter as the mountain gorilla. Modern studies by researchers such as Dr George Schaller and Dian Fossey, have shown that far from

21

being a savage man-eater, this giant ape is a gentle and intelligent vegetarian. It is also highly endangered, hunting and habitat erosion have depleted its numbers to between 300-400.[15]

Gorillas also occur in Zaire's lowlands, but differ from the mountain subspecies by way of their shorter fur and jaws, smaller teeth, and longer arms. They are now classed as a separate subspecies – *G. g. graueri*, the eastern lowland gorilla.[16] Conversely, the so-called pygmy gorilla, dubbed *Pseudogorilla mayema* in 1913 by Dr Daniel G. Elliot and known from several skins,[17-18] is not recognised today as a genuinely distinct form.

Saga of the sea mink – the history of a tragedy

The official description of the sea mink in 1903 was no cause for scientific celebration; instead, it brought to a sorry close the tragic story of a remarkable species driven into extinction before science had even become aware of its existence.

As late as the 1850s, fur trappers working for the European fur industries and based along the coasts of New England and western Canada were familiar with an extremely large form of mink. It was not only half as long again as the longest recorded individuals of the common American mink *Mustela vison*, but also much fatter, so that it yielded a pelt twice the size of any from American mink. It was further distinguished by the coarser texture and pale, reddish colouration of its pelage; its body odour was also said to be totally different. As for its habitat, whereas the American mink is an inland species, the giant form was apparently a coastal dweller, confined exclusively to the shores and offshore islands within its recorded distribution range – thus it was known to the fur trappers as the sea mink.[19-20]

Despite its distinctive appearance and specialised habitat, the sea mink attracted no interest from science; specimens were presumably dismissed as nothing more than freakishly large individuals of the ordinary American mink. The trappers, on the other hand, were only too keen to take notice of it, because its large pelt made it a highly sought-after fur-bearer (especially the males, which were about a fifth larger than the females).[19-20]

By the 1870s it had become much rarer and, in 1880, a specimen killed on one of the islands of the Maine township of Jonesport (and sold to a fur buyer) may have been the very last sea mink in existence. Even without its tail it measured more than 26 in long (thereby exceeding the *total* length of the longest New England specimens of *M. vison*). However, there is also a single record of a very large mink of pale colouration taken later in 1894 or thereabouts on New Brunswick's Campobello Island.[19-20]

Even so, it had certainly died out by the turn of the century, when piles of its remains, discovered in Indian shell-heaps along the New England coasts, attracted the attention of American scientist Dr Daniel Webster Prentiss. These convinced him that this giant mink was a genuine species in its own right and he formally described it in 1903, christening it *Mustela macrodon* (emphasising its large teeth).[19-20] The sea mink had finally gained scientific recognition – but more than a decade (if not two) after it had become extinct. There seems little doubt that if it had been identified earlier, it could have been saved by captive breeding. Indeed, the great value of its oversized pelt would surely have been encouragement enough for the establishment of such an enterprise. Instead, it had died as it had lived, in zoological obscurity, and remains today one of the least-known of all modern-day mammalian carnivores, rarely accorded even the briefest of mentions in books.

Dwarf siamang – an ambiguous ape

In 1821, the world's largest species of gibbon, the siamang *Symphalangus syndactylus* of Sumatra, was described by Sir Stamford Raffles. Almost a century later, zoologist C.B. Kloss discovered what seemed to be a dwarf counterpart, living on South Pagi, one of the Mentawi Islands off Sumatra's western coast. Much smaller and rarer than the true siamang (only half the size), with very soft, silky black fur, it was described in 1903 by Smithsonian Institution mammalogist Dr Gerrit Miller,[22] but its precise affinities remained somewhat controversial. Certain authorities maintained that it was most closely related to the siamang and referred to it as *S. klossi*. Various others installed it within a genus all to itself, *Brachytanites*; but nowadays most researchers prefer to ally it with the other gibbons, thereby naming it *Hylobates klossi*.

Pacarana – Count Branicki's 'terrible mouse'

1904 was a momentous year for mice, for it marked the rediscovery of a rodent known to science as the 'terrible mouse', due to the fact that it was as large as a fox terrier.

Needless to say, any mouse the size of a small dog is no ordinary mouse, and in truth this species is not a bona fide mouse at all. If anything, it more closely resembles a long-tailed, spineless porcupine in shape, and sports a handsome grey-black pelage decorated with longitudinal rows of white spots, which compares well with that of the South American paca *Cuniculus paca*, a fairly large relative of the guinea pig. Indeed, in its native Andean homeland, the 'terrible mouse' is known locally as the pacarana ('false paca'). Yet it is neither paca nor porcupine. Instead, it is sufficiently removed from all living rodents to require an entire family to itself, thereby making it one of the most important mammalian discoveries of the past 150 years – not to mention one of the most elusive.[23]

Measuring up to 3.25 ft long, the pacarana is the world's third largest living rodent (exceeded only by the capybaras and beavers), and was discovered in 1873 by Prof. Constantin Jelski, curator of Poland's Cracow Museum. Financed by Count Constantin Branicki, Jelski was engaged in zoological explorations in Peru when, one morning at daybreak, he observed an extremely large but wholly unfamiliar rodent. It had very long whiskers and a fairly long tail and was wandering through an orchard in a hacienda near Vitoc, in the eastern Peruvian Andes. He swiftly dispatched the creature, and sent its skin and most of its skeleton back to Warsaw where it gained the attention of Prof. Wilhelm Peters, director of Berlin Zoo, who meticulously studied its anatomy. Recognising that this huge rodent represented a dramatically new species, by the end of 1873 he had published a scientific description of it, in which he named it *Dinomys branickii* – 'Branicki's terrible mouse'. The pacarana had made its scientific debut.[23-4]

Peters's studies disclosed that its anatomy was a bewildering amalgamation of features drawn from several quite different rodent families. In terms of its pelage and limb structure, it compared well with the paca, but unlike the five-toed (pentadactyl) configuration of the latter's paws, the pacarana's each possessed just four toes. Many of its cranial and skeletal features (not to mention its long, hairy tail) also set it well apart from the paca, especially the flattened shape of the front section of its sternum (breast bone), and the development of its clavicles (collar bones). Certain less conspicuous features of its anatomy were reminiscent of the capybara, but various others (including the shape of its molar teeth) corresponded most closely with those of the chinchillas. There were also additional characteristics that seemed to ally it with the West Indian hutias (see p. 53). Little wonder then that Peters elected to create a completely separate taxonomic family for it.[23-4]

The pacarana was clearly a major find – yet no sooner had it been discovered than it vanished. For three decades nothing more was heard of it, and zoologists worldwide feared that it was extinct. But in May 1904, Dr Emil Goeldi, director of Brazil's Para (now Belem) Museum, received a cage containing two living pacaranas (an adult female and a subadult male). These precious animals had been sent from the upper Rio Purus, Brazil, and proved to be extremely docile, inoffensive creatures, totally belying their 'terrible mouse' image. They were swiftly transferred to Brazil's Zoological Gardens, but tragically the adult female died shortly afterwards, following the birth of the first of two offspring that she was carrying.[23,25]

In 1919, an even more unusual pacarana was described by Alipio de Miranda Ribeiro. Instead of being greyish-black in colour, it was brown, and so Ribeiro designated it as the type specimen of a new species, christened *D. pacarana*. Three years earlier, the first pacarana recorded from Colombia had been collected (near La Candela, Huila);

in 1921, this became the type of a third species, *D. gigas*. During the early 1920s, a series of pacaranas was procured by Edmund Heller from localities in Peru and also Brazil, so that by the 1930s a number of museum specimens existed, which were then examined carefully by Dr Colin Sanborn in the most detailed pacarana study undertaken at that time. Publishing his findings in 1931, he revealed that *D. pacarana* and *D. gigas* were merely forms of *D. branickii,* which meant that only a single species existed after all.[26]

A rarely-glimpsed inhabitant of mountain forests, the pacarana feeds on leaves, fruit, and grass, and is hunted as a source of food by its Indian neighbours, but little else is known about its lifestyle in the wild. It is currently classed as an endangered species, yet as a result of its secretive habits and inaccessible habitat it may be more common than hitherto suspected.[23]

Giant forest hog – the world's largest pig

Those critics of cryptozoology who believed that the okapi had to be the last large mammal that would be discovered in Africa were effectively silenced less than three years after its debut, when in 1904 this ever-startling continent offered up another zoological surprise – a previously undescribed species of wild pig attaining quite colossal proportions.

As far back as 1668, in his *Naukeurige Beschryvinge der Afrikaensche gewesten van Egypten,* Dr Olfert Dapper had spoken of an extremely large black pig from Liberia, known to the natives as *couja quinta.* Two centuries later, during his Emin relief expedition of 1888-90, Sir Henry Stanley collected reports of a gigantic pig, reputedly reaching 6 ft in length, which allegedly

Giant forest hog – exhibiting this species' grotesque, fungus-like facial swellings.

inhabited the Ituri Forest. At much the same time, rumours of a comparable creature were also issuing from Kenya. Some of these eventually reached the ears of Lieutenant (later Captain) Richard Meinertzhagen of the British East-African Rifles, who happened to be stationed in Kenya in 1903, and as a keen hunter he became determined to track down this formidable animal.[2-3,27]

His first piece of good fortune came in February 1904, when he learnt that one of these creatures had been killed by native hunters at a small village on Mount Kenya. By the time he reached the spot, however, the carcase had been badly damaged, but one of his companions obtained from it a couple of pieces of skin. Meinertzhagen readily recognised these as being from some form of pig, but none that was known to him. Not long afterwards he was more successful, discovering in a village on the mountain's southeastern slopes an almost complete, relatively fresh skin, plus a second, somewhat older skin. Parcelling all

his finds together, he sent them to Oldfield Thomas at the British Museum, and resolved to seek out additional evidence of the giant pig's existence.[2-3,27]

Meinertzhagen's crowning triumph came in May, when he learnt that another individual had been killed, this time in the Nandi country near Lake Victoria. He arrived on the scene in time to secure not only a further piece of skin, but also an entire skull which measured 3 ft in length. He also obtained an incomplete skull from a somewhat older specimen. Well-pleased with his good fortune, and anxious to discover whether they were of any scientific significance, Meinertzhagen sent these latest specimens to London, and awaited Thomas's verdict. This proved to be far more exciting than anything he had dared anticipate.[2-3,27]

The giant forest hog, as it soon became known, was indeed a new species, and so unlike anything seen before that it warranted the creation of a new genus, *Hylochoerus*. In recognition of the valiant efforts made by its discoverer to bring it to the attention of western science, Thomas named it *H. meinertzhageni* in his official description of the species, published on 15 November 1904.[27]

Taxiderm specimen of the giant forest hog – the world's largest wild pig, it can exceed 7 ft in length, but eluded formal detection until 1904.

The most striking features of the giant forest hog, other than its huge size – it can exceed 7 ft in length, and reach 3 ft at the shoulder – are its relatively long legs and massive head; its bristly, shiny black or dark brown coat; the pair of formidable curved and bulky tusks projecting from its upper jaw; a huge pair of fungus-like warts positioned beneath its eyes and stretching down as far as its cheeks; and a most peculiar but very noticeable indentation on top of its head, large enough to accommodate a man's fist.[27]

A predominantly nocturnal denizen of dense jungles, the giant forest hog is now known to exist in three principal localities across Africa. One comprises those regions of Kenya and Tanzania that border Lake Victoria, and stretches northeastwards into Zaire and southern Ethiopia. The second overlaps Cameroon and the People's Republic of the Congo (where it was once believed to constitute a separate species, named *H. gigliolii*). And a third, deep in West Africa (where it was once believed to comprise another separate species, named *H. rimator*), extends over the border region between Ghana, Burkina Faso and the Ivory Coast, westwards into Liberia. There are also unconfirmed reports that it exists even further west, in Guinea and in Guinea Bissau.[8,27-8]

Regrettably, however, it is rare in all of these areas, although this was not always the case. Judging from native testimony, prior to the late 1800s it was apparently much more common, but in 1891 domestic pigs throughout Africa were devastated by rinderpest, a disease to which the giant forest hog seems to be particularly susceptible, and which almost certainly had a profound effect upon its numbers. Fortunately, although uncommon, its continuing survival does not appear to be threatened. Indeed, it has become a somewhat unexpected tourist attraction – thanks to its occasional forays into the forests overlooked by the famous Kenyan hotel Tree Tops.[8]

Goeldi's perplexing little primate

In 1904, with a skull-less, incomplete skin as his evidence, Oldfield Thomas described a new species of monkey that was destined to disrupt the traditional division of South American primates into two distinct taxonomic families – the marmosets and tamarins (Callithricidae) and the true monkeys (Cebidae). The skin had been obtained from Brazil's Para Museum, and Thomas named it *Midas goeldii*, after the museum's director, pacarana rediscoverer Dr Emil Goeldi.

In December 1911, a small female monkey, formerly living in the Para Museum's adjoining zoological gardens, was described by Alipio de Miranda Ribeiro under the name *Callimico snethlageri*, as Ribeiro considered it to be sufficiently different from all other South American species to require its own genus.[29] When Thomas examined its remains in 1913, he agreed with Ribeiro's views concerning its distinctness, but he also recognised that this specimen and the incomplete skin that he had personally described back in 1904 clearly belonged to the same species. Accordingly, the rules of nomenclatural precedence dictated that the species would thereafter be known as *Callimico goeldii*, Goeldi's monkey – a monkey that embodies a unique combination of features from both families of New World primate.[29-30]

Externally, it appears quite an ordinary-looking animal, superficially resembling a predominantly black or dark brown marmoset, with an average head-and-body length of 8 in, and an extra 10-13 in of tail, plus a mane of fur over its neck and shoulders. However, examination of its cranial, dental, and skeletal features, exposes its bemusing intermediate position between the two primate families. Whereas the claw-like nails and the overall skeletal structure of its feet, plus the basic configuration of its face, are all more comparable to those of genuine marmosets and tamarins, its dentition and cranial structure are more like those of South America's true monkeys.[30]

So how can it be classified? Even today, there is no firm agreement concerning Goeldi's monkey. Some authorities (like Oldfield Thomas) have chosen to house it within a subfamily of Cebidae (as a peculiar true New World monkey), others (like Reginald Pocock) within its own subfamily of Callithricidae (as an aberrant marmoset). A few (like Captain Guy Dollman) have preferred to place it within a family of its own – Callimiconidae. Goeldi's perplexing little primate succinctly demonstrates that however well-established a system of classification for a given group of species seems to be, there is always the possibility that a new species will come along and completely overturn it.[30]

A shoal of new seals

The Hawaiian monk seal *Monachus schauinslandi* is the world's most recently-described, accepted species of seal, named in 1905 by Dr Paul Matschie after Prof. H.H. Schauinsland, a German zoologist who had reported its existence around the Hawaiian island of Laysan.[31] Up to 9 ft in length, with grey-brown upperparts and silvery-hued underparts (sometimes acquiring a greenish sheen caused by growth of algae amongst its fur), this was once an abundant species.

Relentless hunting by man, however, has reduced its total population to 1000-1500 individuals, so that today it is one of the world's rarest seal species.[32]

The taxonomic status of two other seals described this century is still a matter of some dispute. In 1904, a new species of fur seal, *Arctocephalus galapagoensis*, was described from the Galapagos Islands, but some authorities merely treat it as a subspecies of the South American fur seal *A. australis*. Similarly, the Australian fur seal *A. doriferus*, described in 1925 by F. Wood Jones, is usually demoted to a subspecies of the South African fur seal *A. pusillus*.[32] In 1963, a new species of seal from the Pacific's Kurile Islands was reported by a Russian scientist, but its separate specific status is again nowadays rarely accepted..[33]

The emperor who should have been a mandarin

One of the most delightful and frequently illustrated species of South American monkey is the emperor tamarin of northwestern Brazil. Yet it was unknown to science until 1907, when it was officially described and named by Dr Emil Goeldi. With a principally black head and body measuring up to 9 in long, and a rufous-coloured tail around 12 in long, the emperor tamarin is instantly recognised and distinguished from all other species by way of its enormous white moustache, which sweeps majestically downwards in faithful imitation of a venerable Chinese mandarin's moustache.[34]

Its 'imperial' title arose through a mistake made by the taxidermist responsible for preserving the species' type specimen. As he had never seen a living example, he apparently assumed that in life its extraordinarily large moustache would curl

Emperor tamarin – it derives its name from a misconception.
(A. van den Nieuwenhuizen)

upwards, just like that of the German emperor Wilhelm, and so that is how he arranged it. Accordingly, this engaging little monkey became known as the emperor tamarin, and Goeldi duly christened it *Midas imperator* (later changed to *Saguinus imperator*). Of course, the procurement of more specimens swiftly exposed the true appearance of this species' moustache, but by then its imperial appellation had become too widely used to be dropped[10].

Lorises small, intermediate – and tailed

Those Asian, tailless relatives of lemurs, the lorises, were known only from two species – the slender loris *Loris tardigradus* and the slow loris *Nycticebus coucang* – until 1907,

when a third was described by J.L. Bonhote. Its type specimen had been collected by a Dr Vassal on 13 November 1905 at Nha-trang, Annam; and although an adult, measuring a mere 8 in long it was only half the total length of the slow loris. Its dentition was also very distinct, and so Bonhote dubbed it *N. pygmaeus*, the pygmy slow loris.[35]

Intriguingly, a single adult female *Nycticebus*-like loris was obtained many years later from Hoa Binh, northern Vietnam, which was midway between *N. coucang* and *N. pygmaeus* in size, inspiring D.V. Tien to designate it as the type of a new species, which in 1960 he suitably named *N. intermedius*. But few zoologists accept this. Far more extraordinary were the white-coated, woolly-furred *Nycticebus*-like lorises captured and photographed near Fort Lungleh in Assam's Lushai Hills in December 1889 (but undocumented until 1908). With short but stout limbs, a large rounded head, flat face and small muzzle, short roundish ears, large eyes each encircled by a dark triangular patch, and a narrow black stripe running from its skull's occipital region along its back's entire length, this form differed dramatically from all other lorises in one very conspicuous way – it had a thick bushy tail.[35] Unless it is a teratological, freak variety of *N. coucang,* a radically new species of slow loris still awaits official recognition – for which I propose, as a suitable name, *Nycticebus caudatus,* the tailed slow loris.

While speaking of pygmy primates, another controversial form has recently gained taxonomic respectability. In 1921, an unusually small specimen of tarsier (less than 1ft long) collected four years earlier from upper montane rainforest in Central Sulawesi (Celebes), became the type of a new species, dubbed *Tarsius pumilus,* the pygmy tarsier. However, its status as a valid species was not generally accepted until 1987, when an extensive study of this mysterious mammal by Dr Guy G. Musser and Marian Dagosto demonstrated unequivocally that it deserved separate specific status, thereby adding (after 70 years as a primatological *persona non grata*) a fourth tarsier to the zoological catalogue of formally recognised species.[36]

Andrews' beaked whale – starting a seafaring septet

Beaked whales are medium-sized cetaceans, superficially dolphin-like in shape but characterised by a pair of longitudinal grooves that meet on the throat, and by long tapering jaws that usually house no more than one or two pairs of teeth (depending upon the genus concerned). Of the seven new species of beaked whale discovered so far this century, five belong to the genus *Mesoplodon*, each species of which has only a single pair of teeth.

The first of this quintet to receive scientific attention was Andrews' beaked whale *M. bowdoini*. Distinguished by the splayed manner in which its lone pair of teeth projects from its jaws, it was described in 1908 by Dr Roy Chapman Andrews of the American Museum of Natural History. The type specimen, a mounted adult skeleton, had been purchased by the museum four years earlier, and had originated from a stranded individual that had met its death on Brighton Beach, near Canterbury, New Zealand. Since then, at least six more specimens have been obtained for study, all originally stranded on various shores of New Zealand, mainland Australia or Tasmania, and with an average total length of 13 ft. Anatomically, this species seems in many ways to be a smaller, southern counterpart of Stejneger's beaked whale *M.*

stejnegeri; but with no available records or studies relating to living examples, Andrews' beaked whale remains one of the least-known cetaceans.[32,37-8]

Mountain nyala – Buxton's major surprise from Ethiopia

Again, just when it seemed that Africa had exhausted its supply of significant zoological surprises, yet another new mammal of magnitude was discovered. In mid-December 1910, zoologist Dr Richard Lydekker received the skull, spiralled horns, and grey-coated skin of a handsome kudu-like antelope, courtesy of Rowland Ward, proprietor of the famous Piccadilly firm of taxidermists. They had been sent to Ward by Major Ivor Buxton, who had shot the animal that summer in southern Ethiopia, and Ward believed that it represented a new species. Upon examining the relics, Lydekker came to the same conclusion.[39]

Lydekker duly wrote a letter to *The Times*, which was published on 23 September. As a result, he was contacted shortly afterwards by Major Buxton, who informed him that the antelope's precise provenance was a locality to the west of the Arusi plateau of Gallaland, on the open stony ground of Ethiopia's Sahatu Mountains, at an altitude of about 9000 ft. Equipped with this information, Lydekker published a formal description of the new species, which was published on 29 September in *Nature*, and in which he named it *Strepsiceros buxtoni* (thereby allying it with the kudus). However, in a later account, appearing in *The Field* on 22 October and based upon his examination of some additional material received from Buxton, Lydekker changed his mind. He now announced that the antelope was actually most closely related to the nyala *Tragelaphus angasi*, suggesting that it should therefore be referred to popularly as the mountain nyala and be known scientifically as *T. buxtoni*.[40]

The common and mountain nyalas are indeed closely allied; however, there are some morphological differences that readily distinguish them externally. The mountain nyala is almost 1 ft taller, standing 52 in or so at the shoulder, and it lacks the other species' very striking series of transverse creamy-white body stripes, although it does bear a longitudinal line of nine white spots on each haunch.

Subsequent investigations within its native habitat concluded that the mountain nyala was very rare, numbering less than 2000 individuals in total, but in 1966 this assessment was shown by a joint World Wildlife Fund/American Geographic Society survey to be an underestimate. Nevertheless, the mountain nyala is by no means abundant, and is still one of the least-studied of Africa's larger antelope species.[8,40]

Quarles's mountain anoa – a bantam-weight buffalo

With a shoulder height of little more than 3 ft, the lowland anoa *Anoa depressicornis* is a small but nonetheless belligerent species of dark-coated, white-legged, southeast Asian buffalo, native to the lowland forests of Sulawesi (Celebes). Smaller still, however, is its relative the mountain anoa *A. quarlesi*, which inhabits Sulawesi's montane forests, and has a shoulder height not exceeding 2.5 ft. This species was officially described in 1910 by Major P.A. Ouwens, director of the Botanical Gardens at Buitenzorg, Java, who had received two living specimens that year from the mountains of Sulawesi's central Toradja region. They were distinguished from the lowland anoa not only by their smaller size and shorter tails, but also by

their thicker, lighter-coloured coats, the absence of white colouration on their legs, and by the conical bases of their horns (those of the lowland anoa are triangular).[41]

There has been much confusion and controversy regarding anoa taxonomy over the years, and some authorities attest to the existence on Sulawesi of a *third* anoa species, even smaller than the mountain anoa, measuring no more than 27 in at the shoulder, and sharing the montane habitat of the latter species.[42] Most researchers, however, prefer to treat these two forms as one. The mountain anoa is also referred to in some publications as *A. fergusoni*; this is the name given by Dr Richard Lydekker in 1905 to a zoo specimen of anoa long thought to have been a mountain anoa but now known to have been a lowland anoa – hence '*A. fergusoni*' is nowadays suppressed in favour of '*A. quarlesi*' for the mountain anoa.[41]

Hero shrews – strongmen of the small mammal world

The year 1910 saw the discovery of the first of two very small but thoroughly amazing species of mammal known as hero shrews. Their name derives from the belief held by some native tribes that if they consume (or wear as an amulet) any part of these animals, they will become indestructible. Named *Scutisorex somereni*, this species was found in rainforests near Kampala, Uganda; and in 1913 a second species, later christened *S. congicus*, was revealed in Zaire's Ituri Forest.[43] (Today, some authorities class these two as a single species.)

Measuring no more than 9 in long (half of which comprises the tail) and weighing only a few ounces, these diminutive species outwardly look much like other shrews, but their skeleton possesses an incredible secret.

Skeleton of a hero shrew revealing its backbone's extraordinary degree of protective reinforcement, which enables it to withstand immense pressure. (Neg. No 37485/Photo: Kay C. Lernskjold/Courtesy Department Library Services. American Museum of Natural History)

This was first disclosed with *S. congicus*, when in 1916 a team of American mammal collectors (led by Herbert Lang) visited the terrain of the Ituri's Mangbetu tribe. Prior to this, science only had skulls and skins of hero shrews, and therefore was totally unaware of their unique capability – one that the Mangbetu people exposed in what initially seemed to be a singularly barbaric manner.[44]

A tribesman placed a shrew on the ground, and then to the American collectors' horror, stood on top of its back, balancing on one foot! Naturally, the Americans fully expected the tiny creature to be instantaneously squashed to pulp. Instead, to their astonishment, not only was the shrew completely undamaged, but when the man finally stepped off its back several minutes later, it merely shook itself and scampered back into the undergrowth, clearly unaffected by the experience.[44]

This extraordinary episode's denouement came when the American team sent back some complete *S. congicus* skeletons for anatomical study at the American Museum of Natural History (*S. somereni* skeletons were also obtained in due course). These revealed the hero shrew's backbone to incorporate an unparalleled degree of protective reinforcement. The vertebrae were much broader than those of other shrews and the surface of each was effectively buttressed with a formidable array of bony knobs, ridges and spines. These interlinked so closely and tightly with those of the vertebrae immediately in front and behind that the backbone constituted an invincible bridge resistant to immense pressure, pressure that would instantly crush the backbone of much larger animals, let alone other shrews.[44]

Most mysterious of all, however, is the reason why the two species of hero shrew have evolved such an exceptional skeleton, because their insectivorous lifestyle does not seem to differ from that of normal shrews.[44] Eight decades have passed since the hero shrews' discovery, but science has yet to provide a convincing answer to this baffling riddle.

Congo hero shrew – although it only weighs a few ounces, it can readily support the weight of an adult man on its back.
(Neg. No. 36883/Photo: Julius Kirschner/Courtesy Department Library Services, American Museum of Natural History)

Pygmy hippopotamus –
resurrection of a very large dwarf

The common hippopotamus *Hippopotamus amphibius* has been known to the western world for many centuries, but in 1849 Dr Samuel Morton, vice-president of Philadelphia's Academy of Natural Sciences, described a second, much smaller species, based upon two skulls which originated from Liberia. He dubbed it *H. minor*, but changed that to *H. liberiensis* when he found that *H. minor* was already the name of a fossil species. In 1852, the new hippo's name changed again, this time to *Choeropsis liberiensis* ('pig-like creature from Liberia'). This name was given to it by anatomist and fossil-seeker Dr Joseph Leidy, whose own examination of the two skulls convinced him that the presence of certain pig-like features rendered this species sufficiently distinct from the much larger, familiar hippopotamus to warrant its own genus.[45]

This marked the beginning of a long and heated dispute in scientific circles, with some authorities supporting Leidy's views, others preferring to retain it within the genus *Hippopotamus*, and some even dismissing this so-called 'pygmy hippopotamus' as a freak, stunted variety (i.e. a dwarf) of the ordinary species, or as an immature form of it.

Over the years, some other skulls and a few skeletons were brought back to the west from Liberia, but these could not stem the flow of conflict that ensued whenever the pygmy hippo attracted scientific discussion. In 1870, there was even a living specimen on show in Europe, when an extremely small individual arrived at Dublin Zoo from Liberia. True to form, it was initially dismissed as a very young common hippo; but when it died a few weeks later, it was carefully examined by Irish zoologist A. MacAllister, who announced that it was a juvenile specimen of the controversial pygmy hippopotamus.[46]

MacAllister's subsequent detailed study of the species' external appearance led him to recognise that its critics were totally wrong in assuming that it was merely a scaled-down version of the common hippopotamus.[46] He found that it was much more pig-like than its larger relative, with proportionately smaller head, longer limbs, and an arched back, and was much lighter in overall build. No longer were its porcine parallels confined to cranial characteristics. Nonetheless, its basic skeletal structure, as well as its large jaws and the absence of a delineated snout, confirmed its closer affinity to the hippopotamus family than to that of the pigs.[46]

Yet despite such findings as these, the 'stunted freak' identity still drew a surprising amount of support from scientists. And, to make matters worse, when little more news reached the west

Early photo of a pygmy hippopotamus – discounted as a freak, stunted variety of the common hippo until its rediscovery in 1911.

concerning this perplexing pygmy, zoologists finally wrote it off as extinct (as if to rid themselves of a troublesome enigma).[2]

Fortunately, the famous animal trader Carl Hagenbeck was not prepared to let this matter rest. When he learnt from one of his collectors that Liberians still spoke of a strange beast called the *nigbwe* whose description sounded suspiciously similar to that of the pygmy hippo, he decided to sort out this taxonomic tangle once and for all by sending to Liberia the renowned explorer-naturalist Hans Schomburgk. If anyone could find an answer to this anomaly, Schomburgk could.

Indeed after diligent searches and long periods of time spent patiently questioning the natives, Schomburgk did succeed. On 13 June 1911, he found himself standing face to face with a living pygmy hippopotamus, deep in the Liberian forests. Sadly, however, he did not have the means to catch it, and he did not wish to kill it – his trip had been primarily a fact-finding mission, to determine whether or not the species still existed. Now that he knew it did, Schomburgk took scant notice of the disbelief and disdain that he received from scientists when he returned home to Europe empty-handed. Instead, he assembled the necessary equipment to catch some pygmy hippos, arrived back in Liberia at the end of 1912, and captured a living specimen on 1 March 1913. Bringing his search to a triumphant conclusion, he returned home in August accompanied by no less than five thriving pygmy hippos, and a wealth of information concerning this 'extinct' species.[47]

No longer could there be any doubt. The pygmy hippopotamus, less than 6 ft long and only 2.5 ft high, with a glossy black skin and a preference for terrestrial life in forests rather than an aquatic existence in lakes and rivers, was indisputably a valid species in its own right. Another Dark Continent denizen had finally acquired scientific recognition.[48]

Spectacled porpoise and True's beaked whale

At the turn of the 19th century, an exceptionally handsome porpoise was captured off Argentina, and taken to the Buenos Aires Museum, where scientists were in little doubt that it represented a hitherto unknown species. Its jet black upperparts contrasted sharply against its snowy white flanks and underparts; but most distinctive of all were its eyes, each of which, housed within the white portion of its head, was encircled by a black ring.[38,49]

Tragically, however, before this unique specimen could be studied fully it was somehow lost, but in 1912 a second specimen appeared, stranded at Punta Colares on Argentina's Rio de la Plata. This time, a detailed examination was carried out by the museum's whale specialist Fernando Lahille, who confirmed that it was a species new to science and, in recognition of its most striking external feature, named it *Phocaena* [now *Phocoena*] *dioptrica*, the spectacled porpoise.[49] It is a relatively small species, no more than 6.5 ft in length. Less than 15 specimens have been obtained since 1912, and no living individual has ever been studied. As many cetaceans are notoriously elusive, however, rarity of collected specimens is by no means synonymous with rarity of species[38].

True's beaked whale also became known to science in 1912, when a specimen was stranded on Bird Island Shoal, outside North Carolina's Beaufort Harbour. The following year it was described fully by mammalogist Dr Frederick True, who named it *Mesoplodon mirum* [now *mirus*].[50] Dark greyish-blue dorsally, with paler, sometimes yellowish underparts (often speckled with small spots), and averaging 17 ft or so in total length, True's beaked whale has since been recorded elsewhere in the U.S.A.'s New England area, as well as from beaches in western Britain on the opposite side of the North Atlantic. There is also evidence to suggest that it inhabits the southern temperate waters off South Africa. Like those of certain other *Mesoplodon* species, the females do not have teeth emerging through the gums, but the males have a single, flattened pair of small, triangular teeth at the end of the lower jaw.[38,50]

Two surprising civets – one insectivorous, one amphibious?

Two of the world's most mystifying members of the viverrid family (housing the civets, genets, and mongooses) came to zoological attention within the space of just two years.

Owston's banded civet *Chrotogale owstoni* is an obscure Asian species measuring up to 3.5 ft in length. It is named after Alan Owston, whose native collector procured its type specimen on 16 September 1911 at Yen-bay, on Tonkin's Song-koi River in southern China. It was officially described in 1912 by Oldfield Thomas, who designated it as the sole member of a new genus. Its visually arresting pattern created by contrasting light-and-dark, transverse bands on its body and the basal portion of its tail closely resembles that of the banded palm civet *Hemigalus derbianus*, but the latter species lacks the dark spots visible on the neck, shoulders, flanks, and thighs of *Chrotogale*.[48,51]

Owston's banded civet – an obscure, possibly insectivorous species discovered in 1911, and still known from only a handful of specimens.
(Dr Karl Shuker)

Anatomical comparisons also uncovered distinct differences in cranial structure and dentition between the two species, differences sufficiently marked to warrant these civets' respective residence in separate genera. Most remarkable of these contrasts were the very slender muzzle of *Chrotogale*, and its incongruous incisors – these teeth are surprisingly broad and close-set, and arranged almost in a semi-circle, a condition more comparable to that of certain insectivorous marsupials than to any species of viverrid. Whether it too is predominantly insectivorous, however, is unknown, as it remains to this day a very mysterious animal, known from less than two dozen preserved specimens originating variously from northern Vietnam, Laos, and from Tonkin and Yunnan in China,[48,51] plus a live individual captured in Vietnam in 1991.[51]

Even more enigmatic, however, is the second member of this duo of new viverrids. Unrecorded by science until 1913, never studied alive by scientists, and even virtually unknown to the local natives, the water civet *Osbornictis piscivora* is one of the world's most mystifying mammals.

It is an exceedingly handsome, strikingly-coloured creature, with a densely-furred chestnut head and body, a black bushy tail (comprising almost half of the animal's total length of 3 ft), and white facial markings. The type specimen of this secretive species was obtained on 1 December 1913 in a forest stream at Niapu, in northeastern Zaire, by Drs James P. Chapin and Herbert Lang during the American Museum of Natural History's famous Congo Expedition. Six years later, the species was formally described by J.A. Allen from the museum; its scientific name honours Prof. Henry Fairfield Osborn (who was greatly interested in the Congo Expedition), and records its apparent fish-eating proclivity.[48,52]

Although its anatomy suggests that it is most closely related to the genets (despite its civet appellation), the water civet exhibits several features markedly at variance with typical genet morphology. Most obvious of these is its vulpine colouration, totally different from the black-and-white coat patterning of spots and bands synonymous with genets. In addition, the soles of its paws are unfurred, its teeth are much weaker and narrower than those of similar-sized genets, its nose is smaller, its muzzle shorter, and its overall size rivals that of the giant genet (see p. 20), the largest of all *Genetta* species.[52]

Most books state that the water civet was totally unknown to the natives prior to its scientific discovery in 1913; this is not true. Along with the holotype, Lang and Chapin also obtained an incomplete specimen (lacking skull, tail and feet) from a native;[52] and in the local Kibila and Kipakombe languages, it has its own specific name – *esele*.[53] Nevertheless, for the most part it is truly as much a mystery to them as it is to science, with virtually no information available concerning its natural history, and very few museum specimens.

Baiji – Chinese river dolphin or reincarnated princess?

The baiji or Chinese river dolphin *Lipotes vexillifer* is revered in China as the reincarnation of a drowned princess, and has therefore been featured extensively in generations of Chinese poetry, legends and literature stretching back as far as 200 BC. All of which makes it particularly surprising that this distinctive cetacean's existence only became known to western science as recently as 1916 (not 1914, as many books allege). On 18 February 1916, a visiting American, Charles M. Hoy, killed a specimen in Lake Tung Ting, about 600 miles up the famous Yangtze River, and sold its skull and neck vertebrae to the United States National Museum, where they were examined by mammalogist Dr Gerrit S. Miller. He perceived that they were from a completely new species, which he described in 1918, assigning it to a new genus.[54]

Few specimens have been taken since, but many have been accidentally killed through entanglement with fishing equipment, and the species is gravely endangered. It is now restricted to stretches of the Yangtze downstream from Yidu, and numbers no more than 300 individuals.[36,48] Attempts at semi-captive breeding are being made at Tongling, where the baiji is the municipal mascot and is honoured by a spectacular sculpture depicting five baijis leaping out of the water (see colour section).[55]

A very attractive, fish-eating species measuring 7-8 ft in total length, the baiji is silver-grey dorsally and almost pure-white ventrally (*baiji* translates as 'white dolphin'), with a long and slender upturned beak, a triangular dorsal fin, squat flippers, and almost sightless eyes.[55] According to local reports, it frequently emits loud roaring sounds at night.[38,48] Worth noting is that similar noises have been reported from certain remote Chinese lakes that supposedly house mysterious water monsters. Could these monsters be forms of freshwater dolphin, perhaps even species still undescribed by science? Support for this possibility was provided in 1985 by the discovery of the pesut (see p. 92).

Wyulda – a scaly-tailed puzzle

Whereas most Australian possums are marsupial equivalents of squirrels, tree rats, dormice, or other rodents in basic appearance, the scaly-tailed possum more closely resembles the Madagascan lemurs. Unlike lemurs, however, and unlike other possums too, most of its tail is hairless. Only the basal portion is furred, the remainder being covered with thick, non-overlapping scales, from which it derives its common and scientific names.[56-7]

It has short pale-grey fur bearing a dark stripe that runs along its back from shoulders to rump, a fairly wide head, and uses its unique tail for tree climbing. This unusual species was unknown to science until 1917, when a female specimen was captured alive at Violet Valley Station, near Turkey Creek in north Western Australia's Kimberley district. In 1919 it became the type specimen of a new species (and genus), named *Wyulda squamicaudata* by W.B. Alexander (*wyulda* is the scaly-tailed possum's Western Australian aboriginal name),[56] and was maintained thereafter in captivity at the South Perth Zoological Gardens.[57-8]

Following this, the scaly-tailed possum eluded scientists for 23 years, until in 1942 a second specimen (this time a male) was obtained, by the Reverend J.R.B. Love, close to his mission at Kunmunya – once again in the Kimberley district but on the opposite peninsula coast to the first specimen's provenance. In 1954, Specimen No. 3 was recorded – a female containing a baby in her pouch, collected at Wotjulum Mission, south of Kunmunya, by Kenneth Buller of the Western Australian Museum. No others were obtained until 1965 – so despite extensive searches, from 1917 until the mid-1960s only three adults and one infant had been documented, suggesting that this species was exceedingly rare.[42,48,57-8]

At the end of 1965 and early 1966, however, a number of specimens were procured by Harold Butler at Kalumburu Mission, near to Western Australia's northernmost edge, thereby greatly increasing the species' known distribution range. Furthermore, Butler learned from one of the older aborigines in the area that this possum's numbers fluctuated quite considerably; mostly it was rare, but sometimes it became quite common, although the reason for such oscillations in numbers (if true) has yet to be ascertained. It is quite possible that the recorded 'rarity' of Western Australia's wily *Wyulda* is not so much an accurate assessment of its status as a reflection of the fact that it seldom seems to frequent areas inhabited or studied to any extent by western man.[48,57-8]

Ameranthropoides – South America's problematical 'ape'

Without a doubt, South America's 'ape' is one of the most debated (and debased) animal discoveries of the century, a creature so controversial that its very existence (let alone its taxonomic identity) is still disputed by all but the most open-minded of zoologists.

Officially, South America is not known to harbour any primates larger than its marmosets and true monkeys, except for man, but in the 1920s a noteworthy item of evidence for the existence of a South American ape-like beast much bigger than any of these latter New World species was brought to public attention. The item in question comprised a very striking close-up photograph of an allegedly bipedal (capable of walking on its hind legs), tailless, 5-ft tall primate, one of two encountered in 1920 within forests on the Colombia-Venezuela border. It was shot when it threatened to attack a team of geologists led by Dr François de Loys (its partner escaped, unharmed). The specimen itself (a female) was not preserved, but the photograph of it taken shortly after its death appeared in an account of the entire episode penned by Dr de Loys and published by the *Illustrated London News* (15 June 1929), initiating a singularly acrimonious series of interchanges within the scientific community.[2,23,59]

The photo's principal champion was the eminent French zoologist Prof. George Montandon, who was sufficiently convinced that it depicted an unknown species of ape-like primate to confer upon the latter creature a formal scientific name – *Ameranthropoides loysi* ('Loys's American ape')[59]. Many other scientific luminaries, however, (most notably the English anthropologist Sir Arthur Keith) declared that its subject was nothing more exciting than a spider monkey, and intimated that the monkey had been purposefully manipulated to resemble an ape for the photograph – in short, it was widely

Ameranthropoides loysi – Dr François de Loys's controversial South American 'ape', whose taxonomic identity remains an enigma.
(Fortean Picture Library)

considered that Dr de Loys and his colleagues had attempted to perpetrate an elaborate hoax.[2,23]

Such a theory, however, fails to take into account the fact that, during their time in South America, the team had been constantly subjected to the most harrowing hardships, and had been more than adequately occupied with the life-saving tasks of avoiding onslaughts from venomous fauna, virulent diseases and murderous ambushes by the region's hostile Motilone Indians (plentifully-equipped with poison-tipped arrows) – hardly the most conducive of situations for fostering any inclination or opportunity to stage an elaborate hoax with which to attempt to fool the scientific community.[23] In addition, ape-like entities are well-known to the natives of many parts of South America (and are even depicted in ancient sculptures discovered among the crumbling remains of

long-demised civilisations there). Natives refer to these creatures by such names as the *didi* (in Guyana), *mapinguary* (Brazil and Bolivia), and *vasitri* (Venezuela). There also seems to be no good reason why the South American primate lineage could not have given rise to a branch of ape-like forms, paralleling the anthropoids' evolution in the Old World; there are certainly appropriate ecological niches for apes in South America.[2,23]

Today, de Loys's perplexing photo and the equally perplexing creature it portrays are largely forgotten, and are very rarely alluded to in wildlife literature, which is a tragedy. They are mysteries in dire need of satisfactory resolution – which will only be achieved by confronting the problems that they raise, not by ignoring them in the hope that the zoologically-inconvenient issues that they embody will simply cease to exist if left undisturbed.

King cheetah – a striped enigma

A bizarre beast known to Zimbabwean natives as the *nsui-fisi* ('leopard-hyaena') was assumed by zoologists to be a myth until the skin of one of these creatures was brought to scientific attention. This was in 1926, when Major A.C. Cooper of Salisbury (now Harare) documented in *The Field* for 14 October the existence at Salisbury's Queen Victoria Memorial Library and Museum of an extraordinary skin obtained from a strange felid now known to have been trapped at Macheke, about 62 miles southeast of Salisbury. Royally adorned with ornate blotches and curved stripes upon its flanks and upper limbs, a series of longitudinal stripes running along its back

and shoulders, and distinctive rings encircling much of its tail, this handsome skin was ultimately identified by Reginald Pocock of the British Museum (Natural History) as that of a cheetah – but one that was drastically different in coat patterning from the typical spotted version.[60-1]

Pocock was convinced that this wonderful striped cheetah constituted a hitherto unknown species, and in his scientific description of it, published in 1927, christened it *Acinonyx rex* – the king cheetah, a name inspired not only by its regal coat but also by its prominent mane. By 1939, however, he had changed his mind – other 'king' skins had been obtained by this time, and some seemed distinctly intermediate between the type specimen recorded by Cooper and 'normal', spotted cheetah skins. This suggested that the king cheetah was nothing more than a freak – a genetic mutant variety of the spotted cheetah *A. jubatus*. Accordingly, from that time onwards it was simply referred to as *A. jubatus* var. *rex*.[60-1]

King cheetah – a simple mutant of the spotted cheetah, or an emerging species in its own right? (Lena and Paul Bottriell)

Breeding experiments during the early 1980s at the de Wildt Cheetah Breeding and Research Centre of Pretoria's National Zoological Gardens confirmed this, revealing that the king cheetah's spectacular coat pattern was due to a recessive mutant allele (an often-hidden abnormal version of a gene), probably homologous (equivalent) to the allele creating the blotched tabby pattern in the domestic cat. Nevertheless, the mystique of the king cheetah has not been completely dispelled.[60-1]

Current interest in this most elegant of felids is due largely to the extensive investigations carried out since the late 1970s by king cheetah experts Lena and Paul Bottriell. Not only have they tracked down and filmed living king cheetahs and over 20 preserved skins, they have also exposed some anomalous facets of the king cheetah's natural history that cannot be readily reconciled with the belief that it is nothing more than a simple mutant of the normal cheetah. For example, hair samples have revealed that the cuticular scale pattern of king cheetah guard hair more closely resembles that of the leopard than that of the spotted cheetah. Moreover, whereas the spotted cheetah is primarily a diurnal savannah-dweller, its striped counterpart appears to favour a nocturnal, forest-inhabiting lifestyle, one in which its richly-marked coat would be of particular benefit, providing it with effective camouflage.[60-1]

Hence in 1987 the Bottriells boldly postulated that the king cheetah may actually be demonstrating evolution in action – the divergence of a mutant form from the normal, wild-type, which, if separated reproductively from the latter for a sufficient period of time via habitat and behavioural differences, might ultimately become a separate species in its own right.

Perhaps Pocock's original view concerning the king cheetah's taxonomic status was not incorrect after all, but merely in evolutionary terms a little premature.[60-1]

Also of note in the felid world during the mid-1920s was the discovery in 1925 of a strange wildcat-like skull in China, for its finding marked the rediscovery of *Felis bieti*, the Chinese desert cat – one of the world's most obscure felids, previously known solely from two skins purchased in the Tibetan fur markets of Torgolo and Tatsienlu in 1889 by a collector of zoological specimens for Prince Henry d'Orleans.[62]

Longman's beaked whale – a marine mystery

In 1822, a very eroded whale skull, nearly 4 ft long and originating from a male individual, was discovered on a beach near Mackay, Queensland, Australia. It was presented by E.W. Rawson to the Queensland Museum, where it lingered in scientific obscurity for the next 104 years. It finally received formal attention in 1926, when it was included by H.A. Longman in a paper dealing with cetaceans of Queensland. Longman could see that the skull had clearly belonged to some form of beaked whale, but as it did not correspond with any of the species hitherto recorded, he designated it as the type specimen of a new one – which he named *Mesoplodon pacificus*, because the skull's structural characteristics most closely resembled those of the *Mesoplodon* species.[63]

Nothing more was heard of this species until 1955, when a second skull was found, albeit in a somewhat unexpected location – the floor of a fertiliser factory near Mogadiscio, Somalia. Fortunately, its discoverer, Italian scientist Dr Ugo Funaioli, recognised its worth, and traced its origin by learning that it had come in only a few weeks earlier, having been collected on a beach near Danane by some local fishermen. This second skull, which proved to be from a female, was sent by Funaioli to the University of Florence, where in 1968 its identity as a Longman's beaked whale was confirmed by cetologist Maria Azzaroli.[64] That year also saw the creation for this species of its own genus, *Indopacetus,* by Dr Joseph Curtis Moore, an expert on beaked whales, who cited the skulls' very long beak and shallow tooth sockets as features justifying separate generic status for their species.[65]

No additional specimen of Longman's beaked whale has ever been obtained. Consequently, its external appearance and skeletal anatomy remain unknown – although estimates based upon its skull size indicate that it may attain a total length of up to 25 ft when fully mature, thereby making it one of the largest species of beaked whale. Whether large or small, it is unquestionably the most mysterious.[63-5]

There is, however, a tantalising post-script to this account. In 1987, Robert L. Pitman documented an unidentified form of beaked whale that has been regularly reported from the eastern tropical Pacific, and can be either uniformly grey-brown or black-white in colour (different sexes or ages?). One of the identities contemplated by Pitman for it, is Longman's beaked whale.[66]

Denouement of *Dasogale* – a misidentified Madagascan

Indigenous to Madagascar, tenrecs are small, insectivorous mammals that can be readily divided into two major groups – spiny hedgehog-like species, and soft-furred shrew- or mole-like species. For every good rule, however, there is usually an exception to test it, and in the case of the tenrecs the exception was, until very recently, *Dasogale fontoynonti.*

This species was discovered in 1928 in the forests of eastern Madagascar and described a year later by G. Grandidier (who named it in honour of Dr Fontoynont, a former president of the Madagascan Academy). It is exceptional not only because it is known from just one specimen, but also because that specimen's skull and dental characteristics are perplexingly intermediate between those of the hedgehog tenrecs and those of the other group. Externally it is also transitional, with spines on its back and flanks, but not on its head or underparts.[48,67]

Inevitably, this anomalous little creature has attracted notable zoological interest, and its extreme scarcity earned it a longstanding place in the *Guinness Book of Records* as the world's rarest mammal. In 1987, however, its celebrity status finally ended, when, after detailed comparative studies of tenrec anatomy, Dr R.D.E. MacPhee of North Carolina's Duke University stated that its type (and only) specimen was actually an immature individual of the greater hedgehog tenrec *Setifer setosus.* Another memorable zoological mystery was solved.[68]

Pygmy chimpanzee – a new ape, incognito

Until the mid-1920s, science only accepted the existence of one species of chimpanzee, the familiar common species *Pan troglodytes,* generally divided into three subspecies. In 1928, however, zoologist Dr Ernst Schwarz was examining some specimens at the Congo Museum in Tervueren, Belgium, when he came upon a series of skeletons and skins of a chimpanzee type that appeared very different from any that he had seen before.[2-3,69]

Obtained by a M. Ghesquiere, they revealed that this strange form of chimpanzee was smaller in size than the common species, and was much more slender in build. Its head was smaller too, but its face was longer and narrower, its dense fur was also long and was uniformly black except for a small white patch on the rump, and it lacked the common chimpanzee's familiar white beard. Schwarz discovered that these odd-looking chimps had been collected in an area of tropical rainforest on the south bank of the Congo River – all previously recorded chimpanzees had been obtained from localities north of this river.[2-3,69]

Evidently, the southern chimps comprised an important find, and their distinctive morphology persuaded Schwarz that they represented a currently undescribed

subspecies. Hence in 1929 he formally documented it within the museum's journal, naming this new ape *P. t. paniscus* – the pygmy chimpanzee. Five years later, it was elevated to the level of a full species – *P. paniscus*.[2-3,48,69]

Once science became aware of this primate, investigations uncovered that the Tervueren examples were not the only specimens of pygmy chimp to have been collected without recognition of their separate taxonomic status. The British Museum's collections had contained one in 1895, for instance, and a living example of what was almost certainly a pygmy chimp had been on show for a time in 1923 at New York's Bronx Zoo.[10] Similarly, John Edwards, a Fellow of London's Zoological Society, has kindly brought to my attention a picture postcard in his private collection depicting a chimp housed in Amsterdam Zoo, again during the early 1920s, which was quite obviously a pygmy chimpanzee.

Since the species' 'official' discovery, specimens (correctly identified) have been exhibited at several zoological gardens, particularly in European collections such as Antwerp Zoo and Vincennes Zoo. In 1962, Frankfurt Zoo succeeded in breeding pygmy chimps for the first time in captivity, and has repeated this feat on a number of occasions since. Studies of captive individuals such as these have revealed that the pygmy chimpanzee is much more docile and even-tempered than its less placid, better-known relative.[10]

There has been a fair amount of controversy concerning the pygmy

Pygmy chimpanzee – this particular specimen was actually on show at Amsterdam Zoo several years before the pygmy chimpanzee's official scientific discovery.
(John Edwards)

41

chimpanzee's precise taxonomic identity. Whereas some experts are so convinced of its distinct specific status that they have placed it within its own genus, as *Bonobo paniscus* (*bonobo* is its native name), certain others still prefer to treat it merely as a subspecies of the common chimpanzee. Recent biochemical and genetic comparisons between common and pygmy chimps, however, indicate that the latter ape is certainly sufficiently distinct to justify classification as a separate species (though whether separate *generic* status for it is warranted is still a matter for conjecture).[70]

It seems surprising that a new species of ape could remain undetected by science until as recently as the late 1920s, especially when specimens were actually preserved in scientific museums and exhibited alive in zoos. In fact, there is an even more ironic twist to the tale. Following extensive research on the subject in the 1960s, Vernon Reynolds revealed that the individual designated by Linnaeus way back in 1758 as his type specimen for the common chimpanzee was actually a pygmy chimpanzee![42]

Giant panda – return of the world's favourite

The giant panda is a leading contender for the title of the world's most popular wild animal, and a favourite of the cuddly toy industry. As a modern-day endangered species, its fight for survival has engendered international interest, concern, and assistance on a scale equalled by few if any other forms of threatened wildlife. In view

of this evidence for the giant panda's popular appeal, it is difficult to believe that there was once a time prior to 1929 when zoologists feared that it had been allowed to slip into extinction through lack of interest – neglected by science, and largely unknown to the world outside China.

Referred to by the Chinese as *bei-shung* and prized for its extremely handsome fur (used in earlier days for making ornamental and sleeping rugs), the giant panda was 'officially' discovered by western science in the second half of the 19th century, thanks to the enquiring mind of French missionary-naturalist Père Armand David. At that time, western scholars were aware that ancient Chinese paintings sometimes featured a strange bear-like creature that was predominantly white in colour, but these were generally assumed to be depictions of polar bears brought back to China by hunters – even though the creatures in the

The world's favourite wild animal? A young giant panda – Lan Tian ('Blue Sky') – at China's Wolong Panda Reserve in 1987.
(Mail Newspapers p.l.c.)

paintings usually had black legs, hardly a typical feature of polar bears.[2,71]

On 11 March 1868, while residing with a landowner at his home in Szechwan, Père David noticed that his host possessed a skin of China's mysterious 'black-legged polar bear', which revealed categorically that the paintings had represented the animal accurately and that, whatever it *was*, it certainly was *not* a polar bear. His interest keenly awakened, Père David was anxious to see some complete specimens of this exotic-looking species – an inhabitant, he learnt, of the bamboo forests of the Hsifan Mountains.[2,71]

Accordingly, the hunters he employed for the procurement of specimens captured a young panda, which, unhappily, they killed in order to transport it more conveniently. Père David received it on 23 March 1869 and on 1 April it was followed by another dead specimen, this time an adult.

Suspecting that their species was a member of the bear family, and one that was new to science, Père David named it *Ursus melanoleucus* ('black-and-white bear'), but when his specimens reached Europe they were examined by mammalogist Prof. Alphonse Milne-Edwards, who came up with a very different identity. Although the creature was indeed new and indisputably bear-like in outward appearance, a number of its dental and skeletal features (including the structure of its feet) convinced Milne-Edwards that in reality it was not a bear, but rather a giant relative of the raccoons – and especially of a fiery furred Chinese mammal known as the lesser or red panda *Ailurus fulgens*, described in 1825 by Baron Cuvier and held to be the only living Old World member of the raccoon family.[72-3]

Consequently, when he published his views on this matter in 1870, Milne-Edwards changed the scientific name of Père David's 'black-and-white bear' to *Ailuropoda melanoleuca* ('black-and-white with panda's feet'), emphasising its apparent affinity to *Ailurus*.[72-3] Thus began an extraordinary saga of conflict and contradiction regarding the taxonomic relationship of *Ailuropoda* – one that has persisted right up to the present day. With respect to this animal's common name, in 1901 its large size and supposed kinship with the lesser panda (which, until then, had simply been called the panda) led to its becoming known as the giant panda.

Its unique appearance and taxonomic interest made zoologists anxious to learn more about the giant panda, and to observe it alive in its native habitat – a desire that proved singularly difficult to satisfy. A few specimens were shot shortly after its official discovery and then found their way into various western museums. There is even an unconfirmed report that Père David had sent some *living* specimens to Europe, where they were reputedly displayed for a time in Paris, although most authorities believe that this story arose from nomenclatural confusion, when reports of lesser pandas (i.e. *Ailurus*) were erroneously interpreted as giant pandas.[71]

On the whole, however, this intriguing bicoloured beast remained elusive. Except for a single specimen, a young cub given to German zoologist Hugo Weigold as a pet by the local people during his expedition to China's Wassu Province in 1916, no living giant panda was seen by any westerner from the 1880s to the late 1920s. Sadly, the cub died after only a few days, in spite of every effort made by Weigold to rear it. Eventually, western science began to fear that this mystifying sui generis of the mountains had died out.[2,71]

Not everyone, however, shared this pessimistic view and among those who intended to spy a living panda were a number of notable big-game hunters from America – eager to add a near-legendary creature to their array of trophies. So it was that the morning of 13 April 1929 found Colonel Theodore Roosevelt and Kermit Roosevelt – sons of the famous U.S. president 'Teddy' Roosevelt – clambering through the snow near Yehli in the Hsifan Mountains, seeking a giant panda to shoot. After following panda tracks for 2.5 hours, they found one peacefully asleep in the hollow of a huge spruce tree. As they drew near, it arose and, still half asleep, looked slowly from side to side before ambling towards some nearby bamboo – whereupon the Roosevelt brothers opened fire simultaneously, the resulting hail of bullets killing the poor animal instantly.[2,71,74]

News of this 'success' – the shooting of a half-asleep, inoffensive panda adding a further page of triumph to the hallowed annals of 'sport' – was flashed around the world, enticing other hunters and inciting further killings over the coming years, in what must surely be a uniquely macabre manner of celebrating the rediscovery of a long-lost species.[2,71]

Ironically, although the Roosevelts' shooting of their panda is hardly likely to be commemorated by conservationists, it did have one effect that has acted very much in the giant panda's favour ever since, and which is now the major force behind worldwide attempts to prevent the species from dying out. It brought the giant panda to public notice, introducing a creature hitherto little-known beyond scientific circles, which exuded charm and appeal. And it did all of this extremely successfully. By the mid-1930s the craze for panda shooting was past, and a new objective had emerged – to bring back a living giant panda to the west.

On 18 December 1936 this goal was accomplished, when the first giant panda known (officially) to have reached the western world alive was gently carried off the *President McKinley* liner at San Francisco, to be greeted with the kind of rapturous welcome normally reserved only for the Hollywood elite. Su-Lin had arrived. Still only a cub, she had been captured by Ruth Harkness, widow of William Harvest Harkness Jr, who had failed in his own earlier attempts to achieve this zoological coup.[75] Tragically, less than two years after her arrival in America, Su-Lin choked on a branch at her home in Chicago's Brookesfield Zoo and died; but in the years to come, other giant pandas would arrive in the west, most would thrive for many years, and all would be mammalian mega-stars.[71,76]

Equally well-publicised have been the many vain attempts to breed giant pandas successfully in the west – the most celebrated, long-running episode involving the chaperoned visits, back and forth between London and Moscow, by Chi-Chi and An-An. In contrast, giant pandas in Chinese zoos have been successfully bred and reared for many years.[71,76]

Needless to say, the adoration that giant pandas inspire in the west has not gone unnoticed by the Chinese, whose awareness of their country's most popular animal swiftly turned to alarm as they recognised that it has progressively become one of its rarest. Current estimates place the total number of wild pandas in China at less than 1000. For many years, therefore, the Chinese government has been at the forefront of efforts to perpetuate the species in its native habitat. For example, as the giant panda feeds principally upon bamboo shoots, large areas of bamboo forest have been set aside as protected zones. In

Sichuan's Wolong Panda Reserve the punishment for harming or killing a giant panda is often the death penalty.[77]

To end the giant panda story – an update on the much-debated matter of its taxonomic allegiances. Just what is this species – an enormous raccoon, or a small bear? Drawing upon anatomical comparisons and considerations, both schools of thought have acquired formidable champions. Dr Dwight Davis (Mammal Curator at Chicago's Field Museum of Natural History), for example, supports the bear candidature; while Dr R.F. Ewer (Ghana University carnivore expert) is among the raccoon identity's adherents. There is even a middle-of-the-road contingent, promoted by (among others) Dr George Schaller (Vice-President of the New York Zoological Society), recommending that the giant panda should be classed within a family of its own (or with the lesser panda as its only other member).[71]

In short, a century's worth of anatomy-based arguments has failed to provide a conclusive answer to the problem. The year 1956, however, marked the beginning of a different approach, when a paper was published by Kansas University researchers Dr Charles Leone and Alvin Wiens. They had carried out a painstaking serological study of the giant panda, and their results indicated a bear identity for it.[78] This was followed by other, more detailed and specific biochemical research, culminating in 1983 by utilisation of the most accurate and advanced tests so far devised for investigating a species' taxonomy – DNA hybridisation.[79]

Carried out by Dr Stephen O'Brien and colleagues at the U.S. National Cancer Institute, this basically involved making direct comparisons (via a complex means of chemical 'pairing') of the giant panda's genetic material (DNA) with that of bears and raccoons, to discover which of these displayed the greatest similarity to it – and which was therefore the giant panda's closest relative. Additional tests, of a more straightforward biochemical nature, were also run to check for consistency. The results obtained were indeed consistent, and provided some notable surprises. They indicated that whereas the lesser panda was truly a raccoon, the giant panda represented a specialised side-branch of the bears. Everyone had been wrong! The two pandas were only distantly related, and the giant panda was truly a bear – just as Père David had believed, more than a century earlier![79]

Moreover, those western scholars who had assumed (prior to the giant panda's discovery by Père David) that the white bear-like beasts depicted in ancient Chinese manuscripts were polar bears may not have been completely wrong after all. Since 1964, a number of creamy-white bears have been captured in Shennongjia, China, and some are currently housed in various Chinese zoos. Previously unknown to western science, these bears have naturally attracted much interest – especially as some Chinese researchers have expressed the opinion that they do not merely comprise an albinistic morph of the brown bear *Ursus arctos*, but may instead constitute a form quite separate from all others previously documented.[80-1]

In *The Giant Panda Book* (1981), Jenny Belson and James Gilheany offer a wonderfully succinct summary of the entire history of this, the world's most charismatic animal:[76]

Once Giant Pandas were hunted down and killed for their coats. Now they are treated like royalty, their courtships, births, and deaths chronicled around the world with an almost obsessive curiosity. The Giant Panda is the ultimate Chinese puzzle: one of the few creatures left on Earth which continue to mystify zoologists.

Judging from the recent discoveries recorded above, it seems more than likely that the giant panda will succeed in its profound ability to mystify for a long time to come.

Golden hamster – from extinct enigma to popular pet

Many pet owners will undoubtedly be surprised to learn that the world's most popular species of small pet mammal was virtually unknown to science until 1930, and that its rediscovery that year apparently snatched it from the very jaws of extinction. All of this, and more, feature in the remarkable history of the golden hamster.

It began in 1839, when the skin of a hamster-like creature, smaller than known hamsters and captured near Aleppo, northern Syria, was described by George R. Waterhouse at a meeting of London's Zoological Society. He named it *Cricetus auratus* – the golden hamster – after that particular specimen's unusually rich fur colour. Nothing more emerged regarding this newly-described species until 1879, when some live examples were brought back to England by James Skene, who had been working in the diplomatic service in Syria. These thrived and bred for 30 years (during which time their species was renamed *Mesocricetus auratus*); but when, in 1910, the newest generation of progeny descended from those original specimens died without issue, the golden hamster once again sank into obscurity.[82]

During the late 1920s, zoologist Prof. Israel Aharoni, from Jerusalem's Hebrew University, was reading through some

Golden hamster – amazingly, all of today's many millions of pet golden hamsters are descended from three specimens captured in Syria in 1930.

ancient Aramaic and Hebrew documents when he came upon a passage telling of a special kind of Syrian mouse. The passage described how it had once existed in the district of Chaleb (nowadays the site of Aleppo), and had been taken to Assyria, where specimens had been kept as docile pets in cages by children. Aharoni was very intrigued by this, as he knew of no living species of animal from the Aleppo area that fitted the description in the ancient document. In April 1930 he visited Aleppo, and there, in an 8-ft-deep earth burrow, an adult female golden hamster and eleven young were found, whose appearance tallied with that of the ancient text's mysterious 'Syrian mouse'. (Later that same month, three old females were also caught, and are now preserved at Berlin's Zoological Museum.) Aharoni brought back nine of the eleven young, which he reared and presented to his university's parasitology department in July 1930. Five escaped and a sixth was killed, but the remaining three – two females and one male – survived and bred successfully in captivity. To safeguard this rediscovered species' continuing existence, specimens were later sent to universities and zoos all over the world, thereby ensuring that if one establishment's stock was lost or somehow destroyed, there would still be many others elsewhere.[82-3]

The golden hamster soon became very popular as a laboratory species, particularly in the study of genetics as it bred so readily in captivity. Even more significantly, as a result of its docility it carved out a peerless niche for itself as a children's pet throughout the world, so that its numbers are today counted in the many millions. Most remarkable of all, however, is the fact that every single one of these is descended from the three specimens housed at the Hebrew University's parasitology department in the 1930s, because no others were obtained in the wild until Dr Michael Murphy procured 12 at Aleppo in 1971 (these were afterwards maintained at the National Institutes of Health at Bethesda, Maryland). In 1978, two more were brought from Aleppo to the U.S.A., this time by Bill Duncan of the Southwestern Medical School in Dallas, Texas.[83]

Desert rat kangaroo – the case of the missing marsupial

Closely paralleling the golden hamster's early history is the saga of the desert rat kangaroo *Caloprymnus campestris*. It is a small, sandy-furred species of hopping marsupial, characterised by its long ears, naked muzzle and enormous hind feet. It was first made known to science in 1843,

when three specimens were collected from an unrecorded locality in South Australia by Sir George Gray, who sent them to the British Museum (Natural History). Nothing more was heard of it until the early 1930s, when it was rediscovered by Adelaide University zoologist Dr H.H. Finlayson, who recorded in September 1931 that he had sighted a number of specimens in a large expanse of plains country within Lake Eyre Basin, straddling the borders of South Australia and Queensland.[84] Since then, however, no additional, conclusive observations have been reported, so that many fear that this scarcely-known marsupial, the only member of its genus, is extinct. Yet in view of its previous success at remaining hidden, and acknowledging that its terrain's harsh nature deters most people from visiting this region, there must still be hope that it survives.

Tasmacetus – world's most primitive beaked whale

Nine years after the type specimen of Longman's beaked whale *Indopacetus pacificus* had been officially documented, another, even more unusual, species of beaked whale made its existence known to science. On 7 November 1933, the carcase of a dead beaked whale (with pale underside but dark back and flippers) was washed onto a beach at Ohawe, in the New Zealand province of Taranaki. Over the next month, various reports concerning its appearance ashore, and subsequent disappearance back into the sea, were published in a local newspaper, the *Hawera Star*.[85] In early December, one of these attracted the attention of G. Shepherd, curator of the nearby Wanganui Alexander Museum, who alerted beach patrols to look out for its possible restranding. And sure enough, a

47

features conspicuously different from those of other species. In fact, it appears to be the most primitive of all known present-day beaked whales, and this is indicated by its most noticeable characteristic – in contrast to the mere handful (at most) of functional teeth possessed by all other beaked whales, *Tasmacetus* has no less than 90. Also of interest is that its lower jaw is slightly longer than its upper one.[86]

few days later the decomposing remains were once again cast up onto the shore. News of this was duly passed to Shepherd, who came over the next morning with two assistants to undertake the unenviable task of dissecting out all existing skeletal and dental material, braving the stench arising from the putrefying carcase of the 16-ft-long, one-month-dead whale.[85-6]

Well-wrapped and liberally soaked in lysol (in an attempt to counteract the smell), the precious material was transported back to the museum for preservation and study. During the examination that followed, it soon became clear that the remains were from a quite extraordinary and totally new species, so Shepherd invited cetologist Dr W.R.B. Oliver, director of the Dominion Museum at Wellington, to prepare a formal description. This was published in 1937, and in recognition of Shepherd's commendable actions in procuring and preserving its type specimen, Oliver named the new species *Tasmacetus shepherdi*.[86]

Sole member of a new genus, Shepherd's beaked whale possesses a number of cranial

By the early 1970s four more *Tasmacetus* specimens had been identified, all from New Zealand, but in 1973 a beached individual was recorded from Patagonia, followed later by a record from Chile, these examples expanding its known distribution range considerably. A beached example was also subsequently reported from South Australia. There are also records of possible sightings of *living* specimens from earlier years. In 1964 one such sighting was made by William Watkins from a cliff top near Christchurch, New Zealand;[38] and similarly, J. Vollewens's detailed account and sketch of a mysterious sea creature sighted by him in 1904, while he was serving on the steamer *Ambon* in the Straits of Bab-el-Mandeb (between the Red Sea and the Gulf of Aden),[87] readily calls to mind images of a Shepherd's beaked whale. If this was indeed the creature's identity, we have on file an eyewitness record of a seldom-seen species made almost 30 years *before* that species' discovery by science.

Solenodons – living fossils from the Caribbean

Although not prepossessing in appearance – they look like large rats with very long, attenuated snouts – solenodons have great zoological significance, as they represent the last of an ancient line of insectivorous mammals stretching back 30 million years. Now wholly confined to the West Indies, there are just two surviving species – the Hispaniolan solenodon *Solenodon paradoxus,* and the Cuban solenodon *S. cubanus.* Both are extremely rare, and have been written off as extinct on several occasions in the past.

The black-and-red Hispaniolan solenodon, measuring almost 2 ft in length, was formally described in 1833, but was seldom thereafter reported, and following the introduction of the mongoose onto Hispaniola in 1870, seemed to have totally vanished. However, in 1907 it was rediscovered in the island's northeastern interior by A. Hyatt Verrill. Five specimens were captured alive and sent to Washington Zoo and New York's Bronx Zoo. A few further specimens were caught – and then the species disappeared once more, not turning up again until 1935, when it was tracked down by German animal collector

Paul Thumb, assisted by his dog. Some live specimens were obtained and sent to various German zoos in the hope that they would breed and thrive in captivity, but although some lived for up to 11 years, the greatly-desired establishment of a captive breeding population was never achieved.[19]

The last pair in any European zoo died in 1973 at Frankfurt, the female in August and the male on 12 December. The latter, named Soli, was a very friendly little creature, who enjoyed climbing into the laps of visitors and poking his damp nose and extremely sensitive snout into their ears! Soli's species is totally protected on its island home, but is still very much on the endangered animals list.[88]

The Cuban solenodon was once represented by two readily differentiated subspecies – the very distinctive black-and-white *S. c. poeyana* and the buff-headed *S. c. cubanus.* The species as a whole was first brought to attention in 1838, and scientifically distinguished from its slightly larger Hispaniolan relative in 1863. Intermittently reported and captured for the next two years, it vanished afterwards until the capture of a living specimen in Cuba's eastern mountains in 1909. Sadly, this individual died only a short time later, and its species promptly disappeared again, remaining undetected for over 30 years. By the early 1940s, however, there were examples in Cuba's La Habana Zoo, and subsequently in the private zoo of a school in Santiago de Cuba as well, but these were all dead by the mid-1950s. No specimen of the buff-headed subspecies has been reported since 1944, but in 1974 a single male of the black-and-white *poeyana* version was caught, and small

Cuban solenodon – lost and found many times since its original discovery in 1838.
(Fortean Picture Library)

numbers, wholly protected, have been recorded in Cuba's eastern section. Even so, it remains extremely scarce.[19,88] The solenodons' main hope for future survival seems to be in successful captive breeding.

Another family of unusual insectivores exclusive to the West Indies consisted of the nesophontids – shrew-like mammals of varying sizes (one species was as large as a chipmunk) that supposedly died out during the 17th century on the cluster of Caribbean islands comprising their homeland. In 1930, however, some nesophontid bones and tissues extracted from a mass of owl pellets discovered in the Dominican Republic, Hispaniola, were found to be so fresh that it seemed clear that the individual(s) from which they had derived had been killed only a short time before. This encouraged Smithsonian Institution zoologist Dr Gerrit Miller to speculate that some nesophontids may still survive after all.[19,89]

No further evidence for such survival, however, has been obtained, but given the extremely elusive nature of their solenodon relative on this same island, perhaps there may indeed come a time when the nesophontid family will be resurrected.

Kouprey – an important new mammal from Cambodia

A favourite subject for temple carvings and statues of the Khymer Culture of 400-800 years ago,[90] and one of Asia's largest mammals, yet undescribed by science until the 1930s and still of uncertain identity more than 50 years later, the wild grey ox of Cambodia is a pre-eminent paradox in the annals of zoology.

During the early 1930s, various scientists visiting northern Cambodia's hilly areas took note of native reports describing a large, dark-bodied, white-limbed type of wild ox, standing a little over 6 ft at the shoulder, bearing a very long, pendulous dewlap (flap of skin) extending from its throat to its mid-chest region, and armed with a pair of lengthy, slender, widely-spreading horns. It was known locally as the kouprey.[2-3,91]

Such information greatly interested Prof. Achille Urbain, the director of Vincennes Zoo near Paris. In 1936, while visiting northern Cambodia, Prof. Urbain met resident vet Dr R. Sauvel and saw at his home a most impressive set of ox horns allegedly from a kouprey. Intrigued by these, Urbain implored Sauvel to do whatever he could to capture a living specimen for exhibition at Vincennes Zoo, a request that Sauvel succeeded in fulfilling not long afterwards, when he captured a young bull. This bull became the first and only kouprey to be displayed at any zoo in the world. Dr Sauvel also shot an adult bull kouprey which he allowed Urbain to examine closely.[91]

Based upon these two specimens, Prof. Urbain officially described the kouprey in late 1937, classing it as a new species and naming it *Bos sauveli*, thereby allying it with the other two species of large Asian wild ox – namely the comparably-sized banteng *B. banteng,* and the somewhat larger gaur *B. gaurus*.[91]

In addition to its grey-black body colour, white 'stockings' and prominent dewlap, the kouprey is distinguished from other Asian oxen by bearing only a very insignificant ridge along its back – differing markedly from the well-developed version exhibited by the other species. Furthermore, its horns are distinctive not just on account of their length, slender form and wide span, but also by way of their fringes. Just behind the tip of each horn in adult male koupreys is a fringe of horny splinters – the remains of the juvenile horn sheath that has been pierced by the permanent, adult horn which grows underneath as the kouprey matures. In all other species of oxen, this fringe of splinters is swiftly removed when the animal rubs its horns on the ground, so that only a ridge is left behind. The complete curve of each of the adult male kouprey's horns, however, is such that this type of rubbing is not possible, so the fringe stays in place for a long time afterwards.[2-3,10,91-2]

The kouprey also has many internal distinguishing anatomical features. Indeed, following his meticulous examination of the kouprey's anatomy, in 1940 Harvard University mammalogist Dr Harold Jefferson Coolidge was so convinced of the kouprey's distinctly separate scientific status that he proposed a new genus for it – *Novibos* ('new ox').[93]

Kouprey – Cambodia's rarely-spied grey ox in its native homeland.
(Dr Pierre Pfeffer/World Wide Fund for Nature)

All of this, therefore, makes all the more surprising the many claims since then that the kouprey is not a genuine species, and controversy regarding its precise scientific identity continues to the present day. The reason for this uncertainty is the kouprey's unexpected amalgamation of features from different species of oxen.

For example, some of its cranial and external characteristics are more comparable to those of the gaur and (especially) the banteng, but certain others appear closer to those of the domestic zebu *B. indicus*. Consequently, some researchers, such as F. Edmond-Blanc, have suggested that the kouprey may be a hybrid form, probably descended from interbreeding between the above species. Yet Urbain sighted entire herds of kouprey after its discovery – the existence of herds would not be expected if it were merely a hybrid.[10,92]

In contrast, Dr Charles Wharton has opined that the kouprey may have been domesticated during the early Khymer Culture but became feral after the latter's decline, so that today's koupreys are modified versions of the original stock. Certain others have expanded upon this theory, suggesting that the kouprey may actually have *originated* as a domestic breed, produced deliberately by banteng-zebu crossbreeding, later running wild, and existing ever since in a feral state.[10,90,92] Confounding matters even further, there are (or were) domestic cattle in the same locality as the kouprey that combine certain of its features with those of the zebu. Such cattle are known as boeufs des Stiengs (named after the area's people, the Stieng).

Whether or not the kouprey is itself of domestic origin, however, is another matter entirely. Mammalogists Dr H. Bohlken and Dr Theodor Haltenorth feel that it is wisest to consider the kouprey as a genuine wild species as long as there is no conclusive evidence pointing to its derivation from a feral domestic form.[10,90,92] Zoologist Prof. Colin Groves considers that the kouprey may be a last surviving remnant of the wild species that gave rise to the zebu. A similar viewpoint has also been proffered by mammalogist Braestrup, who thereby regards it as the world's most primitive species of wild ox alive today. Finally, cattle expert Dr Caroline Grigson has suggested that the banteng, gaur, kouprey, zebu, and boeuf des Stiengs are all members of an extensive species complex.[90,92]

Of course, comparisons of the kouprey's DNA with that of the above oxen would be greatly beneficial in shedding light on this much-muddled matter, but with available kouprey material virtually non-existent, there seems scant hope at present that such analyses will take place. When officially described in 1937, it was believed to number at least 1000 in Cambodia, with similar counts in Laos, Vietnam and Thailand. By 1953, however, it had seemingly died out in Thailand, and disturbance by hunters brought its numbers down dramatically elsewhere. In spite of being chosen by Prince Sihanouk as Cambodia's national animal in 1964, the kouprey continued its downward gallop towards extinction. This was hastened along after 1970 by years of intensive warfare within the major portion of its distribution range between the Khymer Rouge and the collective Vietnamese and Kampuchean forces. Indeed, for some time zoologists feared that the kouprey had completely died out, but sporadic reports during the 1970s of small numbers in various localities within southern Laos and northern Cambodia

refuted this. Moreover, during 1980 it was rediscovered in Thailand, in Si Sa Ket Province's Dongrak mountain range, on the border with Cambodia, prompting the king of Thailand to proclaim the setting aside of 79,000 acres in the province as a kouprey sanctuary.[90,94-5]

In 1988, the entire world total of koupreys was estimated by biologists working in Indochina at no more than 300, most of which exist in Cambodia, with 100 at most in Laos, plus a few specimens recently sighted in Vietnam. The Thailand contingent appears to consist of individuals that wander back and forth across the border with Cambodia. It is indisputably one of the world's rarest wild animals.[90,96]

Any attempts to safeguard the kouprey from demise in the wild are fraught with problems arising from its relatively remote habitat, and its vulnerability to local hunters, who see a 6-ft-tall ox as too good a source of fresh meat to be missed. Obviously, the best hope for the kouprey would be the establishment of a captive herd, enabling the species to multiply in safety, and also enabling some specimens to be sent periodically to other zoos or parks around the world in order to establish additional herds, thereby mirroring the Duke of Bedford's highly successful efforts with Père David's deer *Elaphurus davidianus* earlier this century.

The need for a captive breeding herd was recognised by Hanoi University zoologist Prof. Vo Quy. In November 1988, after two years of planning, and sponsored by many zoos around the world as well as by the World Wide Fund for Nature and the International Union for the Conservation of Nature, he led a team of workers into a region of Vietnam where a kouprey sighting had been made in 1987, in the hope of capturing some specimens. This herd was to be maintained in one of Vietnam's wildlife parks, but some specimens were to be sent to various of the funding zoos. So far, however, the search has not been successful, but if specimens are eventually captured this would finally provide zoologists with the opportunity to carry out DNA comparisons between koupreys and other forms of ox.[96] In short, within the next few years if all goes well, not only might the kouprey finally be freed from the imminent threat of extinction, but it may also reveal its true scientific identity, so that we will at last know just what this beast really is.

Selevin's dormouse – an insectivorous rodent

In 1938, zoologist W.A. Selevin discovered an extraordinary little rodent on the sandy plains of Kazakhstan, near to the village of Betpak-Dala. Accordingly, when formally described the following year by Soviet scientists Drs B.A. Belosludov and V.S. Bashanov, it was named *Selevinia betpakdalaensis*.[97] Although only mouse-sized, it looks rather plump, because of its relatively long hair, and it behaves in a most un-rodent-like manner. Instead of following a predominantly vegetarian diet, it is exclusively insectivorous, devouring grasshoppers and other insects. Generally referred to as the desert or Selevin's dormouse, it does bear a superficial resemblance to dormice, but its collective anatomy is sufficiently distinct from this family of rodents (and, indeed, from all others) for it to be housed in an entire family of its own.[97] Despite its relatively recent scientific debut, this unique little

creature's nomadic human neighbours, the Kazakhstans, have always known of its existence (even though it is mainly nocturnal), and refer to it as *shalman-kulak* or *kalkan-kulak*, both names inspired by the species' large round ears.[10,97]

Hutias – hide-and-seek rodents of the West Indies

Hutias are large coypu-related rodents indigenous to the West Indies, and famed for their long-running series of impromptu appearances and disappearances during the 20th century. One of the most celebrated examples involved Cuvier's hutia *Plagiodontia aedium*. Described by, and named after, the eminent French naturalist Frederick Cuvier in 1836, and based upon a single specimen obtained in 1826 by Alexander Ricord from Hispaniola, no more specimens or reports of this 1.5-ft-long species were brought forth for over a century. So zoologists felt more than justified in classing it as extinct. Thus it was with much surprise that they learnt in 1947 that a living individual had been captured in a little-explored area of the island, and that according to local hunters it was quite common there.[19,98]

Hutia – several of these West Indian rodents have famously appeared or reappeared during the 20th century.
(Fortean Picture Library)

When first discovered in the 19th century, Cuvier's hutia was thought to be the only modern-day member of its genus, but in 1923 Hispaniola proved science wrong when a second living *Plagiodontia* species was collected in the island's northeastern section, within the Dominican Republic. Based upon 10 adults and three young obtained close to Samaná Bay that year by Dr W.L. Abbott, the new species was christened *P. hylaeum*. The Dominican hutia is distinguished from Cuvier's by its narrower feet and sharper, longer claws, its proportionately larger body and shorter tail, and its darker fur.[99]

The Cuban dwarf hutia *Capromys nana* first became known to science as a seemingly extinct species, officially described in 1917 from some apparently ancient jawbones found in cave deposits in the Sierra de Hato Nuevo and near Limones in Cuba's western-central region.[100] Independently, however, 1917 also saw the discovery of some living specimens, collected in the island's famous Zapata Swamp[19] (from where a new wren, *Ferminia cerverai*, would be formally described in 1926, and a new rail, *Cyanolimnas cerverai*, in 1927[101]).

A couple or so centuries ago, there were many more species of hutia alive in the West Indies than are present today; the disappearances of those no longer living can be largely attributed to indirect interference or deliberate destruction by man. Unhappily, such extinctions have not ceased – indeed, certain species of hutia have been described in recent times only to disappear completely thereafter. In 1967, for example, a new species, named Garrido's hutia *Capromys garridoi*, was described from a single individual collected on the tiny islet of Cayos Maja, off southern Cuba; only two others have been sighted (in 1989, on two

nearby islets).[102-4] The year 1970 saw the discovery of the little earth hutia, restricted to Juan Garcia Cay, also sited just off southern Cuba. Four specimens were collected, two of which were captured alive and maintained at Cuba's Institute of Biology by L.S. Varona, who named their species *C. sanfelipensis*. Sadly, however, no others have been recorded since.[103,105] Similarly, Cabrera's hutia *C. angelcabrerai*, confined to the Cayos de Ana Maria islets, once again situated just off southern Cuba, is known only from a small series of specimens collected there during the 1970s.[103,106]

There seems little doubt that some if not all of those latter hutias are extinct; their island homes are so small that it is unlikely that viable populations could remain hidden, especially when, as in the case of the little earth hutia in 1980, scientific expeditions arrive specifically to seek out all existing specimens and are unable to find any.

Jentink's duiker – return of the world's rarest antelope

Duikers are diminutive, short-limbed, primitive antelopes native to tropical Africa. They derive their name from their tendency to dive for cover into nearby foliage at the slightest indication of danger; *duiker* is Afrikaans for 'diver'.

With a shoulder height of no more than 31 in, Jentink's duiker *Cephalophus jentinki* is actually one of the tallest species. Regrettably, however, it also lays claim to the much less desirable title of the world's rarest antelope. It first came to attention in 1884, when a female was collected near the Liberian coast by F.A. Jentink, working for F.X. Stampfli. Two more were obtained in 1887, and in 1892 the species was described and named by Oldfield Thomas of the

Jentink's duiker – the largest duiker, the rarest of all antelopes, and lost for 61 years until rediscovered in 1948.
(Gladys Porter Zoo)

not only in Liberia, where it inhabits deep, secluded forests, but also in the Ivory Coast, where the natives call it *nienagbé*. Nonetheless, it is believed to number only in the low hundreds, and is considered to be gravely endangered.[42,103]

British Museum (Natural History), which still has the type specimen. Reports of its existence in Sierra Leone also emerged at that time, but were not confirmed.[42]

Jentink's duiker exhibits a very unusual, diagnostic colour scheme. Except for its white muzzle, its head, neck and shoulders are jet black, whereas the rest of its body is medium grey, and the two contrasting colours are separated by a wide collar of very light grey that encircles its body from the back to the lower chest. The outer side of each limb is the same shade of grey as the body, but the inner side is much paler. Its tail is also pale, but terminates in a darker tuft of hair. Its horns are very small, almost straight, and pointed.[42]

It is clearly not an antelope to be overlooked or confused with any other, which is why zoologists later began to fear that it was extinct. Following its scientific description, nothing more was heard of Jentink's duiker for half a century. Not even an unconfirmed sighting or two were reported; it was as if this distinctive antelope had never existed. Then in 1948, P.L. Dekeyser and A. Villiers successfully refuted that impression when they obtained the skull of an adult male in Liberia's Dyiglo region. Later searches revealed that it was present

On 1 December 1971, the Gladys Porter Zoo in Brownsville, Texas, achieved a significant captive-breeding coup with the birth of Alpha, the first Jentink's duiker ever born in captivity. Happily, Alpha, a female, thrived, and by 1979 she had not only been joined by a mate, Beta, but also had given birth to two offspring. These are believed to be the only specimens of Jentink's duiker currently in captivity anywhere in the world.[107]

Most recently, in 1988, this reclusive species was rediscovered in Sierra Leone, ending decades of doubt as to whether it had ever existed here to begin with.[108]

Andean wolf – a mystery mammal from the mountains

The maned wolf *Chrysocyon brachyurus* is a highly distinctive species whose pointed muzzle, bright chestnut coat and bushy tail make it look more like a fox than a wolf, except for its extremely long, slender legs, which instantly set it completely apart from all true foxes, and which enable it to peer over the tall grass of its pampas homelands, extending from Brazil to Argentina. Its unusual appearance is described very aptly by its native name – *aguara guaza* ('fox on stilts').

Prior to the 1920s, the maned wolf was believed to have no close relatives; it appeared to be a species well-delineated from all other members of the dog family. Then in 1927, German animal dealer Lorenz Hagenbeck was visiting Buenos Aires when he saw a most unusual pelt for sale. It was reminiscent of the maned wolf's, but was much longer, thicker and darker in colour, varying from black on its upperparts to dark brown on its neck and underparts. Like the maned wolf, it possessed a particularly dense, mane-like covering over its neck, but its ears were much smaller and rounder. Making enquiries, Hagenbeck learnt that the pelt belonged to a strange dog-like beast from the Andes.[2,23,109]

Hagenbeck bought the pelt and submitted it for scientific examination upon his return to Germany. Its unusual appearance generated a great deal of discussion and bemusement, but the final verdict was that it seemed to represent a previously unrecorded mountain-dwelling counterpart of the maned wolf. Naturally, however, such an opinion was very provisional – a complete specimen, or at least a skull and/or other remains, would be needed to ascertain more accurately its status. The problem with a unique pelt (especially a unique canid pelt), however distinctive it may be, is that there is little way of determining whether it is from a genuinely discrete species or merely from some strange hybrid or mongrel.[2,23,109]

One of the experts who inclined towards the identity of a mountain maned wolf for the pelt was mammalogist Dr Ingo Krumbiegel – especially when he learnt from Hagenbeck in 1947 that during his Buenos Aires visit he had seen three other pelts of that same type. Canid hybrids are notoriously variable, hence the known existence of at least four similar pelts favoured the reality of a distinct species, rather than crossbreeding between domestic dogs and/or wild species, as the most likely explanation for them.[2,23,109]

In addition, Krumbiegel recalled to mind an odd-looking canid skull that he had examined in 1935, and which had been present within a collection of specimens originating from the Andes. At the time, he had dismissed it as an unusual maned wolf skull, but now he sought it out again, and meticulously re-examined it. Although it did indeed have close similarities to maned wolf skulls, with a length of 31 cm, it was more than 5 cm (2 in) longer than the average recorded from a sample of 23 from this species. Moreover, the maned wolf is an exclusive plains-dweller, not known from mountainous areas. But what if it had a high-altitude counterpart? What would such a creature look like? Krumbiegel realised that it would certainly be a densely-furred, short-eared form, which would conserve heat more efficiently than the typical shorter-furred, large-eared maned wolf, and would therefore match the appearance of Hagenbeck's obscure pelt. [2,23,109]

It all seemed to fit, and so, in 1949, Krumbiegel published a cautious formal description of this putative mountain-modified maned wolf, which he named *Oreocyon hagenbecki* (Hagenbeck's mountain wolf), commonly referred to as the Andean wolf. In his paper, he provided comparative sketches of the typical maned wolf, and the likely appearance of this newly-described Andean equivalent, which, in addition to the pelt characteristics and shorter ears already noted, would most probably have shorter limbs and more powerful claws. Not long afterwards, he discovered that the name *Oreocyon* had already been given by palaeontologist Othniel Charles Marsh to a primitive species of fossil carnivorous mammal called a creodont in 1872. Consequently, he had no option but to change the name of the Andean wolf, rechristening it *Dasycyon hagenbecki* in 1953, thereby emphasising the thickness of its coat.[2,23,109]

Krumbiegel and the rest of the zoological community waited eagerly for fresh specimens with which to resolve the issue of the Andean wolf's identity, but nothing else has been obtained so far. In the meantime, Dr Fritz Dieterlen has carried out some detailed hair analyses, using samples of the fur from its type (and only) pelt and comparing their form and structure with those of fur from other canid specimens. He concluded that there were certain similarities between the Andean wolf's fur and that of the alsatian (German shepherd dog), but that they were not sufficiently strong to confirm a direct relationship (i.e. a derivation of the Andean wolf from some form of hybrid between alsatians and other dogs, etc). In contrast, three years later Dr Angel Cabrera unequivocally classed the Andean wolf pelt as that of a domestic dog.[23,110]

More than forty years after Krumbiegel's description of *D. hagenbecki*, its mystery remains unsolved. Is it merely some unusual crossbreed, or does a large and highly significant species of wild dog exist in the Andes, still awaiting official acceptance by science?

Don Felipe's aquatic weasel

The early 1950s were good years for mammalian discoveries in South America. The black-shouldered opossum *Caluromysiops irrupta*, a new genus and species of marsupial native to Peru and Brazil, was first revealed in 1950,[111] and the following year saw the discovery of what would seem to be a South American counterpart of the water-loving mink.[112]

On 2 October 1951, mammalogist Dr Philip Hershkovitz (affectionately known to the locals as Don Felipe) captured an unusual weasel at Santa Marta, near San Agustin in Huila, Colombia. An adult specimen with very dark upperparts and pale buff-orange underparts, what made it so unusual was the presence of distinct webbing between its toes, particularly extensive between the second, third, and fourth on each foot, indicating an aquatic lifestyle. On 29 September 1956, another specimen, an adult male, was collected – this time by Kjell von Sneidern at Popayán, Cauca, in Colombia.[112]

Both of these specimens were presented to Chicago's Field Museum of Natural History; yet surprisingly, the new species that they clearly represented remained undescribed and un-named until as recently as 1979. In that year the necessary duty was undertaken by Drs Robert J. Izor and Luis de la Torre, who named it *Mustela felipei*, after its discoverer.[112] Since then, a further skin has been procured, this time from Ecuador; and most recently a living specimen was captured in Colombia's Cueva de los Guacharos National Park.[113] Its species is usually referred to as the Colombian or aquatic weasel.

Pygmy killer whale – a little-known little whale

Whereas the common killer whale *Orcinus orca* is one of the world's most familiar cetaceans, the pygmy killer *Feresa attenuata* is one of its least known, and at no more than 9 ft long is less than one third of the length of its mighty relative.

The first two specimens – just a couple of skulls – were obtained in the 19th century, after which this scarcely-known sea-dweller was not recorded again for more than 70 years. In 1952 it was rediscovered when a specimen was obtained near Taiji, on Honshu, Japan, providing scientists with the first opportunity of gaining a complete skeleton of the species.[114] Many others have since been procured, mostly from dead stranded individuals, frequently from Japanese waters, but also documented from the Caribbean, southern Africa, Hawaii and the Gulf of Mexico. Thus, this principally black cetacean with white lips and chin is now known to be widely distributed, but its natural history remains virtually unknown.[38]

Incidentally, the pygmy killer whale should not be confused with the dwarf killer whale. The latter is something of a mystery species, formally described by a team of Soviet cetologists in 1981, who named it *Orcinus nanus*,[115] but its status as a valid species is not widely accepted at the present time. In 1983 another allegedly new species of killer whale was described, this time by Drs A.A. Berzin and V.L. Vladimirov, who named it *O. glacialis*, and recorded it from Prudes Bay in the high latitudes of the Antarctic's Indian Ocean sector. But again its classification as a separate species has not gained widespread acceptance so far.[116]

Pygmy otter shrews

Discovered in 1861 by the French-American explorer Paul du Chaillu, the giant otter shrew *Potamogale velox* of West Africa is an extraordinary creature. Although its closest relatives are the hedgehogs, moles and the other insectivores, its pursuit of an aquatic existence comparable to that of otters has engineered, via evolutionary convergence, a corresponding outward appearance, so that it very closely resembles a miniature otter,

measuring just over 2 ft in total length. For almost a century *Potamogale* was believed to be the only species of otter shrew in existence, in a family all to itself, but in 1954 a hitherto unknown second species was officially described.

Discovered at Ziéla, at the foot of the Nimba Mountains in the Guinea Republic, it was only 10 in long, looked more like the familiar water shrews (*Neomys*) than an otter shrew (or an otter), and had a rounded tail instead of the noticeably flattened version used so effectively by *Potamogale* for propulsion through the water. It didn't even have webbed feet. Nonetheless, internal anatomy clearly indicated a close relationship with the giant otter shrew; and so to underline this, while concomitantly stressing its much smaller size, the new species was named *Micropotamogale lamottei* – 'Lamotte's pygmy otter shrew' (after French zoologist Dr M. Lamotte, who collected animal specimens in West Africa).[117]

Only a year later, a second species of pygmy otter shrew was described. Originally named *P. ruwenzorii* but subsequently reclassified as a *Micropotamogale*, it was somewhat intermediate between *M. lamottei* and *Potamogale*. For although it was most similar to the former in overall appearance, it was longer, reaching up to 14 in, and, like *Potamogale*, had webbed feet. Its type specimen had been obtained in 1953, caught in a native basket fish-trap set at Mutsora, on the River Talya – a River Lume tributary on the western slopes of the Ruwenzori Mountains in Zaire.[117]

Close examination of the few pygmy otter shrew specimens on record indicate that they form a link with the Madagascan tenrecs (see p. 40), so nowadays tenrecs and all three species of otter shrew are usually classed together within a single family.[48]

Golden langur – a new, brightly-furred monkey from India

One of Asia's most attractive primates eluded capture and classification by science until as recently as 1955. Yet as far back as 1907, E.O. Shebbeare recorded reports of sightings of an unidentified form of monkey with light silvery-golden fur from the hills of northern Assam, close to the India-Bhutan border. No specimens were obtained, however, and the monkeys gained little scientific notice, as they were simply assumed to be golden snub-nosed monkeys *Rhinopithecus roxellanae* from Bhutan that had wandered southwards into India.[118]

Then, in 1947, while spending some time at the Jamduar Forest Rest Home on the eastern bank of the Sankosh River in northern Assam's Goalpara District, sportsman-naturalist C.G. Baron made his own sighting of these unexamined, brightly-furred monkeys, and judged them to be an unidentified species of langur. Also known as leaf monkeys, langurs are slender, long-bodied and lengthy-tailed simians – their gracility contrasting with the more robust build of the golden snub-nosed monkey. There are many species of langur spread through much of Asia, but none matched the description of the mysterious examples from northern Assam.[118]

By now they had attracted the attention of E.P. Gee, a noted authority on Indian wildlife, and in November 1953 he visited the Jamduar Forest area to see them for himself. On the river's eastern bank at a locality close to Bhutan, he spotted two troops, collectively comprising more than 40 individuals, which he photographed, filmed and observed closely for many days. They were certainly langurs, but their exquisite colouration distinguished them at once from all others known. During the next year, Gee communicated with various primatologists concerning them, and in January 1955 his films and photos had attracted the keen interest of Dr S.L. Hora, director of the Zoological Survey of India, who sent a party in search of some specimens to enable the form to be officially classified.[118]

Six were duly collected in April 1955 from the forests around the Jamduar Rest Home, by the party's leader, zoologist Dr H. Kharjuria. Upon examination of these, Kharjuria decided that although its cranial characteristics were similar to those of the capped langur *Presbytis pileatus*, the paler colouring and various other pelage differences were sufficient to necessitate the new monkey's delineation as a separate species – which, in honour of its leading investigator, he named *P. gcci*. In popular parlance, it is most commonly termed the golden langur.[119]

No more than two years had elapsed before another new species of langur was named – the white-headed langur *P. leucocephalus*, discovered in China's Fusui County (Funan, southern Kwangsi). Initially known from a single skin obtained in 1953 during a scientific expedition led by T'an Pang-Chien, by 1957 ten more skins had been collected from the same area, convincing him that this eyecatching monkey (known to the locals as *paiyuan* – 'white ape') truly constituted a distinct species. Most other authorities, conversely, prefer to regard it merely as a subspecies of the crested langur *P. cristatus*.[120]

Fraser's dolphin – the world's most common 'rare' sea mammal

Fraser's dolphin is a species with an eventful

and unusual scientific history, which began as far back as 1895, when its type specimen was collected by Charles Hose at the mouth of the Lutong River, Baram, in the portion of Borneo nowadays called Sarawak. Its remains eventually arrived at the British Museum (Natural History) in the company of several specimens of the Indopacific humpback dolphin *Sousa chinensis* – which led in 1901 to its own classification as a member of that species. It attracted no further attention for the next 54 years – until 1955, when merely by chance its remains were noticed by cetologist F.C. Fraser, who swiftly realised that it was something markedly different from any form of humpback dolphin. He proceeded to study it very carefully, and perceived that its anatomy combined certain features characteristic of the ploughshare dolphins (*Lagenorhynchus*) with others more typical of the common dolphin *Delphinus delphis*.[38,121]

It was without question a new species, and one worthy of a new genus too – so in 1956 Fraser created the genus *Lagenodelphis*, stressing its shared affinities with *Lagenorhynchus* and *Delphinus*. Its full scientific name is *Lagenodelphis hosei*, honouring its discoverer.[121]

Following its official recognition by science, cetologists avidly awaited fresh news regarding this newly-unmasked species, but their expectations were not fulfilled. At the beginning of the 1970s, the *Guinness Book of Records* referred to Fraser's dolphin as probably the world's rarest species of marine mammal, known only from the single Sarawak specimen – but what a difference a few months can make. For by the end of 1971, this cryptic cetacean had become one of the world's most widely distributed dolphins.[38]

The explanation for such a tremendous turnabout was that within the first five months of 1971, a number of stranded specimens had turned up in a variety of widely separated localities – from Cocos Island in the eastern Pacific, and New South Wales in Australia, to an area of shoreline close to Durban in South Africa. More recently, Fraser's dolphin has also been recorded from the Caribbean, as well as the coasts of Japan and Taiwan. Sometimes, entire schools have been sighted too, so that the species is now known to be relatively common – a far cry from its earlier status.[38]

A small cetacean, attaining a mere 8.5 ft in total length when fully grown, and characterised externally by surprisingly short fins and snout, Fraser's dolphin has medium-grey upperparts and pinkish-white underparts, with two distinctive lateral stripes – the upper one pale grey and stretching from just above its eye to its tail's base, the lower one a more striking, jet-black band spanning its eye and anus.[38]

Japanese beaked whale – teeth like the leaves of the maidenhair tree

The first specimen of the Japanese beaked whale *Mesoplodon ginkgodens* to come to scientific attention did so in a particularly tragic way. In September 1957, a large, uniformly blue-black whale swam close to the shore at Tokyo's Oiso Beach, attracted by the sight of some boys playing ball at the water's edge and no doubt inquisitive to learn more about their activity. In reply, the boys waded into the water and promptly clubbed the poor animal to death with their baseball bats. The only positive aspect to emerge from this unpleasant incident was that the whale's body was salvaged and carefully examined by cetologists Drs M. Nishiwaki and T. Kamiya from the Japanese Whale Research Institute. They found that its relative body proportions and certain anatomical features set it apart from all other beaked whales, so in 1958 they designated it as the type specimen of a new species.[122]

Yet another member of the genus *Mesoplodon*, its specific name is derived from the most unusual, diagnostic shape of its single pair of teeth (sited midway along the lower jaw in males, but failing to erupt through the gums in females), because when viewed from the side these teeth bear a close resemblance to the lobe-edged leaves of the Chinese maidenhair tree *Ginkgo biloba*, one of the plant kingdom's most famous 'living fossils'.[38,122]

In 1963, a second specimen appeared, washed ashore at Ratmalana, Sri Lanka. This was initially described as another new species, and given the name *M. hotaula*, but then a third specimen turned up, originally cast up onto Delmar's public beach in southern California during 1954 (though not identified at that time). Comparisons of these three individuals by beaked whale expert Dr J.C. Moore revealed that they were all of the same species, so that *M. hotaula* thereafter became a synonym of *M. ginkgodens*.[38,123]

During his studies on the Japanese beaked whale (which appears to attain a total length of up to 17 ft when mature), Moore uncovered some other preserved remains previously unrecognised as being of *M. ginkgodens* identity. Some fresh specimens were also washed ashore on Japanese beaches, and a single individual was recorded from Taiwan. Yet even though it may be widely distributed throughout the warmer regions of the tropical Indopacific, the small number of specimens and sightings on record imply that the Japanese beaked whale is either fairly rare or fairly elusive (or both).[38,123]

Cochito – a petite porpoise from the Gulf of California

The Japanese beaked whale was not the only new cetacean to be described in 1958. Back in 1950, an unusually small, sun-bleached porpoise skull, resting above the high tide line on a beach at Punta San Felipe in the Gulf of California, was sighted and brought back to the University of California by Dr Kenneth Norris, one of the university's mammalogical researchers. At first it was merely assumed to be from an undersized specimen of the common porpoise *Phocoena phocoena*, but some fresh, similarly diminutive skulls were obtained from the Gulf of California in the next few years. After comparing these with each other and with known *P. phocoena* specimens, certain other morphological differences between the latter and the smaller skulls were noted, and Norris and his Cornell University co-worker Dr William McFarland decided that a new species was present. In 1958 they christened this petite porpoise *Phocoena sinus*.[124]

In general parlance, it is referred to as the Gulf of California porpoise, or the cochito – the name by which it is known among local fishermen, in whose nets it frequently becomes entangled. Dark grey on top, creamish-white underneath, the cochito attains a maximum length of only 5 ft, thereby laying claim to the title of the world's smallest species of cetacean. Unhappily, however, on account of what seems to be a comparably minute population size, a very limited distribution (apparently confined to the Gulf), and alarmingly high mortality incurred by accidental death in fishing nets, it would also seem to be one of the rarest. Following considerable publicity roused upon its behalf by the Defenders of Wildlife organisation, in 1985 the U.S. government officially classed the cochito as an endangered species, but with few (if any) confirmed cochito sightings in recent years, its chances of survival do not seem very promising.[38,103]

Liberiictis – a mysterious mongoose from West Africa

By the early part of 1958, Heidelberg University ethnologist Dr Hans Himmelheber had amassed an impressive collection of mammal skulls from northeastern Liberia. He had collected some of these himself while undertaking research at villages in that area, retaining the skulls of animals killed by the village hunters for food. Others had been sent to him by missionaries working in the area.[125]

His collection was examined by fellow Heidelberg University scientist Dr Hans-Jurg Kuhn, who became particularly interested in eight large mongoose skulls that he was unable to assign to any known species. So, while attending the fifteenth International Congress of Zoology, held at London during July 1958, he took the opportunity of visiting mammalogist Dr R.W. Hayman of the British Museum (Natural History), where he showed him one of these eight anomalous skulls. Hayman readily discerned its distinct nature, and after later examining the other seven he announced that they were from a hitherto undescribed species, and one so far removed from all other mongooses that it deserved an entire genus all to itself.[125]

Designating the first skull he had examined as the new mongoose's type (which had been collected some time between October 1957 and April 1958 at the village of Kpeaplay – the most northerly of two different villages bearing this same name), he christened the species *Liberiictis kuhni*.[125]

Structurally, the skulls of the Liberian mongoose compared most closely with those of the cusimanse mongooses (genus *Crossarchus*), but differed from them by virtue of their larger size, the possession of an extra pair of upper and lower premolars, their longer muzzle, and relatively smaller, weaker teeth. These latter characteristics suggested to Hayman that the Liberian mongoose was probably insectivorous, rather than a predator of more substantial animals such as rodents or reptiles.[125]

And so yet another taxonomically significant new mammal had become known to science – or at least its existence and its cranial features had become known. Science still did not know what it looked like in life – a situation that lasted for quite a time. Then in summer 1971, during an expedition to Liberia's northern Grand Gedeh County, two specimens were obtained near the town of Tar. One, an adult male, was captured in cutover High Forest by a local farmer on 7 July. The second, a juvenile female, was caught 22 days later in a burrow near a termite's nest, again in cutover High Forest. Except for its pale-shaded neck (which bears a stripe along each side, running from ear to shoulder), the elusive *Liberiictis* proved to be principally dark brown in colour, and it had long claws – which would be of use in ripping apart termite mounds in search of the insects inside, assuming the validity of Hayman's postulated insectivorous diet for this species.[103,126]

In 1989 a male individual was captured in Liberia's Gbi National Forest, and is currently housed at Canada's Metro Toronto Zoo. Efforts are now being made to capture a female to initiate a captive breeding programme.[103,126]

Ufiti – the friendly 'ghost' of Nkata Bay

One of the most mystifying of this century's mammalian discoveries involved a female chimpanzee named Ufiti. In August 1959, local inhabitants of Nkata Bay, on the western shore of Malawi's Lake Nyasa, began to report sightings of a strange ape-like entity in the fringes of the adjacent forest. Such reports were readily confirmed, because the animal in question became very interested in the construction work that was taking place on a new bridge and road at the nearby Limpasa River, and stayed in the vicinity to observe the proceedings. And as its amiable curiosity largely eclipsed its fear of humans, it could be closely approached.[18,127-8]

When questioned, the local westerners asserted that it was new to them, and the natives referred to it as *ufiti* – meaning 'ghost'. It was not a ghost, however, but a mature female chimpanzee – which came as a great surprise to zoologists, because chimpanzees had never before been recorded in Malawi. Indeed, the nearest colony on record was at least 480 miles northwest of Nkata Bay, in Tanzania's Nkungwe Mountains, on Lake Tanganyika's eastern shore.[18,127-8]

In March 1960, a field expedition from the Rhodes-Livingstone Museum, headed by Drs B.L. Mitchell and C.S. Holliday, travelled to Nkata Bay to observe and photograph Ufiti, to obtain tape recordings of her vocalisations, and to study the prevailing ecology of the area.[18,127-8] The information gathered during that expedition was then sent to anthropologist Dr W.C. Osman Hill, for his remarks and opinions, which in 1963 he documented within an article published by London's Zoological Society in a symposium of primate research.[128]

The photos and observations obtained during the expedition revealed that Ufiti, although definitely a chimpanzee, exhibited certain unexpected features. In view of her provenance, she should have been most similar in appearance to East African chimps – but instead, her completely black face, ears, hands, and feet, and her short, dense coat, allied her more closely with western forms. Equally strange was the presence of a saddle-like area of pale grey fur across her back – a feature characteristic of mature male gorillas.[128]

Prior to Hill's article, the predominant opinion among zoologists was that Ufiti was merely an escapee from captivity. However, the morphological features documented by Hill argued strongly against such an identity. The only explanation that seemed to fit the facts was that Ufiti represented a hitherto unknown type (subspecies?) of chimpanzee, native to Malawi and normally concealed in this country's dense forests, with Ufiti herself presumably being a wanderer, or an individual cast out of the population by its other members. Indeed the Nkata Bay area is well known for harbouring a number of animal and plant species more closely related to West African forms than to East African ones. Moreover, Hill later received accounts of chimpanzee-like creatures from Malawi that considerably preceded Ufiti's debut. So was Ufiti a major discovery?[128]

Sadly, the truth may never be known. In March 1964 she was captured and sent to Britain's Chester Zoo. Unhappily, however, her health was found to be deteriorating rapidly; and so, to prevent her from suffering any further, not long after her arrival the zoo had no option but to put her down.[18] With Ufiti's passing, the issue of Malawi's putative chimpanzee population was soon forgotten, so that more than 30 years after her first appearance the world is still waiting to learn the true identity of the friendly 'ghost' from Nkata Bay.

Red goral – a rug revealed its existence

The red goral must assuredly be the only species of animal whose type specimen was very nearly a carpet! Gorals are goat-like relatives of the antelopes, and live in various mountain ranges of eastern and southern Asia. For many years, science only recognised the existence of a single grizzled greyish-brown type, *Nemorhaedus goral*, the grey goral, whose distribution extends northwards from Burma through northeastern China to Korea and the lower reaches of Siberia.

Yet as far back as 1863, as reported by naturalist Edward Blyth, the natives of Assam, bordering Burma, knew of a quite different, smaller form of goral, whose coat was bright foxy-red in colour, and much softer in texture than that of the grey goral. Similarly, in 1912, the existence of a rufous-pelaged goral in the area of Sanga Chu Dzong in southeastern Tibet was substantiated by Lieutenant-Colonel F.M. Bailey, who learnt that the red-furred coats worn there by various of the local inhabitants had been made from the pelage of this scientifically-undescribed animal. During the next decade, a number of red gorals were shot in Assam's Mishmi Hills, but none was presented for inspection to any scientific establishment. Fortunately, this situation was rectified in 1931, when a specimen shot in northern Burma's Adung Valley by the Earl of Cranbrook was presented by him to the British Museum (Natural History), where it was examined by mammal specialist Captain Guy Dollman.[129]

It seemed that the mystery of the red goral would soon be resolved, because Dollman proposed to prepare a formal description of it, complete with an official scientific name. Surprisingly, however, he never carried out his promise, probably preferring to await additional specimens for absolute confirmation of the red goral's merit as a valid species – but no fresh material arrived. Hence the red goral was soon forgotten, its lone available specimen lingering in the British Museum still un-named and undescribed until 1960.[130]

During that year, the museum received a very attractive rug, made up of skins from a trio of rufous-coated mammals, which was sent to the museum by a Mr H.L. Cooper who wanted to identify the pelts. He reported that the skins were from three of the handful of red goat-like creatures that he and some native tribesmen had shot in the Mishmi Hills during 1922. Museum mammalogist R.W. Hayman compared the rug with the red goral skin donated by the Earl of Cranbrook, and recognised straight away that they were all from the same species. In 1961, Hayman fulfilled the pledge that Dollman had made 30 years earlier, by publishing a full description of the new species, which he named *N. cranbrooki*.[130]

Three years later, science received its first opportunity to observe a living example of this species, when on 9 January 1964 a female red goral, caught near Lashio in Burma's Northern Shan State, arrived at Rangoon Zoo. An extremely agile animal, it was capable of substantial bounds and leaps, and in memory of its former mountainous home it chose not to sleep *inside* its hut but preferred instead to sleep *on top* of it, the roof of which was more than 5 ft above the ground.[131]

Worth noting is that as long ago as 1914, renowned zoologist Reginald Pocock had described a new species of goral, which he named *N. baileyi*, and which is generally referred to as the brown goral, because of the rich brown, ungrizzled shading of its pelage. Its description was based upon a single skin and skull collected on 3 July 1913 by Lt.-Col. Bailey at Dre, Yigrong Tso, Po Me, in southeastern Tibet.[132] No other specimen has ever been recorded. It was eventually demoted to the status of a grey goral subspecies, but when the existence of the red goral became established, some researchers wondered whether the brown form actually represented the latter species' summer coat phase. Hayman, however, closely compared red goral skins with the unique brown goral skin, and discovered various fundamental differences that readily dismissed this possibility, so he concluded that the brown goral was a genuine species.[130]

However, more recently, Prof. Colin Groves reported that new surveys of the western Yunnan mountains, lying between the respective type localities of the red goral and the brown goral, have found red goral there, thus linking the two types geographically. In the opinion of Groves, this therefore makes it fairly clear that, in spite of Hayman's belief, the red goral and the brown goral are in reality one and the same species.[133] It is to be hoped that thorough investigations of the brown goral will be instigated, to determine once and for all the precise identity of this taxonomically ambiguous form.

Also deserving a brief mention here is the golden takin *Budorcas taxicolor bedfordi,* a relative of the gorals, which remained undetected by western science until 1911, when it was discovered in eastern China's Shensi and Kansu Provinces.[2]

Banana bat – a winged 'rhinoceros'

Described in 1960, and named *Musonycteris harrisoni,* the Mexican banana bat is a small but instantly recognisable species – due to its unforgettable profile. The total length of this brown-furred bat scarcely exceeds 3 in, and in proportion to this its head would be relatively small – were it not for its extraordinarily long muzzle, so greatly elongated that it accounts for more than half of the skull's entire length. And as if to accentuate the muzzle's already bizarre appearance, perched incongruously at the very end is a pointed flap of skin, standing upright like a miniature rhinoceros horn just behind the bat's nostrils.[48,134]

Seemingly a rare species, and the only member of its genus, it was first discovered in 1958, when three specimens were captured within a grove of blooming banana trees, situated just over a mile southeast of Pueblo Juarez, Colima. Since then, others have also been recorded from the southwestern Mexican states of Michoacan and Guerrero.[48,134]

Leadbeater's possum – return of the non-gliding glider

Several squirrel species have a membrane of skin between forelimb and hindlimb on each side of the body. If, when leaping from a tree, these membranes are extended, the squirrels can sail through the air for considerable distances. Such species are termed flying squirrels (although they glide rather than fly). In Australia, the possum family contains some very close marsupial counterparts to these, known as flying phalangers – they are squirrel-like in general appearance and have comparable gliding membranes.

The most familiar flying phalanger is a small species called the sugar glider *Petaurus breviceps.* In 1867, however, Sir Frederick McCoy, director of the National Museum of Victoria, described a species that, although very similar superficially to the sugar glider in many respects, was nonetheless immediately distinguished from it by its lack of gliding membranes. With a head and body length of roughly 6.5 in, a thin club-shaped tail of comparable length, and distinctive spatulate (shovel-shaped) toes, this densely-furred form, brownish-grey above, paler grey below, with a dark stripe running from forehead to tail base, was christened *Gymnobelideus leadbeateri* – sole occupant of a newly-created genus.[57]

Leadbeater's possum, as it came to be known, was named after J. Leadbeater, an assistant at the National Museum who had discovered the very first specimen a little while earlier. Two specimens had been collected in the Bass River Valley, 60 miles southwest of Melbourne, in Victoria's South Gippsland. A third example from this same area was received by the museum in 1900, followed by one obtained in 1909 from the edge of the Koo-Wee-Rup Swamp, 30 miles north of the Bass River.[57] Except for a lone specimen discovered in 1931 within a collection of sugar glider skins and originally obtained from East Gippsland's Mount Wills, nothing else materialised concerning Leadbeater's possum for more than half a century, despite a number of extensive searches for it in eastern Victoria. The flying phalanger that couldn't fly (or even glide) seemed to have drifted into extinction, almost before science had even become aware of its existence.[57]

In 1959, naturalist Graham Pizzey began conducting a mammal survey in eastern Victoria's Healesville, Warburton and Marysville ranges. On Easter Monday 1961, he was accompanied by H.E. Wilkinson from Victoria's National Museum on a trip to Cumberland Valley, 11 miles east of Marysville at an altitude of 3000 ft, an area not previously visited by him during his survey. There, alerted by a slight rustling noise on the trunk of a blackwood wattle tree close by, Pizzey briefly saw the first recorded specimen of a living Leadbeater's possum for 52 years. At first, they were so stunned that they could scarcely convince themselves that it really was a Leadbeater's. During that evening, however, after having driven 5 miles in the direction of Marysville to a spot abundant in mountain ash known as Tommy's Bend Creek, they succeeded with the aid of a torch in observing another specimen, this time for a continuous period of about 10 minutes, as the light 'froze' it into immobility. With binoculars, Pizzey was able to check its salient features – club-shaped tail, spatulate toes, absence of gliding membranes. They all pointed to a single, undeniable identity – Leadbeater's possum. It was not extinct after all.[135]

He returned with colleagues to Tommy's Bend Creek five nights later, saw three possums, took photos, and collected a specimen which was subsequently confirmed to be *G. leadbeateri*. Two months

Leadbeater's possum – formerly one of Australia's most famous 'extinct' animals, it made a celebrated comeback in 1961.
(Zoo Operations Ltd)

later, a live individual was captured, which Pizzey was permitted to look after for a time, courtesy of the Fisheries and Wildlife Department. His priceless pet, which he named Jimmy, proved to be wholly nocturnal (which may explain at least in part how the species eluded detection for so long), and his spatulate toes functioned as effective suction pads, thanks to the large, damp pads on their undersurfaces.[135]

Since then, small colonies have been found in this same general area, and as long as Tommy's Bend Creek can remain undisturbed it is likely that Leadbeater's possum will continue to thrive there. Some specimens have also been discovered further afield.[48,135]

Hubbs's beaked whale

Hubbs's beaked whale was discovered by beaked whale expert Dr J.C. Moore during his *Mesoplodon* researches of the early 1960s. While examining some skeletons obtained over the years from America's North Pacific coasts and hitherto classed as Stejneger's beaked whale *M. stejnegeri*, he realised that three of these clearly belonged to a quite different species, not previously scientifically documented. He also discovered that a specimen stranded alive in 1945 at La Jolla in California, and identified by biologist Dr Carl Hubbs as an Andrews' beaked whale *M. bowdoini*, belonged in reality to the undescribed species (thus making the La Jolla specimen the earliest of this 'new' whale to have been preserved). And a beaked whale stranded off Japan in 1958 was shown to be yet another of its representatives.[38,136]

So in 1963, Moore christened this newly-detected species *M. carlhubbsi*, honouring its type specimen's initial researcher.[136] Measuring up to 17 ft long, and relatively

similar in external appearance to *M. stejnegeri*, Hubbs's beaked whale has one notably distinctive characteristic – the colour of its beak, which for much of its terminal portion is pure white, readily differentiating it from all other *Mesoplodon* species.[38,136]

The dwarf blue sheep of Batang

The blue sheep *Pseudois nayaur* is hardly the most aptly named of animals. Also known as the bharal (its Hindi name), it is not a true sheep (hence *Pseudois* – 'false sheep'); in fact, in terms of its habits and its structural anatomy, it seems to be midway between sheep and goats. As for its blue colouration (in reality, brownish-grey infused with slaty blue), this is present only in its first winter coat.

A mountain-dwelling species native to the Himalayas and western China, *P. nayaur* was long thought to be very distinct from all other living forms, the sole member of its genus. Then in 1934, during an expedition to the Tibetan plateau region, Dr E. Schaefer discovered an isolated population of blue sheep, in the Yangtze gorge near Batang, whose members were smaller in size and had proportionately shorter limbs than any previously recorded blue sheep. Three years later, Schaefer documented them as representatives of a new species, but did not give it a formal scientific name. This situation was not rectified until 1964, when Dr Theodor Haltenorth officially named it *P. n. schaeferi*, thereby classing it as a subspecies of the blue sheep.[137]

Popularly referred to as the dwarf blue sheep, it differs from its larger relative not only in terms of size but also by virtue of its drabber coat colouration, brightened only by a silvery sheen. It also exists in much smaller social groups.[137-8] After taking these distinctive features into account, in 1978 – 41 years after Schaefer's original pronouncement – mammal taxonomist Prof. Colin Groves elected to restore the dwarf blue sheep to its former status, namely that of a valid species in its own right.[138]

Iriomote cat – a revelation from the Ryukyus

By the end of the 19th century, zoologists were confident that all of the world's cat species had been described and named – but this belief received a most unexpected challenge in 1965. This was the year in which Japanese author-naturalist Yukio Togawa (sometimes spelled 'Tagawa') learnt of a strange, unfamiliar cat form said to inhabit Iriomote – a tiny insignificant dot of an island in the Japanese Ryukyu chain, almost completely covered with dense mountainous rainforest, and little-explored by scientific researchers. By a fortuitous quirk of fate, work commitments led Togawa to visit Iriomote later that year, and once there he investigated its feline mystery, a creature referred to by the natives as *pingimaya*. Togawa hoped to obtain specimens for formal identification, but was initially foiled by the inconvenient tendency of the natives to eat any such specimens they encountered.[60,139]

Happily, however, two pelts and a skull finally found their way to the University of Okinawa, where they were studied by Togawa and by Ryukyu zoologist Prof. Tetsuo Takara, after which the specimens were passed on to the Japanese mammalogist Prof. Yoshinori Imaizumi at Tokyo's National Science Museum. During a later visit to Iriomote, Togawa succeeded in obtaining three more skulls and a skin, which were once again sent to Prof. Imaizumi. After studying these, together with some additional examples that included at least one living animal, in 1967 Imaizumi published an extensive description of the Iriomote cat, which he deemed to be so distinct from all others that he placed it in a brand-new genus, naming it *Mayailurus iriomotensis*.[60,140]

Little larger than a domestic cat, with greyish-brown fur, the Iriomote cat could easily be dismissed on first sight as nothing more than a feral domestic, and also superficially resembles the common Asian leopard cat *Felis bengalensis*. However, its rounded ears with black backs spotted with white, the 5-7 longitudinal dark lines running along the nape of its neck to end on its shoulders, the distinctive vertical bands of spots on its body, and its 28-tooth dentition constitute just a few of the features that collectively distinguish it from both of these felids. Its tooth count is particularly unusual – on the one hand separating it from the normal 30-tooth dentition of most other Old World cats, yet on the other hand providing an unexpected correspondence with the mountain cat *F. guigna* from Chile.[60,139-140]

This odd assemblage of characteristics inspired Imaizumi to postulate that the Iriomote cat was an extremely primitive species uniting the Old World's small cats with those of the New World. Later studies, however, suggested that its unusual dental complement arose independently of the Chilean mountain cat's, thus undermining its claim to fame as a feline 'missing link'. Nowadays, it is placed within the genus *Felis*, containing all of the small cats.[60,139-140] Recent analyses of its proteins, moreover, confirm that its closest relative is the leopard cat (in fact, some authorities class it as nothing more than a well-marked island subspecies of this felid), but it is nonetheless an important find, wholly restricted as it is to a single tiny island with a total surface area of less than 113 square miles.[60,141]

Nor is the Iriomote cat this island's only zoological distinction. During an expedition here in 1974, a hitherto unknown form of dwarf wild pig was discovered, which seems to be only a little larger than the world's smallest species, the pygmy hog *Sus salvanius* (see p. 75).[142]

There has also been a more recent feline find in Japan. In winter 1989 it was announced that a new species of cat had been discovered on one of the two rocky Japanese islands of Tsushima, sited in Korea Strait, but the IUCN Cat Specialist Group has now suggested that it may merely be a subspecies of the leopard cat.[143]

Return of a lost lemur

In 1875, Dr Albert Günther of London's Zoological Society described a new species of Madagascan lemur, a small brown form with hairy ears. Its type specimen was a skin at the British Museum (Natural History), and it was christened *Cheirogaleus* [now *Allocebus] trichotis*, becoming known as the hairy-eared dwarf lemur. Two other skins were sent to the Paris Museum a few years later, but remained incognito until rediscovered there in 1956 by one of the world's leading lemur experts, Dr Jean-Jacques Petter. Otherwise, the species was a complete mystery – until 1966, when a living specimen was obtained by some natives close to Mananara on Madagascar's eastern coast, and given to Dr Petter's assistant, André Peyrieras.[144] Most recently, in April 1989, Ruhr University zoologist Dr Bernhard Meier discovered this species alive and well in lowland rainforest (Madagascar's

Hairy-eared dwarf lemur – until 1966 it was known only from three 19th century specimens.
(Dr Bernhard Meier)

very last surviving, extensive expanse), once again near Mananara.[145]

Reclusive rice rat

Another lost mammal that reappeared in 1966 – this time in the guise of a skull from a recently-deceased specimen – was the James Island rice rat *Oryzomys swarthi*. This naked-eared, mouse-like rodent from the Galapagos Islands had previously been known only from its type specimen and three others, all collected on James Island in 1906.[144]

White-throated wallaby – a new home in New Zealand

In just over a year, no less than three supposedly long-extinct species of marsupial were rediscovered during the 1960s, the first of which was the white-throated (parma) wallaby *Macropus (Thylogale) parma*. A very handsome animal, dark brown on top, white underneath, with a black stripe running from its neck to midway down its back, it was once plentiful in the Illawarra and Cambewarra mountainous areas of southern New South Wales. But as a result of its woodland habitat's wholesale clearance by man, its numbers rapidly dwindled. By 1932, this attractive mammal was considered extinct.[57,146]

White-throated (parma) wallaby – initially presumed extinct in its native Australia, it was unexpectedly discovered on a tiny New Zealand island in 1966. (Glasgow Zoo)

In 1966, however, it made a reappearance that was particularly unexpected – due to the specific locality in which the reappearance took place, not in Australia but New Zealand, on a 500-acre island called Kawau, sited 30 miles north of Auckland. New Zealand is a country famed for having just two species of native mammal, both of which are bats. So how could the existence on a New Zealand island of an allegedly extinct wallaby from Australia be explained? For once, the answer was quite straightforward.[146]

In 1870, settlers had released several white-throated wallabies onto Kawau, just as they had earlier introduced many other non-native animals onto New Zealand's two principal islands. The wallabies had thrived, and multiplied, so that a healthy population now existed there (alongside those of four other wallaby species also brought here at various times).[146]

To safeguard this species' future, some of the island's white-throats have been sent to zoos around the world to initiate captive populations, just in case disease or some other threat should decimate the Kawau colony. In 1972, moreover, it was rediscovered on mainland Australia too, by G.H. Maynes, who located some notable forest-dwelling populations in an expanse of land stretching from the Hunter River to the Clarence River in northeastern New South Wales, thereby increasing its survival chances in the wild.[146]

Burramys – a possum from the past

One day in August 1966, while residing at the Melbourne University Ski Lodge, high on the slopes of Mount Hotham in the Australian Alps of eastern Victoria, Dr Kenneth Shortman (of the Walter and Eliza Hall Institute) entered the lodge's kitchen, in search of food. What he found just behind the garbage pail and also looking for food constituted one of the most extraordinary mammalogical discoveries of the century.

In 1896, comparative anatomist Dr Robert Broom disclosed that a few fragments of 20,000-year-old fossilised bone, extracted from some owl pellets that he had found in the Wombeyan Caves near to the New South Wales town of Burra, were from a hitherto undescribed species of extinct Pleistocene possum, which he named *Burramys parvus* ('small Burra mouse'). Its fossilised remains were later also found at the Buchan Caves in Gippsland, Victoria. In the years that followed, *Burramys* attracted widespread interest from palaeontologists, as yet another representative of the diverse array of marsupial forms that had failed to survive into Recent (Holocene) times.[42,147]

At least, that was the assumption until August 1966, when Dr Shortman's fateful visit to the ski-lodge's kitchen provided a very different storyline. What he found there was a small, dormouse-like creature with brownish-grey upperparts, paler underparts, and a dark stripe running down each limb. It was evidently a possum, but he could not identify its species. Bemused, he captured the mystery mammal alive and unharmed, and took it to the Victorian Fisheries and Wildlife Department, where to everyone's amazement it was revealed by palaeontologist Norman Wakefield to be a living *Burramys*.[42,147]

It was cared for from then on by Dr John Seebeck, who learnt a great deal concerning the habits of this 'living fossil', noting its principally nocturnal lifestyle, placid temperament, and its dietary preference for insects, apples, sunflower seeds and honey diluted with water.[147]

Searches for more living specimens of *Burramys* (nowadays popularly termed the mountain pygmy possum) were unsuccessful

at first, so that zoologists began to wonder if the ski-lodge trespasser could be a marsupialian Mohican, the very last of its line. Happily, others were found in due course elsewhere in Victoria, securing on a firmer footing the modern-day existence of this highly significant species.[48,147]

Day of the dibbler

Less than a year after the white-throated wallaby's reappearance and the resurrection of *Burramys*, yet another 'extinct' Australian mammal was unexpectedly rediscovered. The species in question was the freckled marsupial mouse *Parantechinus apicalis*, more commonly called the dibbler – its Aboriginal name. Up to 10 in long, with speckled grey fur and a distinctive white ring round each eye, this Western Australian mammal had been last sighted in 1884. It was thought to have preyed upon other mammals and small birds, but little was really known about its lifestyle.[57]

In January 1967, wildlife photographer Michael K. Morcombe was near the Waychinicup River, east of Albany on Western Australia's southern tip, seeking a curious little creature called the honey possum *Tarsipes spencerae*, which lives almost solely upon nectar and pollen (*not* honey!) and seems to be the marsupial equivalent of a hummingbird. To trap some specimens temporarily for photographic purposes, Morcombe prepared some tiny cages and fitted these over the flowers of the nectar-rich bottlebrush and banksia, which are among the honey possum's favourite flora.[148]

Burramys pygmy possum – a fossil that came to life inside a Melbourne ski hut in 1966, after more than 10,000 years of supposed extinction.
(Fisheries and Wildlife Department, Victoria, Australia)

Adult female dibbler – an elusive species that vanished for 83 years, until its accidental rediscovery in 1967.
(Dr Christopher Dickman)

Three weeks passed without any of the cages trapping a single possum. Then the weather grew hotter and drier, and one day Morcombe discovered that his cages had finally snared a couple of specimens – but they were not honey possums. To his amazement and delight, he saw that the two speckled marsupials sitting unharmed inside his cages were dibblers![148] Since then, other specimens have been recorded in southwestern Australia, including a sizeable population on the Jurien Bay islands of Boulanger and Whitlock by Dr Chris Dickman during 1986-1988. Nonetheless, Morcombe's couple remain particularly significant – not only because they were the ones that marked the species' revival, but also because they revealed a hitherto unobserved facet of dibbler lifestyle. In contrast to expectations, the dibbler is not predominantly carnivorous – although it does devour any insects encountered on the blooms of large florescent bushes, its main interest is nectar, especially in dry weather.[148]

Homo pongoides – the iceman cometh

Even more controversial than South America's mystery 'ape' *Ameranthropoides loysi* (see p. 36), the Minnesota iceman has been widely denounced as a hoax, perhaps the most elaborate hoax of this century. If, however, it was genuine – the sustained opinion of at least one of the two very competent zoologists who investigated this contentious case – then it very probably comprises the most sensational zoological discovery of all time.

The case began in the late 1960s, when zoologists Dr Bernard Heuvelmans and Ivan T. Sanderson were informed that a sideshow travelling at that time through Chicago was exhibiting what appeared to be the fresh corpse of a very hirsute man-like entity, preserved within a huge block of ice. Needless to say, the two scientists were very curious to learn more, and their enquiries took them in mid-December 1968 to a farm near Winona, Minnesota, owned by Frank Hansen who ran the sideshow. He led them to a refrigerated, glass-topped coffin, containing the ice-entombed being that was soon to become known worldwide as the Minnesota iceman.[149]

For three days, Hansen allowed the zoologists to observe, sketch, and photograph the iceman, partially visible within its frozen sepulchre, even permitting them to lie directly upon the coffin's glass top to obtain the closest views possible. In overall appearance it resembled an adult human, 5 ft 10 in tall and male, lying on its back, with its left arm twisted behind its head, the palm of its hand uppermost. However, it presented several significant features that readily distinguished it from any form of modern man and recalled the great apes.[149]

Most immediately obvious of these was its body's extensive covering of long brown hair, absent only from its face, and comparable to the hairiness of Africa's gorillas and chimpanzees. Also very noticeable was the ovoid shape of its body's trunk region, greatly differing from the familiar hourglass shape of modern man's. This difference was emphasised by the iceman's more rounded ribcage, and its neck appeared shorter than modern man's. In contrast, its arms were unusually long, its hands and feet were disproportionately large, and its fingers and toes seemed not only relatively longer but also rather more robust than those of modern man. What made these features even more intriguing, however, was that they concomitantly comprised differences from modern man and similarities to Neanderthal man – which supposedly died out around 30,000 years ago.[149]

Most exciting of all: unlike the several famous examples of frozen Siberian mammoths, well-preserved in tombs of ice for many millenia after their deaths, there was one very telling piece of evidence to suggest that the iceman had been alive until very recently. The iceman appeared to have been shot, in the right eye – the path of the bullet had completely dislodged its left eye from its socket, and had blasted away the back of its head.[149]

Heuvelmans and Sanderson soon published their observations and pictorial evidence in various scientific journals. Heuvelmans was so convinced that the iceman represented a genuine form of hominid wholly distinct from modern man, that in his formal description of this specimen he named its species *Homo pongoides* ('ape-like man'). He still considers that even if it is not a separate species, it is at the very least a version of Neanderthal man, and should therefore be known as *Homo neanderthalensis pongoides*.[149]

Sketch depicting the Minnesota iceman – could it have been a recently-killed specimen of our officially long-extinct relative, Neanderthal man? (Ivan T. Sanderson/Society for the Investigation of the Unexplained)

73

Naturally, the scientific world soon became intensely interested in the inscrutable iceman, and the Smithsonian Institution expressed a desire for the corpse to be submitted for examination by its anthropological experts. Hansen, however, refused to comply with this request, alleging that it was not actually owned by him, but was instead the property of a reclusive millionaire who wished to remain anonymous and was not willing for the cadaver to be examined. Shortly afterwards, in accordance with the supposed wishes of its nameless owner, the iceman was withdrawn from public display by Hansen, who announced that it would not be exhibited again; instead, he would display a model of the iceman, which had been constructed from latex and hair on the millionaire's instructions some time earlier, to be used if and when the corpse began to attract unwelcome publicity. Worthy of note here is that the F.B.I. had reputedly become interested in the iceman by then, no doubt on account of the fact that this humanoid entity had been shot.[149]

Since 1969, the whereabouts of the original iceman have remained a mystery; the model, however, (which is visibly different from the corpse) is still being exhibited today. However, the hasty withdrawal of the corpse and its substitution with the model generated appreciable suspicion among scientists – to such an extent that most authorities today believe that there was probably never a genuine iceman at all, and that the corpse examined by the two zoologists was itself nothing more than a skilfully-manufactured model. Sanderson himself, prior to his death in 1973, had begun to entertain doubts as to the iceman's authenticity; and in 1981 it was claimed that expert model-maker Howard Ball had personally constructed the original corpse,

preparing a rubber skin into which millions of hairs had then been painstakingly embedded. Heuvelmans, however, remains adamant that the specimen he observed through its semi-transparent encasement of ice back in December 1968 was a real corpse, not a model; and he recalls that he had even detected the odour of decomposing flesh exuding from one corner of its refrigerated coffin's insulation.[149]

If the iceman was genuine, where had it come from? During the height of its publicity, Hansen issued various contradictory statements. At one point, he said that it had been found by Russian seal hunters (in a subsequent version he referred to them as Japanese whalers) floating in Kamchatka's Sea of Okhotsk in the far eastern portion of the former Soviet Union, entombed within its block of ice. Later, he stated that he had shot it himself, after encountering it in the Minnesota woods; he also claimed that it had been purchased in Hong Kong...and so on.[149]

Heuvelmans, however, believes that it was probably shot during the mid-1960s in Vietnam – where there have been many reports of Neanderthal-like entities, seemingly of the same type as the mysterious humanoid *almas* of Mongolia and *almasty* of Russia – and that its corpse had then been smuggled into the U.S.A. inside one of the 'body bags' used to transport the bodies of American soldiers killed during the Vietnam War.[149]

Today, all that we have to show for this extraordinary episode are the sketches and photographs obtained by Sanderson and Heuvelmans – and the disquieting knowledge that what may have been the greatest zoological discovery of the age was allowed to disappear without a formal scientific examination, after having been publicly displayed for months to countless thousands of unsuspecting observers.

Pygmy hog – rediscovering the world's tiniest wild pig

The 1970s began very promisingly for mammalian finds, with the rediscovery of a delightful creature called the pygmy hog *Sus salvanius*. In keeping with its name, it is the smallest species of wild pig, with a total length of only 20-26 in, and a shoulder height of no more than 12 in. Once widely distributed in grassy swampland along the southern foothills of the Himalayas of Bhutan, Nepal, Sikkim, Bangladesh and northeastern India, by the late 1950s it seemed to have died out – its disappearance blamed upon habitat destruction.[103,150]

Nevertheless, while science wrote it off as extinct, unconfirmed reports of its continuing survival persisted in various localities within its former range. These included a statement made by a forest ranger to noted Indian wildlife expert E.P. Gee that during the 1958-9 winter, pygmy hogs had been seen in Assam's Rowta Reserve Forest, on the northern bank of India's famous Brahmaputra River. This and other accounts greatly intrigued amateur naturalist John Tessier-Yandell, who was living at that time in Upper Assam. By sheer good fortune, in 1967 his official work took him to the Brahmaputra's north bank – right in the heart of pygmy hog territory. He lost no time in pursuing this species' trail, and two years later he learnt that a pygmy hog had definitely been killed not long before on an estate in nearby Mangaldai – sadly, the specimen had been eaten afterwards and the remains discarded. Nevertheless, for Tessier-Yandell there was no longer any doubt concerning the pygmy hog's continuing existence. All that he now needed was conclusive evidence for scientists to examine and confirm.[150]

His investigations continued to uncover fresh pieces of encouraging information during 1970, so that it seemed only a matter of time before the pygmy hog would be formally rediscovered. And on 10 April 1971 that time indeed came, when Tessier-Yandell received a telegram from colleague and fellow pygmy hog pursuer Dick Graves, requesting him to come to Mangaldai at once to identify some wild pigs that had been captured alive and which Graves felt sure were bona fide pygmy hogs. Nine animals in all were present – four young and two adult sows, plus one adult and two immature boars. Tessier-Yandell was thrilled to be able to verify Graves's belief – they were indeed pygmy hogs. Another memorable mammal had made a welcome return to the world list of living creatures.[150]

Since then, specimens have been captured for breeding programmes, but this has not proven successful and the last specimen died a short time ago; unfortunately, therefore, this diminutive creature's future has still to be secured.[103,150-1]

There are two pygmy-sized but nonetheless significant footnotes to this saga. Firstly, an unexpected bonus during the search for the pygmy hog was the capture of a hispid hare *Caprolagus hispudus*, another little-known species hitherto deemed extinct by some authorities.[150-1] Secondly, in 1977 four specimens of a new species of parasitic insect were taken off a pygmy hog in Darrang, northwestern Assam. It was later named *Haematopinus oliveri*, the pygmy hog sucking louse; its male form has yet to be collected.[152]

Kitti's hog-nosed bat – no bigger than a bumblebee

What do a bumblebee and a bat have in common? Not a lot – until 1973, that is. During the early 1970s, Dr Kitti

Thonglongya – at that time Curator of Terrestrial Vertebrates at Bangkok's Centre for Thai National Reference Collections – became increasingly interested in Thailand's chiropteran (bat) fauna, and made a number of important discoveries in that field. The most notable of these comprised a series of exceptionally tiny bats collected by him in October and December 1973, from one or other of two limestone caves in the vicinity of Ban Sai Yoke's Forestry Station and the infamous River Kwai bridge, in southern Thailand's Kanchanaburi Province. Dr Thonglongya's initial examination of these specimens convinced him that they represented something totally new, radically different from any species recorded before by science and at least meriting separate generic status.[153]

Thonglongya's opinion was shared by experts at the British Museum (Natural History); and so, working with British Museum colleague Dr John Edwards Hill, he began to prepare a full-scale scientific description of this new species. Tragically, however, in February 1974 (only four months after he had collected the very first specimens) Thonglongya died, but Hill continued with their paper and published it later that year.[153]

The new bat was certainly very different from all others, exhibiting a bewildering mixture of morphological and anatomical features drawn from several quite separate chiropteran families. Accordingly, Hill deemed it necessary to create a completely new family for it (Craseonycteridae – 'family of bats with mixed features'), a classification still accepted today. As for any vernacular name, two of the bat's most striking external attributes provided a couple of suitable versions nowadays in widespread use. One alludes to its remarkably small size: holder of the Guinness Book of Records title as the world's smallest species of mammal (and quite possibly the world's smallest warm-blooded vertebrate), with a body size no bigger than that of a large bumblebee and only weighing 2 g (0.07 oz), this minuscule mammal soon became known as the bumblebee bat. Equally, its pig-like snout earned it the alternative name of Kitti's hog-nosed bat. Other noticeable characteristics include the relatively large size of the flight membrane connecting its thighs, and its lack of a tail.[153]

Following this species' discovery and description (in which Hill named it Craseonycteris thonglongyai [153]), attempts were made to find out how abundant, or rare, it was. Regrettably, only a handful of examples were located by the early 1980s, and its continuing survival seemed so uncertain that at the November 1984 General Assembly of the IUCN (International Union for the Conservation of Nature), Kitti's hog-nosed bat was named as one of the world's 12 most endangered animal species.[154] By 1986, however, events had taken a more promising turn; over 2000 specimens had been recorded in more than 21 caves, following an extensive search made by Surapon Duangkhae from Bangkok's Mahidol University, armed with geological maps to locate the precise type of cave most likely to house this species, and a high-tech electronic bat-detector.[155]

Even so, faced with the ever-present threat of habitat destruction, as well as with collection of specimens by locals to sell as souvenirs or to display as curios, the smallest but most significant bat species discovered this century is by no means out of danger, and requires full protection to ensure its longterm survival.[155]

On 2 May 1948, a strange tailless fruit bat was caught on a remote coffee estate in southern India's Western Ghats, but was not recognised to be a new species until 1972 – when Dr Thonglongya dubbed it *Latidens salimalii,* honouring the renowned Indian zoologist Dr Salim Ali. No other specimen was recorded until April 1993, when a flock was encountered on the same coffee estate by zoologists Nikky Thomas and Manoj Muni.[156] And another rare Asian bat, Ridley's leaf-nosed bat *Hipposideros ridleyi*, last reported in 1910, made a welcome flight back into being in 1975, when a colony of about 50 individuals was discovered in a forest near Malaysia's capital, Kuala Lumpur.[103,156]

Chacoan peccary – an Ice Age recluse

The present-day existence of only two species of peccary, those pig-like mammals of tropical America, was an immutable and immortal zoological fact that had been faithfully reiterated within each and every zoological work for generations – until a third species was unexpectedly discovered in 1974, making it one of the greatest mammalian finds since the kouprey. Nor was it 'just another species'.

During an extensive series of field studies carried out from 1972 to 1975 in the semi-arid Gran Chaco area overlapping northern Argentina, western Paraguay and southeastern Bolivia, Connecticut University biologist Dr Ralph Wetzel and his co-workers were at first puzzled to discover that the local inhabitants recognised the existence of three different types of peccary. The white-lipped peccary *Tayassu pecari* was referred to as *tâchycâtí* or *tagnicate*, and the collared peccary *T. tajacu* as *cure-í* or *tayté-tou*, but the locals also spoke of a larger, mysterious form variously termed *tagua, pagua,* or, probably on account of its long ears, *curé-buro* ('donkey-pig'). After further enquiries, Wetzel

succeeded in obtaining a series of skulls for all three peccary types from hunters' kills, and morphological comparisons of these duly proved that the 'donkey-eared' peccary was truly a totally separate type, distinct from the two known modern-day species.[157]

Upon his return to the university, Wetzel made an even more surprising discovery. Although previously unknown in living form, the new peccary was not completely unknown to science. In 1930, the first specimen of a new fossil subspecies of Argentinian peccary had been described and named *Platygonus carlesi wagneri*. Eight years later, Rusconi classified it as a species in its own right – *P. wagneri*. Since then, many other fossil specimens of this species have been found, but none of more recent date than the Pleistocene epoch (2 million to 10 thousand years ago), so it has always been catalogued as one of the many large mammals that died out during the Ice Ages. When he compared fossilised skulls of *P. wagneri* and present-day skulls of the 'donkey-eared' peccary, however, Wetzel perceived that they all unquestionably belonged to one and the same species. *P. wagneri* had survived the Ice Ages after all. His studies also led him to conclude that *P. wagneri* was really more akin to members of the genus *Catagonus* than *Platygonus*, so in 1975 he renamed it *Catagonus wagneri,* and it is nowadays commonly called the Chacoan peccary or tagua.[157]

Weighing 100 lb and standing more than 3 ft high, Rusconi's resurrected species is the largest of the three modern-day peccary species, and less closely related to either of the other two than they are to each other. Except for its size, its most noticeable external features are its brown, bristly pelage, its faint collar of lighter hairs across its shoulders, its large head, and its

77

Chacoan peccary – sensationally resurrected from Ice Age extinction in 1974.
(Fred Kleinschmidt/Archiv Zoo Berlin)

the living, news emerged that for a number of years prior to this, and wholly unbeknownst to science, its hide had routinely been used by New York furriers to trim hats and coats.

Yellow-tailed woolly monkey – how a pet restored a 'lost' species

Whereas the common woolly monkey *Lagothrix lagothricha* is one of the most well-known species of South American primate, its yellow-tailed relative *L. flavicauda* was renowned for a very great period of time as the rarest and most mysterious. Its type specimen had been obtained as long ago as 1802, by the famous explorer Alexander von Humboldt, who documented it a decade later, recording its provenance as the Peruvian province of Jaen. Nothing more was heard of this new monkey for more than a century afterwards – until 1926, when three more were obtained by an animal collector called Hendee (working on behalf of the Godman-Thomas expedition to Peru) at Pucatambo, in the Peruvian province of Rodriguez de Mendoza, Amazonas.[159]

It made a fleeting return to the scientific spotlight in 1963, when zoologist Jack Fooden revealed that two monkey specimens held at the American Museum of Natural History and obtained in 1925 from La Leija (in Amazonas) were yellow-tailed woollies, thereby boosting the number of recorded specimens from four to six. Even so, after that it again sank into scientific obscurity, and there it may well have remained indefinitely – had it not been for the interest that its history had aroused in Peruvian zoologist Dr Hernando de Macedo-

relatively long limbs, tail, ears and snout.[157] At first, its existence was known only from the Gran Chaco region of Paraguay and Argentina, but later reports from hunters in Bolivia's corresponding area exposed its presence there too. Yet, disturbingly, due to habitat destruction and to hunting by the local people for its hide and meat, the Chacoan peccary's continuing survival is becoming increasingly imperilled. This grave situation prompted Wildlife Conservation International (a division of the New York Zoological Society) to begin funding an important conservation project in 1983 in an attempt to prevent the species from becoming any rarer. Headed by zoologist Andrew Taber, the goal is to initiate and encourage positive conservation policies in the Chaco Basin region, in order to preserve the Chacoan peccary and the area's many endemic species.[158]

The much-welcomed discovery or rediscovery of a major animal often has its ironic aspects too – and the formal exposure of the Chacoan peccary's present-day existence was certainly no exception. Following its 'official' return to the land of

Ruiz (Head of Mammalogy and Ornithology at Lima's Natural History Museum), Harvard University zoologist Dr Russell Mittermeier and Lima resident B. Anthony Luscombe.[159]

In 1974, this trio of investigators organised and took part in a 12-day expedition to the area in which the six known specimens had been collected, and almost immediately achieved success. On only the second day, they encountered a local hunter carrying the skull and stuffed skin of an adult *L. flavicauda* that he had shot less than a week earlier. Evidently, the species was not extinct. In addition, he supplied them with three other skins and two skulls of specimens that he had killed for food – but their greatest success was still to come. On the very last day of their expedition, Dr de Macedo-Ruiz and company were led by some children at Pedro Ruiz Gallo to the home of a soldier, whose current pet was none other than a juvenile *L. flavicauda*. The team rapidly purchased this unique animal – the very first living yellow-tailed woolly monkey ever seen by scientists.[159]

The team's researches suggested that this species' natural habitat consisted of montane forests at 1665-8330 ft, which were primarily of Amazonian origin, but that its distribution range was extremely limited. Coupling this with the extensive destruction of its habitat through road development and provision of land for agricultural purposes, plus the additional threat to its survival posed by hunting, this rediscovered species was indisputably greatly endangered. Consequently, the team concluded its investigations by recommending the establishment of an official reserve within the monkey's distribution range – a recommendation that led to a formal campaign for conservation, and to the announcement in 1982 that a

national park would indeed be created. And as an extra attempt to secure its future, a captive breeding programme for the yellow-tailed woolly monkey has been proposed at Lima Zoo.[103,159-60]

The novel ningauis and other minuscule marsupials

'Marsupial mouse' is something of a misnomer for the various species of tiny pouched mammal inhabiting Australia that are grouped together under this collective name, because their savage behaviour, insectivorous mode of existence, and sharp-muzzled features are far more reminiscent of shrews than mice. Pairing their diminutive size, moreover, with the extreme elusiveness characteristic of all predators, plus a predominantly nocturnal lifestyle, it can be appreciated that detailed observation and identification of these animals in the wild is in no way an easy task. Consequently, reports from time to time concerning the rediscovery of marsupial mice not seen for some years is usually neither uncommon nor unexpected.

A notable exception, however, occurred in 1975, when a series of such animals was scientifically described that not only comprised two new species, but also required the creation of a totally new genus for them. Various cranial and dental features and relatively short feet set them well apart from all previously known species of marsupial mouse.[161]

The two species were christened *Ningaui timealeyi* (from northwestern Western Australia) and *N. ridei* (from central Western Australia), by marsupial researcher Dr Michael Archer of the Queensland Museum, who disclosed that the specimens representing them had been collected as far back as the 1950s in some cases, but had not been recognised until now as taxonomically distinct from all others. Just prior to the publication of Archer's paper, news services around the world carried reports regarding the capture of a living ningaui (their generic name is now also used as their common name), an adult female measuring just 4 in long, which had been caught in the Billiatt Conservation Park, 100 miles east of Adelaide. Another female, this time with newborn babies (each measuring less than 0.5 in), was also captured, and all were safely transported to Adelaide's Institute of Medical and Veterinary Science.[161]

Incidentally, Archer's choice of generic name for these new species was particularly appropriate, because 'ningaui' is an Aboriginal term alluding to tiny mythological entities that are hairy, have short feet, hunt for food only at night, and eat all food raw – a perfect description of the new marsupial mice and their lifestyle.[161] During the 1980s, several more new species of marsupial mouse were discovered, including a third ningaui. Named *N. yvonneae* in 1983, it hails once again from Western Australia.[162]

Back in 1975, marsupial mouse researchers were also celebrating the rediscovery of a very unusual 'lost' species. First made known to science in 1908 with the procurement of a single specimen at Pilbara in Western Australia,[163] the long-tailed dunnart *Sminthopsis longicaudata* has a tail more than twice as long as its head and body combined, ending in a conspicuous black tuft. After 1908, this distinctive species was not reported again until 1940, when a second lone individual was obtained at Marble Bar. In addition, a preserved specimen not previously identified as *S. longicaudata* was spotted in the National Museum of Victoria's collections.[57] Nothing more was then heard of this tiny marsupial for another 35 years, until 1975, when an adult female was obtained in Western Australia's Gibson Desert.[164] Six years later, two breeding pairs were captured alive there by members of the Western Australian Research Centre, and the species is now believed to be relatively widespread amongst this desert's rocky terrain. As for its extraordinary tail, researchers have surmised that it uses this to lure within range the insects upon which it feeds.[165]

The sandhill dunnart *S. psammophila* was discovered in 1894, when a single specimen was procured by the Horn Expedition in the desert near Lake Amadeus, in the proximity of the Northern Territory's famous Ayers Rock. Nothing else was known of this species until 1969, when farmer M. Andrews collected one on South Australia's Eyre Peninsula, about 650 miles southeast of Ayers Rock. Others have since been found even further southeast.[57,164]

Ningaui – a novel type of minuscule marsupial, named in 1975 after a legendary Antipodean race of tiny beings with small feet and a liking for raw food. (Times Newspapers)

Proserpine rock wallaby

Albeit to varying extents, by 1977 all seven species of Australian rock wallaby known at that time had sharply decreased in number, and some were greatly endangered. Hence the discovery of an eighth, totally new species in that year was the very last thing that zoologists expected. Yet, if science had taken more notice of local testimony, it may well have occurred much earlier – for farmers at Proserpine, eastern Queensland, had often spoken about a strange form of rock wallaby in the area, but no-one had ever sought a specimen. Midway through 1977, however, a single individual of this mysterious marsupial was finally captured, and it provided scientists with a great surprise.[166]

To begin with, it was rather larger in size than any of the known species of rock wallaby; and its tail was longer relative to body size, and, uniquely, was tipped with white. Examination of the living animal's external morphology was succeeded by comprehensive chromosomal and blood-protein comparisons, which demonstrated irrefutably that it was genuinely a species new to science. To ensure that this, the largest of all rock wallabies, did not suffer the marked decrease in numbers experienced by its smaller relatives, recommendations for its habitat's preservation were soon submitted to the Queensland State Government. As for its name, it simply became known as the Proserpine rock wallaby, after its type locality – in turn named after the Roman goddess Proserpina. In order to maintain its nomenclatural link with classical legend, its scientific name was derived from Proserpina's Greek counterpart Persephone, and it was christened *Petrogale persephone*.[166]

Bulmer's fruit bat – the fossil that came to life.

In 1977, the *Australian Journal of Zoology* published a paper by palaeontologist James I. Menzies in which he described a new genus and species of fossil fruit bat, of which 200 incomplete specimens had been excavated at a site called the Kiowa rock shelter in New Guinea's Chimbu Province. The fossils were at least 9,000 years old, and the new (albeit long-extinct) bat was dubbed *Aproteles bulmerae*, Bulmer's fruit bat. Its closest living relative was another New Guinea species, *Dobsonia moluccensis*.[167] Needless to say, the discovery of Bulmer's fruit bat was of great interest to palaeontologists, representing as it did a wholly new fossil genus, but within three years its name would also become of equal if not greater interest to students of present-day wildlife.

In 1980, another paper by Menzies appeared, containing some stunning news. Not long after the publication of his description of Bulmer's fruit bat in 1977, Menzies had examined a collection of current New Guinea animal specimens obtained two years earlier, and had discovered within it two modern-day skulls and two isolated modern-day mandibles (lower jaws) of this fruit bat. In short, *A. bulmerae* was no longer an exclusively fossil form, supposedly extinct since the close of the Pleistocene. Instead, it had plainly survived right up to the present day. Somewhere in New Guinea, therefore, there had to be living specimens of this resuscitated species.[168]

The specimen collection had been made in 1975 by D. Hyndman, while he was carrying out anthropological studies in western Papua New Guinea's Hindenburg ranges. The *A. bulmerae* remains were from specimens that had been shot by bow and arrow in a large cave nearby – and the cave was said to contain numerous bats (more *A. bulmerae?*). Obviously, this cave was the ideal place to search for living specimens.[168] And so, following Menzies's identification of the *A. bulmerae* material within his earlier collection, Hyndman returned there in November 1977 for this specific purpose. To his horror, however, he had learnt upon arrival that, not long before, a native hunter visiting the cave had either driven away or killed all but two members of the entire bat colony.[168]

Happily, the species nonetheless survives. After being written off as extinct during the 1980s, in May 1992 it was formally rediscovered, when 137 living specimens were recorded in a single cave within the Hindenberg ranges.[168]

Fea's muntjac – rediscovering the world's rarest deer

In December 1977, a female specimen of Fea's muntjac *Muntiacus feae,* the world's rarest deer, arrived at Bangkok's Dusit Zoo. It is a small dark-coated relative of India's barking deer. The only previous examples on record had been the species' type specimen (formally described in 1889) and one other, both originating from the borders of southern Burma and western Thailand. During the early 1980s, some more were captured and sent to Dusit Zoo – two females in 1981, followed by three males and three females from Xizang, Tibet, between February 1982 and April 1983, thereby establishing a small herd of this threatened species for captive breeding.[169-70]

One unexpected but exciting footnote to the Fea's muntjac story is that in March 1988 a muntjac was captured in the mountains of Gongshan County, in China's Yunnan Province, that was thought at first to belong to this species. Chromosomal analyses, however, divulged that it was in reality a quite separate species, one that had never been documented by science. It is currently being studied and described by Profs. Wang Yingiang and Shi Liming from the Kunming Institute of Zoology.[171]

Moreover, in 1982 mammalogists Prof. Colin Groves and Dr Peter Grubb described a new muntjac, *M. atherodes,* from Borneo; prior to this, only the common muntjac *M. muntiacus* had been known there. Confirmation of *M. atherodes* as a bona fide species has still to be accepted by some mammalian authorities.[172]

Sulawesi's 'tree-climbing dog'

One of the least-known of all viverrids (civets, genets and mongooses) is the giant palm civet *Macrogalidia musschenbroeki.* A forest-inhabiting species of 5 ft in length (a third of which comprises its brown-and-white banded tail), it has a strikingly dog-like head, large feet, and sports a handsome coat of chestnut-brown fur on its back with a paler brown stomach and a reddish chest. Confined to the southeast Asian island of Sulawesi (Celebes), it was always presumed to be rare, and by the onset of World War II sightings had totally ceased.[173]

So in 1978 zoological circles greatly welcomed the news that a specimen had recently been spied and positively identified by Dr John MacKinnon and Ir. Tarmuji while conducting a WWF survey in Gunung Ambang Reserve, located in the island's northern section. Equally exciting was the announcement that MacKinnon had actually succeeded in photographing it as it sat in full view in a tree – the first time that the giant palm civet had ever been photographed alive in its natural habitat.

Giant palm civet – rediscovered in 1978, this scarcely-known Sulawesi species explains native reports of a mystifying 'tree-climbing dog'.
(Dr John MacKinnon/World Wide Fund for Nature)

(One of these photos is reproduced here.) The Sulawesi natives tell stories of a strange tree-climbing dog termed the *unguno bato* or *anjing hutan*, with hind limbs longer than its forelimbs; and, as MacKinnon has commented, this is evidently based upon sightings of the elusive *M. musschenbroeki*.[173]

Long-footed potoroo – the biggest rat kangaroo

Smaller than kangaroos and wallabies, closer in size to rabbits and hares, the Australian potoroos or rat kangaroos (genus *Potorous*) are characterised by their large canine teeth, short ears and hind legs, and rat-like form. Until 1967, only two species were

known to exist (a third, the flat-faced potoroo *P. platyceps*, had died out a century earlier), but in June of that year a conspicuously large potoroo (an adult male) was caught in a dog trap in the forest southwest of Bonang, Victoria. It was initially assumed to be a three-toed potoroo *P. tridactylus,* but when some other unusually large specimens were obtained at a nearby site named Bellbird (28 miles or so southeast of Bonang) in May 1968 and April 1978, suspicions that they may comprise something more significant were put to the test. Detailed morphological and chromosomal analyses were undertaken by research biologists Drs John Seebeck and P.G. Johnston, and by 1980 they had discovered differences in cranial and foot structure, and in blood proteins, as well as a totally distinct chromosomal complement – confirming that these rangy specimens really did constitute a new species. Its most obvious distinguishing feature gave rise to its scientific and common names – *Potorous longipes,* the long-footed potoroo.[174]

Helmet dolphin – recognition after 135 years

In 1846, British Museum zoologist John Edward Gray described a new species of dolphin based only upon a skull of unknown provenance from a dolphin specimen of equally unknown external appearance. Named *Delphinus metis* – then changed to *Stenella clymene* – this species was later reclassified as nothing more notable than a local variety of the spinner dolphin *Stenella longirostris*, and was omitted from lists of cetacean species for many decades afterwards. Then in 1975, dolphin researcher Dr W.F. Perrin recognised that the skulls of two dolphins that had been obtained from the Texas Gulf coast so greatly resembled that of Gray's *S. clymene* (still housed at the British Museum) that the three skulls had to belong to the same species – but which species? Cranially, they corresponded most closely with *S. coeruleoalba*, the striped dolphin. Yet when photographs taken of the two Texan dolphins while still alive were examined, their body colouration and intricate pattern of markings were most similar to those of the spinner dolphin. Essentially, here were dolphins whose skulls resembled one species, and whose external appearance resembled a second, totally separate species.[38,175]

As a result, Dr Perrin suspected that *S. clymene,* with the British Museum skull as its type specimen and the Texan skulls as paratypes, was a valid species after all. In June 1976, another of these puzzling dolphins was obtained – it had beached itself at New Jersey's Ocean City. This specimen was carefully examined in 1977 at the Second International Conference on the Biology of Marine Mammals, held in Seattle, and its distinct nature was officially confirmed. So in 1981 Perrin and four colleagues fully redescribed *S. clymene,* combining a detailed anatomical report with an extensive account of its external morphology.[38,175]

Now known from Texas, Florida, New Jersey, the Caribbean, the mid-Atlantic and West Africa, this re-elevated species exhibits a more complex pattern of swirling black, grey, and white markings along its flanks than the spinner dolphin, and is also distinguished from it by its shorter beak. Most characteristic of all, however, is the helmet-like series of markings on its beak and forehead; thus it is now widely referred to as the helmet dolphin.[38,175]

Sun-tailed guenon – from dinner to debutant

In 1984, primatologist Dr Mike Harrison returned home to Edinburgh from Gabon, West Africa, with a very beautiful monkey skin that had been left over from the dinner of a local hunter in central Gabon's secluded Forêt des Abeilles (Forest of Bees). The brilliant orange distal portion of its tail distinguished it from l'Hoest's guenon *Cercopithecus lhoesti*, the known species to which it bore the closest resemblance (but which in any event is limited to eastern Zaire). Enquiries by Harrison led to the discovery of some more skins, and a colleague, Rennes University zoologist Dr Jean-Pierre Gautier, located a live specimen kept as a pet in the same area of Gabon. Blood samples taken from this individual revealed that its species' chromosomal make-up differed from that of l'Hoest's guenon.[176-7]

The golden-tailed monkeys obviously comprised a new species, which Harrison duly described in 1988, naming it *C. solatus* ('sunstruck guenon'), emphasising the vivid colouration of its tail's tip, so that its common name became the sun-tailed guenon.[177-8]

This is the latest in a line of surprising new guenons discovered during this century. In 1977, a new species was found in central Zaire, when a Japanese traveller purchased a very strikingly patterned monkey skin from some local hunters. Later named *C. salongo*, it most closely resembles the well-known diana monkey *C. diana* of western Africa.[179] Central Zaire is also the home of the dryas guenon *C. dryas*, formally described in 1932 by Dr Ernst Schwarz and still known only from its type specimen.[180] And 1907 witnessed the description of an intriguing blackish-green species known as Allen's swamp guenon. Hailing once again from the forests of Zaire, as well as from those of the Congo Republic, it was originally named *C. nigroviridis*, but in 1923 Lang rehoused it within a genus of its own (renaming it *Allenopithecus nigroviridis*), on account of certain anatomical and behavioural similarities to the baboons. As it is the only species of *Allenopithecus*, Allen's swamp guenon is particularly important, comprising the most recently-discovered genus of Old World monkey.[48,181]

The Queen of Sheba's gazelle

In the 1950s, while undertaking a study of mammals in the Yemen, Dr Harold Hoogstraal collected many specimens, which were afterwards lodged in Chicago's Field Museum of Natural History. They included five skulls and skins from gazelles that were assumed at that time to belong to the Arabian gazelle's North Yemeni subspecies, *Gazella gazella cora*.[182]

In consequence, they attracted little further attention – until, more than three decades later, mammalogist Prof. Colin Groves and fellow researcher Dr Douglas Lay re-examined them closely, comparing those characteristics of taxonomic importance with their equivalents in known specimens of the North Yemeni Arabian gazelle. To their surprise, they found that the Hoogstraal material was decidedly different (especially with regard to the male skulls' unusually upright, almost straight horns). Indeed, it was apparent that these remains required formal description as the basis of a new species.

In 1985, this was carried out by Groves and Lay, who named the newly-exposed

mammal *Gazella bilkis*, the bilkis gazelle. Since then, some living specimens have been discovered in a private wildlife collection in Qatar, which have revealed the species to be an antelope of extremely elegant, aristocratic appearance. As a result, its common and scientific names are especially appropriate – because Bilqis was none other than the Queen of Sheba; moreover, her kingdom extended over much of what is now North Yemen.[182]

Making a monkey out of an ape-man

Since the earliest times, people from many parts of China have been reporting sightings of strange hairy ape-men, some as tall as man himself (even taller in certain instances) and bipedal, others much smaller and given to running on all fours. The zoological identities of the larger forms, collectively termed the Chinese wildman or *yeren*, are still unknown, but in 1985 the mystery of the smaller version finally came to an end, when one of these elusive creatures was captured alive and unharmed.[183]

Caught near Anhui Province's Huangshan Mountain, and transferred to Hefei Zoo, it proved to be a macaque (i.e. related to the famous rhesus monkey *Macaca mulatta* and Gibraltar's barbary ape *M. sylvana*). However, it is sufficiently larger than any previously recorded species to incite speculation that it may represent a new species, or at least a new subspecies of one of China's two species of stump-tailed macaque.[183] Chinese anthropologist Dr Zhou Guoxing, a *yeren* expert, feels that the Huangshan Mountain specimen is of the same type as the unidentified giant macaque killed on 23 May 1957 near Zhejiang Province's Jiulong Mountain, whose preserved hands and feet he examined in 1982. But further studies and specimens are required to resolve this issue satisfactorily.[184]

Deniliquin wombat – burrowing back from extinction?

In the 1890s, a population of wombats was observed near to the town of Deniliquin, in the Riverina district of New South Wales, Australia. They seemed to represent a species unknown to science, but before they could be investigated they disappeared, never to be seen alive again. In 1985, however, George G. Scott, a researcher with a special interest in wombat taxonomy, working at Canberra's Australian National Museum, learnt that just two years earlier a picnicker had reputedly seen a wombat in the Riverina area, a locality not frequented by common wombats. Investigating this claim, local naturalists discovered some wombat burrows there, which appeared to be freshly-made, but they did not spot any wombats. Other burrows have since been found, some containing hairs that have been shown to match very closely those from a recently-uncovered taxiderm specimen prepared from a wombat now known to have been collected at Deniliquin prior to the 1890s. Searches are continuing in the hope that these marsupial denizens of Deniliquin do survive.[185]

Vanzolini's squirrel monkey

1985 also witnessed the description of Vanzolini's squirrel monkey *Saimiri vanzolinii* – the first new South American monkey to be described and accepted as a valid species since the emperor tamarin in 1907 (p. 27). Named after Brazilian herpetologist Dr Paul Vanzolini, it was found by primatologist Dr Marcio Ayres (from São Paulo's National Institute for Amazonian Research) in a very small area of rainforest between Brazil's Japura and Amazon Rivers. Its facial markings and darker fur colouration distinguish it from its neighbouring species, *S. sciureus*, but ally it with the Bolivian squirrel monkey *S. boliviensis* – even though that species is only found several hundred miles further southwest. The most likely explanation for such a zoogeographically anomalous affinity is that Vanzolini's squirrel monkey evolved from a population of *S. boliviensis* that became isolated from all others of its species when the latter's distribution range shrank during the last Ice Age.[186]

Onza – Mexico's legend becomes a reality

For zoologists, 1986 opened in a dramatic manner with the procurement on 1 January of a legendary creature whose existence had been denied by science for centuries. That evening, Mexican rancher Andres Rodriguez Murillo surprised a very large cat close to his home in the valley behind Parrot Mountain, in Mexico's Sinaloa State. Fearing that it was a jaguar about to attack him, he shot it, but when he examined its body he found that it was neither a jaguar nor a puma, the only other large felid 'officially' existing in Mexico.[60,187]

It did resemble a puma superficially, but its limbs were longer and its body was more slender, giving it a cheetah-like outline; in addition, its ears were unusually big, and the inner surfaces of its forelimbs bore dark markings not possessed by pumas. As Rodriguez had little knowledge of wildlife, he contacted an expert hunter by the name of Manuel Vega to come over and identify it for him. When Vega arrived, he recognised the cat at once – it was an onza, the fabled third large cat of Mexico, whose existence is supported by more than 300 years' worth of local eyewitness accounts (even including the testimony of visiting missionaries and Jesuit priests), yet all of which had hitherto been dismissed by zoologists as reports of poorly-seen or misidentified pumas.[60,187]

Some 20th century accounts of onzas had actually been supported for a short time by complete specimens, though in every case these were somehow lost or destroyed. In spring 1926, for example, hunter-cowboy C.B. Ruggles trapped and killed a supposed onza southeast of Yaqui River in Mexico's Sonora State. After taking some photos of its carcase, and noting that it had very skinny hindquarters, with dark spots on the innerside of its limbs, Ruggles discarded it. A few years later, American naturalist J. Frank Dobie reported shooting an onza caught in traps set on Mexico's Barrancas de la Viboras; regrettably, its skin was subsequently devoured by bugs. In 1938, while in the company of renowned hunters Dale and Clell Lee from Arizona, Indiana banker Joseph Shirk shot an onza on Sinaloa's La Silla Mountain; photos show that, as with all of the others, it resembled an extremely gracile, long-limbed puma with big ears and unusual limb markings. Although much of its carcase was discarded, its skull was retained – only to vanish without trace by being

sent to a museum whose name, frustratingly, does not appear to have been placed on record. The dead body of a large unidentified felid that may well have been an onza was taken to Texas University in the late 1950s, but this cannot be traced either.[188]

J. Richard Greenwell, secretary of the International Society of Cryptozoology (ISC), who has a particular interest in the onza, has succeeded in locating two onza skulls – one from a specimen shot in 1938 on La Silla Mountain by R.R.M. Carpenter while accompanied by Dale and Clell Lee, the other from an onza shot by Jesus Vega (father of Manuel Vega) in much the same area sometime during the mid-1970s. Additionally, another onza investigator, Arizona hunter Robert Marshall (author of *The Onza*, this subject's definitive book), was successful in obtaining the incomplete skull (its lower jaw was missing) of an onza shot during the 1950s at Los Frailes, Sinaloa.[60,189]

More recently, around 1986, an onza was allegedly captured alive, and held for several days in captivity at a ranch in northern Sonora, where it was supposedly photographed. Tragically, however, when

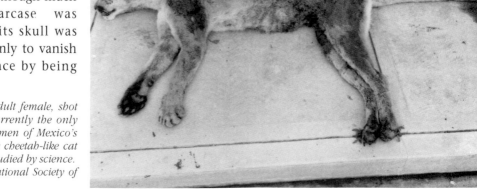

Onza – this adult female, shot in 1986, is currently the only complete specimen of Mexico's once-legendary cheetah-like cat to have been studied by science. (Photo: International Society of Cryptozoology)

no-one showed any interest in it, its owner shot it and threw its body away. As for the photographs, these have yet to make a published appearance. And even more recently, in early 1987, yet another onza was reportedly shot in Sinaloa, this time by a wealthy Mazatlan businessman; but, true to form, its remains were not preserved.[190]

In short, with the exception of three skulls, physical remains of onzas have displayed a disconcerting tendency to disappear beyond the reach of scientists. The Rodriguez specimen, however, changed all of that – for instead of destroying its remains, the ranchers contacted Richard Greenwell. Following a complex series of interchanges, the precious specimen was transported to the Regional Diagnostic Laboratory of Animal Pathology, in Mazatlan, Sinaloa. There it was painstakingly studied and dissected by a biological team headed by American puma researcher Dr Troy Best, who had been working alongside Greenwell during his earlier onza investigations. After the dissection, extensive samples of skeletal material, tissues and blood were taken for examination and analysis in various U.S. research institutions, in a bid to uncover the onza's taxonomic identity. So far, no conclusive results have been obtained, but the research programmes are continuing, and there are three different identities on offer.[60,187]

The onza may simply be a mutant form of the puma, the result of a genetic aberration that has yielded an uncommonly slim, leggy variety. Its gracility is, indisputably, a natural facet of its appearance (rather than starvation-induced emaciation), because the Rodriguez specimen was found to possess adequate amounts of body fat. If not a genetic freak, the onza could be a separate subspecies of puma, kept apart from the Mexican puma *Felis concolor azteca* by behavioural differences and dissimilar habitat preferences. Finally, but most exciting, it could be a currently undescribed species – one that quite possibly descended from the typical puma, but later diverged from it to fill the ecological niche left vacant by the extinction 10,000 years ago of *Acinonyx trumani* – an extraordinary felid now known to have been a true American cheetah (it was first classed as a cheetah-like puma).[60,187]

Yet whatever the onza proves to be, the Rodriguez specimen provides undeniable proof that this distinctive cat form is a corporeal reality, as opposed to a non-existent feline fable, demonstrating once again that local accounts of creatures not known to science can (and often do) lead to the discovery of new animals.

Bewildering bamboo lemurs

Until its rediscovery in 1972 by French zoologist Dr André Peyrieras in a small forest near Kianjavato, situated 63 miles east of the town of Fianarantsoa in southeastern Madagascar, the greater bamboo lemur *Hapalemur simus* was believed to have been extinct since this century's opening years. In 1985, French researcher Corine Dague discovered what seemed at first to be a second colony of this species inhabiting a rainforest near Ranomafana, 28.5 miles east of Fianarantsoa. By comparing these individuals with those back at Kianjavato, however, Ruhr University zoologist Dr Bernhard Meier showed in 1986 that they were not greater bamboo lemurs at all. On the contrary, they represented something even more exciting – a completely new species, never before recorded.[191]

Readily distinguished from the ruddy-grey greater bamboo lemur *H. simus* and from the smaller, grey bamboo lemur *H. griseus* by virtue of its fur's rich golden hue on its throat, cheeks, and eyebrows, as well as by its quite different alarm call, scent-marking glands and high chromosome number, the new species was named *H. aureus*, the golden bamboo lemur. Even its feeding habits are different. It lives exclusively upon the young shoots and branches of bamboo, whereas the other two species also eat fruit and foliage from additional plant species. Two golden bamboo lemurs, a male and female, were captured alive for study, and are currently in captivity at Tsimbazaza Park, in the island's capital, Antananarivo.[191]

Giant striped mongoose

Another mammalian surprise from Madagascar that came to light in 1986 was discovered not in any forest, but in a museum cabinet. Madagascar is home to several very strange-looking mongooses that are overtly unlike any found elsewhere else in the world. One of these is *Galidictis fasciata*, the broad-striped mongoose – named after the three horizontal wide bands of dark brown that run close together along each creamy-white flank, from just behind the creature's ear to the base of its tail. It was once thought to be the only member of its genus, but a second species was described in 1986 by zoologist Dr W. Chris Wozencraft (from Kansas University's Museum of Natural History).[192]

During an in-depth study of mongoose specimens in museums worldwide, Wozencraft had come upon two labelled as *G. fasciata* that differed conspicuously from other recorded examples of this species by way of their longer, sturdier and broader skulls, their larger canine teeth and carnassials, and their widely-spaced,

horizontal brown bands. As a result, Wozencraft designated these as the first recorded representatives of a new species, the giant striped mongoose *G. grandidiensis* – named after the Grandidier collection of specimens from which its type had been acquired. Its second representative specimen, the skin and damaged skull of an adult male, had been collected near to southwestern Madagascar's Lac Tsimanampetsotsa on 15 February 1929, and local villagers in that area have recently confirmed the existence of an animal fitting the giant striped mongoose's description, but it has yet to be observed scientifically in the field.[113,192]

Chaetomys – reappearance of a thin-spined missing link

Variously deemed to be a rat with unusually spiky hair or a porcupine with unusually fine quills, the thin-spined porcupine rat *Chaetomys subspinosus* constitutes a perplexing taxonomic bridge between the spiny rats and the American porcupines, combining features of both families. Even its tail is tantalisingly transitional – whereas those of spiny rats are not prehensile, and those of American porcupines are fully prehensile, the tail of *Chaetomys* is semi-prehensile. This ambiguous but beguiling little animal, not exceeding 2.5 ft in total length, bristling with soft, flexible brown spines, and hailing from the drier forests of southeastern Brazil, was officially described as long ago as 1818. But it has been conclusively sighted only very rarely since, with the last definite report coming in 1952 – accompanied by the first photograph ever taken of the species in the wild. Apart from various unconfirmed reports in later years, nothing more was heard of this intriguing rodent.[48]

In December 1986, however, during a specific search for the species in the vicinity of Valenca, in Bahia State, mammalogist Ilmar Bastos Santos was taken by a local hunter to a tree that contained two thin-spined porcupine rats, one of which was a pregnant female. Additional specimens are now being sought, and it is hoped that a protected breeding area for this taxonomically significant species can be established.[193]

Koopman's tree porcupine *Coendou koopmani*, a new prehensile-tailed porcupine, was formally described in 1992, from Brazil's Amazon lowlands. It is a very small, dark-spined species, no larger than a guinea-pig.[194]

Return of the rhinos

The possibility that animals as large as rhinoceroses could remain unknown to science for decades must seem very remote. Yet between 1986 and 1988, zoologists learnt of two separate cases in which this is precisely what had happened. The first announcement came in 1986, disclosing that up to five specimens of the hairy Sumatran rhinoceros *Dicerorhinus sumatrensis* had been found in Sarawak, on the island of Borneo. Science had hitherto assumed that this species had died out in Sarawak by the end of World War II. Inhabiting a remote valley in the Ulu Baram area, they had first come to the notice of local inhabitants in 1983, and were reported at once to the Sarawak Forest Department's National Parks and Wildlife Office. It decided to keep the discovery secret for a while, however, to allow time for protection measures to be drawn up and implemented.

Sumatran rhinoceros – its startling ability to remain undetected in Sarawak for almost four decades gave the zoological world a great surprise in the 1980s.

They were assisted by Dr Julian Caldecott of the Earthlife Foundation, who spotted Sumatran rhino tracks himself in August 1986.[195]

An even more spectacular revelation occurred just two years later – because this was when the Javan rhinoceros *Rhinoceros sondaicus,* the most critically threatened of all rhino species, supposedly confined totally to Java since the 1940s, was rediscovered on the Asian mainland. In November 1988, a female specimen was shot by a local tribesman in the jungles of southern Vietnam, about 80 miles northeast of Ho Chi Minh City (formerly Saigon). Its remains, together with those of a second shot specimen, were later examined and conclusively identified by Dr George Schaller, Vice-President of the New York Zoological Society, who had been working at the time on a faunal survey with Vietnamese scientists in the jungles of southern Vietnam. In February 1989, Schaller also sighted some Javan rhino tracks, on the banks of the Dong Nai River (75 miles northeast of Ho Chi Minh City), and estimated that as many as 10-15 individuals may still survive in the area. Prompted by this dramatic find, the

Indeed, it is quite likely that a number of other supposed great Indians from the earlier days of zoological parks will ultimately be exposed as incognito Javans.

A bronze quoll and a black tree kangaroo

Australasia's answers to the mustelids (weasels, martens and suchlike) and viverrids (civets, genets and mongooses) found elsewhere in the world are the dasyures, traditionally comprising a quintet of brown-coated, white-spotted marsupial carnivores. Two are commonly referred to as quolls – New Guinea's *Dasyurus albopunctatus,* and eastern Australia's *D. viverrinus* – but in 1987 a third species of quoll was described, from the savannahs of southwestern Papua New Guinea, thereby increasing the total number of dasyure species to six. Dubbed *D. spartacus* by Queensland Museum zoologist Dr Stephen Van Dyck, its common name is the bronze quoll, on account of the deep bronze colouration of its pelage, which is dappled with small white spots (except for its tail, which is uniformly black). It can also be differentiated from the other dasyures by the extreme narrowness of its muzzle measured between the left and right lachrymal canals (channels in the skull for the tear ducts). It first came to light in the early 1970s, when five specimens were collected as part of a mammal survey in the Trans-Fly Plains of southwestern Papua New Guinea during 1972-3, but these were classed as western dasyures *D. geoffroii* until Van Dyck examined them and perceived their distinctness from known examples of the latter species.[197]

Vietnamese government has established a Rhinoceros Conservation Group, and is considering plans to extend the neighbouring Nam Cat Tien Reserve to encompass the entire region housing the rhinos (only a portion is contained within it at present), which would be of great benefit to the long-term survival of this small but priceless population of a species ranked in 1984 as one of the world's 12 most endangered species of animal.[196]

Incidentally, it is often alleged that the Javan rhinoceros has never been maintained in captivity, but this is far from being true. Reproduced here is a photo of an Asian rhinoceros on show at London Zoo from 1874 to 1885 and it is unquestionably a Javan rhino – as evinced by the characteristically scaly, mosaic-like patterning upon its hide, and especially by the fold of skin in front of its shoulder, which runs right across its back (in the great Indian rhino *R. unicornis* this fold does not run right across its back). In addition, as I learnt from John Edwards, of the Zoological Society of London, the large Asian rhino that had lived at Adelaide Zoo until 1907 had always been looked upon as a great Indian until 1948, when researchers revealed that it had actually been a Javan.

The description of a new dasyure from New Guinea in 1987 was followed in 1988 by the discovery on this same island of a very special tree kangaroo – after four years of pursuit by Sydney Museum zoologist Dr Tim Flannery and ranger-biologist Lester Seri. Heavier than Matschie's tree kangaroo *Dendrolagus matschiei* (the biggest species currently recognised), the new form is further delineated by its short face, thick jet-black fur, and unusually short tail (which is also characterised by a striking flash of orange at its base). The biggest mammal native to Melanesia, it inhabits the remote Torricelli mountain range in New Guinea's East Sepik Province, and first came to Flannery's attention when he purchased a strange claw from one of the region's local hunters. Unhappily, he believes that like so many other recently-disclosed animals, the new tree kangaroo (presently awaiting a formal description and name) may be in grave danger of extinction, as he estimates its total number at no more than a few hundred, and its habitat to be only about 10.5 square miles in area.[198]

Lesser beaked whale – a prize from Peru

An important marine mammal, the discovery of which was made public in 1988, was a new species of *Mesoplodon* beaked whale, the fifth to have been discovered so far during this century. Its existence first became known on 2 February 1976, with the procurement of a partial cranium and lumbar vertebra by Smithsonian Institution mammalogist Dr James G. Mead, close to the fish market in San Andres, Peru. Their dimensions suggested a total length of around 11.5 ft for the complete animal. Nine years later, on 1 May 1985, an immature female beaked whale was captured by fishermen about 30 nautical miles off Pucusana, Peru, and its entire skeleton, together with various internal organs, were duly preserved for study. By late 1988, seven more specimens had been obtained, all from along the coasts of south central Peru, and consisting variously of complete carcases and selected portions of carcases. All were carefully examined and compared with other *Mesoplodon* material by Mead and two fellow cetacean researchers, Drs Julio C. Reyes and Koen van Waerebeek (both from Lima's Centro Peruano de Estudios Cetológicos).[199]

Their studies confirmed that these (plus an additional Pucusana example, obtained in June 1989) belonged to a species that was as yet undescribed – a situation rectified in January 1991 with the publication of their official description of this new *Mesoplodon* member, christened *M. peruvianus*, and commonly known as the lesser or Peruvian beaked whale. Uniformly grey above, paler underneath, this is the world's smallest species of *Mesoplodon* beaked whale, with a maximum recorded total length of only 3.72 m (just over 12 ft), and characteristically small teeth that are ovate in cross-section.[199]

The perplexing pesut – extraordinary new species or freak of nature?

The late 1980s presented another surprise for cetologists, following the announcement during February 1989 of a potentially significant find in Borneo. As far back as the 18th century, villagers in the area of Lakes Jempang and Melitany, eastern Borneo, have reported seeing strange water monsters in the remote Mahakam River. Referred to as the pesut, this unidentified mystery creature attracted the considerable interest of French biologist Dr François-Xavier

Pelletier during a visit to the island in 1985.[200-1]

Determined to investigate this baffling affair, Pelletier journeyed there, and found himself taking part in a thrilling chase by canoe along the Mahakam River in the wake of creatures that were not supposed to exist. Finally, with the help of an oceanarium based in Jakarta, Java, he succeeded in capturing alive and unharmed no less than four pesuts, by extending a net across the entire width of the river. The pesuts were swiftly transferred to the oceanarium, where they have since been displayed, delighting large audiences of interested spectators with their underwater acrobatics and engaging friendliness.[200-1]

In appearance, this slender-bodied, blunt-headed cetacean is similar to, but somewhat smaller than, the Irrawaddy river dolphin *Orcaella breviceps*. Whereas the latter has 70 or so teeth, however, the pesut is instantly distinguished by being completely toothless. Teeth are present within its gums, but they do not seem to irrupt through them. Moreover, the pesut has a very distinctive means of obtaining its prey: employing a modus operandi not unlike that of the famous archerfishes, it stuns its prey by shooting a powerful jet of water at it, after which it is sucked into the pesut's gummy jaws. Apparently, the suction capability of these jaws is considerable – Pelletier noted that on one occasion, one of his arms was almost sucked into the mouth of a pesut via its vacuum cleaner-like action.[200-1]

If the pesut's toothless condition is typical for this form (rather than being some developmental fluke limited to just a few individuals), and if its remarkable method of obtaining prey has been reported accurately, this curious creature may genuinely constitute a new species of cetacean. Arguing against that, however, is the inclusion of the Mahakam River within the distribution range of the Irrawaddy river dolphin by certain cetological reference books, thereby implying that the Irrawaddy species and the pesut are one and the same – which in turn would downgrade the pesut's edentate (toothless) condition and associated prey-capturing behaviour to the level of individual aberration or idiosyncrasy.[200]

On the other hand, as the pesut is extremely similar to the Irrawaddy species in superficial outward appearance, it is possible that observers responsible for including the Mahakam River within the latter species' distribution range had mistakenly identified pesuts as Irrawaddy river dolphins, without investigating them more closely.[200] Only time and further researches will determine which of these answers is the correct one. Meanwhile, the pesut remains a perplexing but amiable enigma, cavorting happily within its native waterways while science wrestles with the riddle of its identity.

Golden-crowned sifaka – cryptic yet conspicuous

Less than three years after the discovery of a new species of bamboo lemur in Madagascar came the description of a new species of sifaka from this island. Also known as sun worshippers on account of at least one species' habit of sitting upright with the palms of its hands stretched upwards, as if in supplication to the sun, sifakas are among the largest of lemurs, and derive their name from the sound of their call. Until recently, only two species were known, but in 1974 mammalogist Dr Ian Tattersall observed some odd-looking specimens in a dry forest near Daraina, in the Madagascan province of Antseranana. Tattersall was puzzled by their unique complement of short white fur, brightly-coloured, readily-visible golden crowns, and very large, well-furred ears – a combination of features that differentiated them from both of the known species of sifaka.[202]

Nevertheless, he did not consider at that time that they could represent a new species, and so the incident attracted no attention – until they were spied in the late 1980s by American zoologist Dr Elwyn Simons, from the Primate Center at North Carolina's Duke University, who did recognise that they warranted separate specific status. In early 1989 he duly described the new species, naming it *Propithecus tattersalli* in its honour of its original observer. Commonly called the golden-crowned sifaka, its greatest mystery for Simons was why it had not been discovered much earlier – because its golden crown makes it so conspicuous, it can be readily spotted in treetops up to half a mile away.[202]

Pygmy elephant – the small subject of a giant controversy

For one of this century's most disputed mammalian discoveries, 1989 was a very critical year, because it witnessed publication of the most challenging evidence presented so far in support of this controversial creature's claim to be recognised as a valid species. The mammal in question is the pygmy elephant, whose history is one that closely parallels that of another onetime taxonomic outcast of undersized stature – the pygmy hippopotamus (see p. 32).

Science has traditionally accepted the existence of two distinct subspecies of the African elephant *Loxodonta africana*. The larger of these two is the bush elephant *L. a. africana (oxyotis)*, 9-13 ft tall at the shoulder, with triangular ears, it frequents open savannahs and bush. Somewhat smaller, with a shoulder height of 7.5-9 ft, is the forest elephant *L. a. cyclotis,* named after its much rounder ears, which inhabits forests and jungles.

In many parts of western and central Africa, however, native tribes claim that a third, totally separate form of elephant also exists. It is much smaller than the other two, with a shoulder height rarely exceeding 6 ft, a hairier, reddish skin, a notably truculent temperament in spite of its small size, and a secluded habitat consisting of only the most dense, swampy rainforests, rarely penetrated by the true forest elephant. This pygmy-sized pachyderm even has its own specific range of native names, never used in relation to the other two types of elephant. In Zaire, for example, it is known as the *wakawaka,* in the French Congo and Cameroon it is the *messala,* the *essala* in the Central African Republic, and the *mussaga* in Gabon. Similarly, when elephant hunter W. D. M. Bell was in Liberia during this century's earlier years, he discovered that the pygmy elephant was referred to there as the red elephant, and the larger, greyer forest elephant as the blue elephant.[2,81,203]

Science received its first opportunity to observe one of these intriguing creatures in 1905, when a *messala* was captured in the French Congo by a team of workers employed by the renowned animal dealer Carl Hagenbeck. A 6-year-old male, standing only 3 ft 8 in at the shoulder, it was brought back to Hamburg, where it was examined by Prof. Theodore Noack. The professor was sufficiently impressed by its tiny size and distinctive overall appearance to designate it as the type specimen of a new subspecies of

Pygmy elephant – due at last to receive zoological recognition as a valid species?

African elephant in January 1906. He named it *Elephas* [now *Loxodonta] africana pumilio.* It was purchased shortly afterwards by the New York Zoological Society, and transported forthwith to the Bronx Zoo, where it was christened 'Congo'. Congo lived there for the next 10 years, until he had to be put down on account of an incurable foot infection. At the time of his death in late autumn 1915, he had attained a shoulder height of only 6 ft 8 in; yet his tusks, although very slender, had grown to a formidable length of 23.5 in.[2,204]

Notwithstanding these unusual dimensions, zoologists in general were far from convinced that the pygmy elephant, eventually represented in zoos not only by Congo but also by a series of other specimens, was a genuine subspecies. Instead, they believed it merely to be either a stunted, dwarf form of the forest elephant, or perhaps simply a precocious juvenile version of it – opinions that remained unswayed by periodic sightings and news of pygmy elephants during the decades that followed. Supporters of this derided creature offered such details in its favour as its occurrence in herds that remained totally aloof from herds of the larger forest elephant, its possession of fully-developed tusks despite its small body size, and its liking for semi-aquatic territory (to the extent that Zaire's *wakawaka* is sometimes referred to as the water elephant). In 1914, the *wakawaka* received the scientific name *Loxodonta fransseni,* honouring a Belgian officer, Lieutenant Franssen, who obtained the remains of its type specimen for scientific study; however, this form is nowadays believed to be one and the same as *L. a. pumilio.*[2,204]

Yet in spite of all such attempts to resurrect its taxonomic respectability, official disapproval of the pygmy elephant prevailed, consigning it to the realms of teratology (the study of developmental freaks and abnormalities). There it lingered, unchampioned, until 1989, and the publication of a major vindication of the views of Prof. Noack and this contentious beast's other defenders. This vindication comprised the detailed findings of an extensive investigation into the entire pygmy elephant phenomenon by German zoologists Drs Martin Eisentraut and Wolfgang Böhme, who exhaustively reviewed and assessed all of the evidence for and against this pint-sized pachyderm's claim to taxonomic delineation, and exposed some unexpected, highly significant data. In fact, so significant were their findings, that they concluded their report by calling for the pygmy elephant to be classed not merely as a separate subspecies, but actually as a completely distinct species, *Loxodonta pumilio,* of equal standing to *Loxodonta africana.*[205] The crucial pieces of evidence that they offered in support of their exciting if radical classification, and the conclusions drawn from these, are as follows:

The well-documented existence of discrete troops or herds of pygmy elephants is proof of their distinct taxonomic status, because juvenile forest elephants never dissociate in this way, but always remain fully integrated in family groups. Some researchers have reported seeing pygmy elephants nuzzling female forest elephants, suggesting that they were therefore merely the offspring of these latter, but Eisentraut and Böhme state that such reports were actually based upon genuine juvenile forest elephants, not upon pygmy elephants.[205]

The disproportionately well-developed tusks of pygmy elephants cannot be explained as precocious tusk development by juvenile forest elephants, because dental evidence obtained from a male pygmy elephant examined by animal collector Ulrich Roder during the second half of this century showed that the beast was 16-18 years old. Even more startling was the discovery of a dead female pygmy elephant by French zoologist Dr L-P. Knoepfler at the pygmy village of Makokou in the forests of Gabon, because when the pygmies sliced open the carcase (measuring a mere 5 ft 3 in at the shoulder), it was found to contain a full-term foetus – clear proof that this diminutive elephant was a mature specimen.[205]

Consistently small spoor, as well as a range of cranial and other anatomical features readily differentiating the pygmy elephant from the forest elephant, comprise the additional evidence presented by Eisentraut and Böhme in support of their belief. And certainly, just as the above findings concerning tusks and the full-term foetus refute the possibility that this elephant is merely a juvenile form of *L. a. cyclotis,* its existence in herds of its own kind discounts the likelihood that it is a genetically-induced dwarf. Of course, adverse environmental factors can sometimes create undernourished, under-developed strains of animal, but the pygmy elephant's tropical rainforest domain is an optimal habitat for herbivores, thereby ruling out any identity involving an epigenetic dwarf form (i.e. a creature whose natural growth has been stunted by environmental factors).[205]

Following on from the above, and most significantly of all: as the pygmy and forest elephants share the same geographical area (even though they occupy different habitats within this area), they cannot be subspecies of the same species; by definition, a species' subspecies are geographically separated from one another. This in turn means that the pygmy elephant has to be a separate species in its own right.[205]

The findings of Eisentraut and Böhme will unquestionably provide much substance for future discussion regarding the pygmy elephant's status, but it seems rather more likely now that, after almost a century in taxonomic turmoil, the pygmy elephant's name will ultimately be added to the catalogue of scientifically-recognised mammalian species.

Kellas cat – a short-lived 'species' from Scotland

During the 1980s, several unusual, very gracile fox-sized cats, with notably large fangs and bristly black fur sprinkled with white primary guard hairs, were found near the West Moray hamlet of Kellas and elsewhere in northern Scotland. The first to attract media attention was a specimen trapped in a fox snare at Revack Lodge in 1984. Unfortunately, its body was later lost, but its photograph is reproduced in the colour section of this book. The media speculated that these distinctive felids, known as Kellas cats, were a species new to science. In *Mystery Cats of the World* (1989) and my Kellas cat paper (1990), however, I predicted that they would prove merely to be introgressive (complex) hybrids of domestic cat and Scottish wildcat – an identity now confirmed by anatomical analyses at the Royal Museum of Scotland.[60,206]

Lion tamarins and zebra marmosets

The first major mammalian discovery to hit the headlines in the 1990s was made public on 21 June 1990 – when, at a scientific conference devoted to those handsome, golden-furred New World monkeys called lion tamarins, primatologists announced that a new, fourth species had recently been discovered in Brazil by biologists Drs Lucia Lorini and Vanessa Persson. This species is known as the black-faced lion tamarin, and was officially named *Leontopithecus caissara* after the caicaras (coastal fishermen who live and work on its island home of Superagui, south of São Paulo).[207]

In October 1992, Dr Russell Mittermeier, of Conservation International in New York, announced the discovery of a new marmoset, *Callithrix mauesi*, marked with a hint of zebra-like stripes. It had been found amid a very remote portion of the Brazilian Amazon[208] – in contrast to the black-faced lion tamarin, whose previously undetected existence astonished zoologists because its

home is in one of Brazil's most heavily-populated regions.[207] (This latter scenario was duplicated by the discovery of a new spiny bandicoot. Dubbed *Echymipera echinista* and described in 1990, this slender-snouted marsupial was found in New Guinea's Western Province, an area that had already been extensively explored.[209])

Tatu bola – in the market for rediscovery

Equally unexpected was the mode of rediscovery featuring the three-banded armadillo *Tolypeutes tricinctus*. Referred to locally as the *tatu bola* on account of its ability to roll itself up into an impregnable ball like a surrealistic armoured hedgehog, it is known only from the drought-blighted, semi-arid plains of northeastern Brazil. Its talents offer it protection against natural predators, but not against man, partial to its chicken-tasting flesh. Indeed, as a direct result of this fatal quality of its flesh, the three-banded armadillo had not been reliably reported since the early 1980s, and was feared to be extinct until 1990, when a team of field researchers seeking Lear's macaw (see Birds) in Bahia spotted five living adult specimens of the *tatu bola* being offered for sale at a local market. Needless to say, the team bought all five and transferred them to Minas Gerais Federal University at Belo Horizonte, where two, both female, are still alive. Plans are now underway to seek out more information concerning this endangered species' dietary requirements and reproduction, in order to instigate a captive breeding programme once some male specimens have been obtained.[210]

Debut of the Vu Quang ox

During a field trip to the remote, scarcely-

classification within the cattle subfamily of bovid ungulates, and has thus been dubbed the Vu Quang ox, this major new find may comprise a taxonomic bridge between the oxen and antelopes, as implied externally by its oryx-like horns. In June 1993, MacKinnon and his Vietnamese colleagues formally described their sensational discovery, christening it *Pseudoryx nghetinhensis*.[211]

Standing 32-36 in at the shoulder, with a total length of approximately 4.5 feet and a weight of about 176 lb when adult, the Vu Quang ox is comparable in size to Sulawesi's mountain anoa *Anoa quarlesi* (p. 30), but its horns and slender neck are longer. Its fine-haired coat is deep brown in colour, and its face is decorated with bold black and white markings. There is also a blackish-brown narrow dorsal stripe running on to the short tail, which bears a black fluffy tip, and a whitish stripe on the outer rump.[211]

Notwithstanding its very belated scientific debut (bearing in mind its large size), it does have a sizeable distribution range, encompassing more than 20 different localities inside the provinces of Nghe an and Ha tinh along Vietnam's border with Laos and comprising a collective area estimated to be in excess of 1540 square miles. It inhabits montane forest, never entering neighbouring agricultural lands, but ventures down into the lowlands during the winter season, at which time it is hunted by the local people. They state that it travels in small groups, usually containing two or three animals, seeking the leaves of bushes and fig trees upon which it browses.[211]

According to local testimony, there may be several hundred specimens presently existing within its known distribution

explored Vu Quang Nature Reserve on the Vietnam-Laos border in May 1992, a scientific team led by WWF representative Dr John MacKinnon came upon three strange pairs of horns (one pair with part of the skull still attached) in the homes of local hunters. The horns were long and dagger-like, similar to those of the African and Arabian oryxes – but there was no Asian species known to science that had such horns. Conversely, the locals knew the creature well, referring to it as *sao la* ('spindle horn') or *son duong* ('mountain goat').[211]

Consequently, the Vietnamese participants of this expedition made four return visits to the region in search of additional specimens of this seemingly undiscovered species, and succeeded in procuring over 20 specimens – including three complete skins, one of which has been preserved as a taxiderm exhibit. These important remains were thoroughly examined by a number of mammal experts in Britain and Australia and subjected to DNA analyses in the United States and Denmark, which confirmed that they were indeed from a hitherto undescribed species – one so distinct from all others, in fact, that it required a new genus.[211]

Although it appears to warrant

range, but to ensure its survival the Vietnamese Ministry of Forestry has increased the Vu Quang Nature Reserve from 16,000 to 60,000 hectares (i.e. from roughly 60 to 230 square miles), and has also prohibited logging within the reserve's boundaries. For the moment, therefore, the future seems hopeful for the Vu Quang ox – the biggest new species of mammal to have been revealed in Asia since the kouprey more than 50 years earlier, and one of the greatest cryptozoological triumphs since the okapi's unveiling back in 1901.[211]

Thylacine – rediscovered by computer?

It is nothing if not fitting that the final mammal to be documented here is one whose rediscovery uniquely spans the past and the future. Put another way, the precise date of its rediscovery depends entirely upon whom we consult – on offer are any number of dates from the past, and a comparable range of predictions for the future. This animal will also probably prove to have been the first lost species to have been refound by computer.

Cynically referred to on occasion as Australia's Loch Ness monster and the world's most common extinct animal, this famously elusive mammal is *Thylacinus cynocephalus*, popularly known as the thylacine or Tasmanian wolf. 'Officially', it has yet to be rediscovered; unofficially, few zoologists doubt that it still exists. Indeed, its eventual 'formal' rediscovery is generally deemed to be a mere technicality; and certainly, after surveying the vast body of literature concerning its alleged survival, my own view is that there is sufficient evidence

Tasmanian wolf – the first extinct species to be rediscovered by computer?
(Fortean Picture Library)

available (especially from the 1980s onwards) to justify the thylacine's inclusion within any volume devoted to the 20th century's quota of new and rediscovered animals.

With a total length of 5 ft (including its stiff, 1.5-ft-long tail), the thylacine is the world's largest modern-day species of marsupial carnivore, and closely resembles a yellowish-brown wolf – except for the diagnostic series of 8-20 black or chocolate-brown transverse stripes across its back, hindquarters, and tail base. On account of these stripes (of which males tend to have fewer than females), it is sometimes termed the Tasmanian tiger, a confusing, undesirable name detracting from its spectacular canine convergence.[212]

This impressive creature's history is one of great tragedy and savage irony. Several thousand years ago, thylacines thrived in New Guinea and throughout Australia, but have been conclusively recorded only from Tasmania in historic times (although, very intriguingly, reports of unidentified thylacine-like animals do emerge from Papua New Guinea and the Australian mainland every so often). Following the arrival onto Tasmania of western sheep farmers, the thylacine, still plentiful here at that time, was soon viewed as a severe

threat to livestock, and was frequently blamed for sheep kills that were for the most part much more likely to have been the work of stray dogs. In 1886, the Australian parliament finally yielded to the ever-increasing barrage of grievances levied by Tasmania's farming fraternity, and instigated a 21-year campaign of thylacine annihilation, offering a bounty of £1 per adult thylacine (and 10/- per thylacine pup). Predictably, the campaign was a great success – for the sheep farmers. For the thylacine it was an unmitigated disaster. By 1909, more than 5000 bounties had been paid; and many other dead thylacines had been handed over to settlers, and to skin dealers doing a brisk trade in thylacine pelts, as these recipients paid more than the governmental bounty price for their carcases.[212]

No large species of mammal wholly confined to one relatively small island could possibly withstand such sustained decimation, especially when it was also being ravaged by a virulent distemper-like disease, and its habitat was being destroyed for agricultural purposes throughout much of its range. By 1910, this once-common species' cataclysmic decline had become all too apparent, by way of the dramatic fall in the number of bounties being claimed, thereby persuading the government to terminate its campaign. It was quite evident, however, that the damage had already been done, because reports of thylacines in the years that followed became ever fewer. A handful of specimens remained in zoos, notably Tasmania's own Hobart Zoo, but no efforts were made to establish a thriving captive population. It was almost as if the concept of extinction, when applied to the thylacine, seemed too implausible for anyone on Tasmania to take seriously – there had always been thylacines

here, and there always would be.[212]

The naivety of this impression was demonstrated in 1930, when farmer Wilf Batty unknowingly made history, by shooting a thylacine that had been showing an unhealthy interest in his poultry – for that unfortunate animal is now on record as being the very last fully-confirmed specimen of a thylacine obtained in the wild.[212]

Six years later, in mid-July 1936, the Australian government finally declared the thylacine an endangered species, and accorded it full protection – but by then it really didn't matter any more, because there only appeared to be one thylacine left.[212]

Housed at Hobart Zoo, this last survivor was an adult male called Benjamin, described by his keeper, Frank Darby, as a morose but tame creature, who enjoyed being patted. As a zoo specimen, Benjamin was not in need of governmental protection, but even if he could have benefited it would not have made much difference to him – because on 7 September 1936, less than 2 months after the new law protecting his species had been passed, Benjamin died. The last living known specimen of Tasmania's spectacular marsupial wolf was gone.[212]

In an ironic *avant-face,* once the wolf was extinct everyone began searching for evidence that it still survived, with numerous expeditions setting out in pursuit of thylacines during the late 1930s, late 1940s, late 1950s, and on a regular basis since then. So far, however, not a single post-1936 specimen of a thylacine has been brought to scientific attention, but there is a vast array of eyewitness reports of supposed thylacines on record, each year adding new ones to the ever-proliferating files, and including among their number some very convincing accounts by reliable observers that cannot be easily discounted. The following case is a particularly impressive, recent example.[212]

It took place at approximately 2.00 am one morning in March 1982, when one of Tasmania's National Parks and Wildlife Service rangers awoke from a nap while parked at a road junction in a remote forested area in the island's northwestern portion. As a matter of routine, he picked up his spotlight and scanned the immediate surroundings with his beam, and as he did so it exposed a large wolf-like creature standing to one side of his vehicle, at a distance of around 20-23 ft. The beam revealed that this unexpected visitor had a sandy coat that bore 12 black stripes, and the reflection of its eyes in the spotlight was pale yellow in colour.[213]

The creature opened its mouth, showing its teeth, but otherwise it remained quite still, enabling the ranger to observe it closely for several minutes, until he decided to reach for his camera, whereupon his movements disturbed the animal, which moved away into the undergrowth, disappearing from sight. At this point, the ranger stepped out of his vehicle, in order to seek any traces that his visitor may have left behind, but it was raining heavily and any clues that might have been present were obscured except for a strong, lingering odour.[213]

Nevertheless, his observations of the animal had been more than adequate for the ranger to have no doubt whatsoever as to its identity – in his subsequent report he referred to it categorically as a large adult male thylacine. Bearing in mind that here was no ordinary eyewitness, but one with impeccable qualifications for identifying animals, and whose observation, moreover, had been made at close range, in good lighting conditions, and for a duration of

several minutes, it is little wonder that this ranger's account is deemed to be one of the most compelling pieces of evidence for the thylacine's continued survival.[213]

Nevertheless, in view of today's ultra-technological, computerised world it is perhaps not only appropriate but also inevitable that the single most significant contribution to the search for conclusive proof of this species' existence has been provided not by any human, but by a much more objective intelligence, devoid of any potentially deceptive emotion or preconception – nothing less, in fact, than a computer programme called Bioclim.[214]

The brainchild of Henry Nix, from the Australian National University's Centre for Resource and Environmental Studies, Bioclim can utilise the known climatic, topographical, and other important environmental preferences of a given species of plant or animal to construct a sophisticated computer-generated map that will predict with great accuracy where that species should occur within any specified geographical locality (e.g. Tasmania). Intrigued by the continuing stream of alleged thylacine sightings emerging year after year, Nix consulted the literature dealing with thylacine distribution and habitat preferences recorded during the 19th century and the early years of this century, and instructed Bioclim to construct from this data a detailed map highlighting those areas of Tasmania that the thylacine would most likely inhabit today if it were still alive. Then, from a vast selection of supposed thylacine sightings recorded during the past six decades, he chose those that seemed to be fairly or very reliable, and incorporated into the map the localities that they featured in order to discover whether they coincided to any extent with the programme's predicted areas for thylacines.

101

For both the fairly reliable and the very reliable sightings, the correspondence with Bioclim's predicted areas was almost exact.[214]

The probability of such extreme conformity occurring solely by random chance is virtually nil. Thus, when announcing his results in March 1990 and commenting upon the sightings' potential significance, Nix concluded that 'These people really are seeing thylacines.'[214]

Perhaps by the time this book is published, the predictions of Nix's computer programme will have been unequivocally confirmed by the discovery of a living thylacine, ending one of cryptozoology's most tantalising mysteries. If this triumph is indeed achieved, however, let us all hope very sincerely that everything possible will be done to ensure that this time Tasmania's most splendid animal does not suffer the same terrible fate at the hands of mankind that it experienced during its previous period of 'official' existence.

Monkey-eating eagle

BIRDS

Resurrected Takahes and Peacocks from the Congo

In 1948, a discovery was made in New Zealand that shook the ornithological world out of its usual comatose condition in an incredible manner – no less than the discovery (or rediscovery) of a bird that had vanished, a bird that had, for the last fifty years, been believed to be extinct. It was, to give it its full title, the Notornis or Takahe (Notornis mantelli), *and the whole history of this bird is one of the most fascinating in the annals of ornithology.*

GERALD DURRELL – TWO IN THE BUSH

The story of the discovery of this bird begins with a single feather which I found on the hat of a native at Avakubi in the Ituri Forest in 1913. It was a secondary wing–quill, rufous with regular blackish barring, and from its form and texture seemed to be that of some gallinaceous bird. But after comparison with feathers of many birds of that group, I found myself unable to identify it, nor could any of the many friends to whom I showed it. So I laid it away in safety, but never forgot it...

DR JAMES P. CHAPIN – 'THE CONGO PEACOCK', IN:
COMPTE–RENDU DU IX CONGRÈS ORNITHOLOGIQUE INTERNATIONAL

Some of the 20th century's most celebrated zoological débutantes and restorées have been of the feathered variety – these include the finding of a phalanx of flamboyant new pheasants, and the debut of a bewildering passerine from Peru that continues to defy all attempts to classify it; the reappearance of a trio of long–lost Australians all within the space of just a few months, as well as the recent revival of several 'classic' extinct species; the long–hoped–for (but little–expected) return of a multicoloured wanderer from New Zealand, and the astounding resurrection of a Bermuda seabird previously believed extinct for more than three centuries; plus the successful pursuit of a macaw missing for over 120 years, and the extraordinary history of a pair of dusty taxiderm specimens, neglected and forgotten for years, which became the greatest ornithological discovery of this century.

Fearful owl – small but sufficient

The most spectacular avian discovery made during the 19th century's closing years was *Pithecophaga jefferyi*, the monkey–eating eagle of the Philippines. A magnificent but nowadays greatly endangered, harpy–related species with a mighty 7 ft wingspan, it was discovered on the island of Samar by English naturalist John Whitehead, and was formally described in 1896 by W.R. Ogilvie–Grant[1] – but was not seen in living form beyond the Philippines until 1909, when a live specimen was exhibited at London Zoo.

Compared to such an impressive species as this, the Solomon Islands' fearful owl *Nesasio solomonensis*, one of the most interesting new birds to be discovered at the beginning of the 20th century, with a total length of only 15 in, may not seem particularly noteworthy on first sight. Certainly, its barred upperparts, wings, and tail, and its paler, creamy underparts, are rather bland; only its thick, startlingly white eyebrows are likely to attract a second glance. However, first appearances can often deceive.[2–3]

Viewed more closely, its beak is seen to be disproportionately powerful and sturdy for such a modest–sized owl, and its talons are also exceptionally formidable. The explanation for these unanticipated features seems to be that the fearful owl, despite its small size, is the Solomon Islands' ecological counterpart to the huge, exceedingly powerful eagle owls found elsewhere in the world. In keeping with this status it preys upon such sizeable creatures as possums and large birds, thereby fully meriting its common name.[2–3]

The only member of its genus, the fearful owl was first discovered on the island of Santa Isabel (Ysabel), by Albert S. Meek, but it also occurs on Choiseul and Bougainville. Formally described in 1901 by Ernst Hartert, it inhabits low and hill forests.[2–3]

Rothschild's peacock pheasant – an unexpected 'missing link'

Despite their name, peacock pheasants are not hybrids of peacocks and pheasants. In fact, they comprise a genus of very distinctive grey or brown pheasants (*Polyplectron*), whose males possess a resplendent 'peacock' tail, liberally adorned with mirror–like eyespots (ocelli), which they raise and spread open during their mating displays.

By the end of the 19th century, five species were known to science, and ornithologists were confident that there were no more of these showy species still awaiting detection. The error of this assumption was decisively laid bare in January 1902, when a team of Bornean hunters employed by animal collector John Waterstradt obtained six peacock pheasants (four males, two females) that did not belong to any species already known to science. Procured in the State of Ulu Pahang within the central Malay Peninsula, they proved most interesting, as their species appeared to be transitional between the most primitive species of peacock pheasant and the four more advanced ones.[4]

The most primitive, the bronze–tailed peacock pheasant *P. chalcurus*, has a long pointed tail, and lacks the reflective ocelli decorating the tail and wings of the other species – whose tail feathers, moreover, are broad with rounded tips. Accordingly, the bronze–tailed was initially placed within its own genus, as *Chalcurus chalcurus*. The new species became known as Rothschild's peacock pheasant in honour of Lord Walter Rothschild (a prominent figure in early 20th century zoology). Its males possessed the long pointed tail characteristic of the bronze–tailed, but their tail and wings were embellished with the ocelli exhibited by the four advanced species.[5] So how was it to be classified?

When Lord Rothschild described this new species in 1903, he deemed the shape of its tail to be more significant than the presence of fully–formed ocelli, so he christened it *Chalcurus inopinatus* – its specific name recalling both its discovery and its equally unexpected status as a 'missing link' in the peacock pheasants' evolutionary progression. Eventually, however, this latter attribute became obscured, on account of a name–change – taxonomists ultimately decided that all six species were sufficiently closely related to be included within the single genus *Polyplectron*, so Rothschild's species is known today as *P. inopinatum*.[4–5]

Notwithstanding their striking plumage and chicken–sized build, peacock pheasants are not easy to spot in the wild, because their favoured habitat consists of dense, inaccessible jungle, where they seek cover in the most impenetrable vegetation at the slightest provocation – thus explaining the success of *P. inopinatum* eluding scientific detection for so long. It is also possible that there is at least one species *still* awaiting scientific discovery. The *alovot* is a pheasant–like bird that allegedly dwells only within the densest forests of Sumatra. Those who have been fortunate enough to glimpse it assert that it is chicken–shaped and sized, with a comb–like crest in some cases (present only in the males?) and dark brown plumage dappled with lighter spots. This description compares with certain of the more advanced species of peacock pheasant.[6]

Wake Island rail – described and destroyed in under 45 years

One of the lesser–known casualties of World War II, the following species has the tragic distinction of having been described and destroyed all within the first half of this century. It was a diminutive, flightless, bar–breasted member of the rail family – a multifarious assemblage of birds that includes such familiar species as the moorhen, coot, water rail, and corncrake. *Rallus* [originally *Hypotaenidia*] *wakensis* was described in 1903 by Lord Rothschild from a series of ten specimens obtained by a Japanese vessel in 1892 on Wake Island, a tiny mid–Pacific dot of land that comprised this species' only known home.[7] Nevertheless, it seemed to be in no danger of extinction, and attracted little attention – until 1941, when its island was occupied by a Japanese battalion during World War II.

Food became ever more scarce on Wake Island as the conflict progressed year upon year, until the soldiers faced outright starvation. Inevitably, they ate whatever they could find – including the defenceless rails. By 1946, every single bird had been killed and eaten. World War II had ended – but so too had the life of an entire species.[8]

Mikado pheasant – beauty in blue from Formosa

One of the world's most beautiful pheasants was unknown to science prior to 1906. In that year, W. Goodfellow noticed two very long and attractive tail feathers, deep steely–blue in colour and banded across with thin white stripes, in the head-dress of a hill–native from Formosa (now Taiwan). They clearly belonged to some type of pheasant, but none with which Goodfellow was familiar. Upon questioning the native, he learnt that they had been obtained from a bird killed on the island's Mount Arizan. Goodfellow was able to purchase the feathers, which, as he had suspected, did not match those of any pheasant recorded by science. Hence they became the type of a new species, described later in 1906 by W.R. Ogilvie–Grant, who named it *Calophasis mikado*, the mikado pheasant.[9]

Not long afterwards, Goodfellow succeeded in obtaining a whole skin of a female mikado pheasant on the Racu–Racu Mountains. Other complete specimens, females and males, were subsequently procured, and in 1907 Lord Rothschild produced the first scientific description of the entire bird. Later studies revealed that this ornate inhabitant of Formosa's steep conifer–bearing slopes was closely related to the long-tailed *Syrmaticus* pheasants, so in 1922 William Beebe renamed it *Syrmaticus mikado*, thereby allying it with such comparably elegant species as Elliot's, Humes's bar-tailed, and the copper pheasant.[5,10]

As with most pheasants, the female mikado is fairly drab, its plumage composed of soft, nondescript shades of brown and fawn. In contrast, the male is extremely eyecatching. Much of its head and body shares the dark blue colour of its tail, which at 20 in or so accounts for just over half of its total length of 3 ft. Intruding upon this predominantly blue colour scheme, however, are two white bands and numerous shorter stripes on each wing, white banding across its tail, an expanse of deep metallic green on the lower part of each shoulder, black spotting on its breast and back, and a bright red patch of skin around each eye.[5,10]

Confined solely to Formosa and hunted widely in the past by this island's natives, the mountain-dwelling mikado is one of the rarer pheasant species, but fortunately it breeds well in captivity, thereby offering a means of perpetuating it, and of supplementing its wild populations via reintroduction programmes using captive-bred birds.[5,10]

Mikado pheasant – two tail feathers heralded its ornithological debut in 1906.
(World Pheasant Association)

African broadbill – an out-of-place oddity

In 1908, at an altitude of roughly 6670 ft in eastern Zaire's Itombwe Mountains, bird collector Rudolf Grauer collected a very pretty, principally green-plumaged bird with bright blue cheeks, throat and chest. Grauer's discovery came as an appreciable surprise to ornithology, for although his bird was first thought to be an aberrant flycatcher, it proved to be a hitherto unknown species belonging to the family Eurylaimidae. The members of this family are primitive perching birds popularly known as broadbills, which were previously believed to be exclusively Asian in distribution. In honour of its discoverer, and in recognition of its superficial similarity to the green *Calyptomena* broadbills from the southeast Asian Sunda Isles, Lord Rothschild named it *Pseudocalyptomena graueri* in 1909.[11-12] Bird enthusiasts were naturally most interested in this African anomaly, and eagerly awaited further news of it – but none arrived. It would be another 20 years before a second specimen appeared.

One morning in 1929, after vainly seeking this 'lost' species for days, during an American expedition to the Itombwe Mountains, Alan Moses was sitting down, taking a rest from his search and despairing of ever sighting his elusive quarry. Luckily, he happened to glance up from his gloomy reverie just at the right moment – for one of these mysterious African broadbills was perched on the branches just above his head. He was unable to catch it, but he now knew that its species did still exist, and by the end of the expedition he did acquire a few specimens verifying its rediscovery.[12]

Even so, its continuing survival is far from guaranteed. In 1967 it was discovered in Uganda, near the Bwindi Swamp in the Impenetrable Forest, but has not been recorded in Zaire since 1959. It is currently classed as one of Africa's most endangered birds.[12] More recently, it has lost its unique status as Africa's only species of broadbill. The genus *Smithornis* contains three African species of dull, brown-coloured bird, which were all known to science before *P. graueri*, but were assumed to be flycatchers – until they were closely re-examined during the 1960s, whereupon they were found to be broadbills.

Rothschild's mynah – Bali's only endemic bird

On 24 March 1911, while participating in the second Freiburger expedition to the Moluccas, avian expert Dr Erwin Stresemann collected an adult female of a quite exquisite species of crested starling at Bubunan, on the northern coast of Bali. Except for the black edge to its tail and its black wing tips, its plumage was an immaculate snowy white. In contrast, its unfeathered legs and feet were pale grey, its bill brownish-yellow, and a conspicuous patch of bright blue skin encircled each eye. A new species, related most closely to the mynahs, it was unique to Bali – moreover, it is this island's *only* endemic bird.[13]

In 1912 it was officially described by Stresemann, who created a new genus for it, and named it *Leucospar rothschildi*, as a token of his gratitude to Lord Rothschild for permitting him to spend such a considerable time during his ornithological researches at the magnificent natural history museum at Tring, founded and owned at that time by Rothschild.[13]

The highly attractive appearance of Rothschild's mynah ensured its rapid rise to fame as a popular cage bird, but by being

Rothschild's mynah – Bali's only endemic bird was unknown to science until 1911.
(Dr Karl Shuker)

restricted to such a tiny island (Bali is no more than 2000 square miles in area, of which only the Bubunan portion is inhabited by the mynahs) it is, unavoidably, a species with a small population size. As a result, the depletion of its numbers in the wild by local trappers supplying birds to zoos, aviculturalists, etc, ultimately transformed it into an endangered species.[14]

Happily, however, it breeds well in captivity, enabling its numbers to be built up. Indeed, plans are now underway for the release onto Bali of captive-bred specimens from the Jersey Wildlife Preservation Trust (where 185 mynahs had been bred from an original group of just four by mid-1990) and from certain American zoos, in a bid to boost its wild population to the level at which it had existed before it became a much sought-after aviary species.[15]

Crested shelduck – does it still survive?

The crested shelduck *Tadorna* [originally *Pseudotadorna*] *cristata* is a renowned mystery bird that might well have become known to western zoologists much earlier if they had paid more attention to oriental works of art, because this extremely attractive and unmistakable species was frequently portrayed in Chinese paintings and tapestries, as well as in antiquarian Japanese illustrations and tomes dating back to the early 18th century. Obviously it must have been common in those days, but by the time it had first engaged scientific interest it was virtually extinct.[10]

The first specimen recorded by science was a female obtained in April 1877 near Vladivostok, but this was dismissed by zoologist Philip Sclater as a hybrid of the falcated teal *Anas falcata* and the ruddy shelduck *Tadorna ferruginea*. In the closing weeks of 1913, a pair of specimens was collected at the mouth of western Korea's Kun-Kiang River (the female was later lost), followed in December 1916 by a female obtained on Korea's Naktong River. By now, this unusual species had attracted formal scientific interest at last, and the Naktong River bird became the species' type, officially described and named in 1917 by Nagamichi Kuroda. In summer 1924, a second male was collected, once again at the mouth of Korea's Kun-Kiang River.[10,16-17]

The male of this species is particularly striking, by virtue of its predominantly tricoloured plumage. Its chin and crown, lower neck and upper back, breast, tail and wing flight feathers are dark greenish-black, as is its long, diagnostic drooping crest. These all contrast sharply with the grey, finely-barred plumes of its face, upper neck, lower back, and underparts; and also with its rufous flanks and shoulders – slightly darker than its deep pink feet and bill. The only intrusion upon this three-shaded colour scheme is the whiteness of the covert feathers on its wings. The female is basically a washed-out counterpart of the male in colour, with the addition of a distinctive white ring around each eye.[16]

Except for the lost Kun-Kiang female, all of the above specimens were preserved, which is just as well, because no additional example has ever been procured since. Much more alarming, however, is the extreme scarcity even of sightings since 1924. In late March 1943, an alleged sighting of two individuals was recorded from South Korea's Chungchong Pukto Province. More than 20 years later, on 16 May 1964, V.I. Labzyuk and Yu. N. Nazarov saw three birds, a male and two females, associating with a flock of harlequin ducks on a rocky island southwest of Vladivostok in the Rimski-Korsakov archipelago. The drake's characteristic tricoloured plumage was readily visible, and easily distinguished from the harlequins' equally distinctive appearance. This (or another) specimen was also seen with a female a few days later, on a nearby island, enhancing the report's veracity and significance.[10,17]

Of particular note was a sighting of no less than six of these birds (including two males) at the mouth of North Korea's Pouchon River in March 1971. This offers tentative hope to ornithologists that the exotic crested shelduck does indeed still exist in viable numbers for breeding[17] – a species that might easily have been bred in captivity and thereby granted a secure future, if only science had recognised its existence and its validity as a genuine species a little earlier.

Inaccessible Island rail – a flightless bird from Atlantis

Inaccessible Island is a tiny islet of the Tristan da Cunha group, sited in the south Atlantic roughly midway between southern Argentina and South Africa, which would have little claim to fame, were it not for a very peculiar member of its avifauna. The species in question is a minuscule rail, only 5 in long (little larger than a newly-hatched chicken), and with such tiny, poorly-formed wings that it is totally flightless. Its habit of scampering swiftly through the island's wide expanses of dense tussock grass thus makes it seem to the casual observer more akin to a mouse than a bird. This illusion is enhanced by its strange feathers, which are decomposed (i.e. atrophied) and hair-like. Its upperparts are reddish-brown in colour, its underparts are dark grey, and its belly, flanks, and wing-covert feathers bear paler bands.[18]

A remote spot, Inaccessible Island was well-named. Due to its inaccessibility, its diminutive rail (found nowhere else in the world) escaped scientific attention until 1923, when the Reverend H.M.C. Rogers, resident chaplain on Tristan da Cunha, collected some skins in response to a request made by the Shackleton-Rowett Expedition naturalist, Mr Wilkins. The expedition had visited the island group a little earlier, and had heard the locals speak about the tiny 'island hen' of Inaccessible, but had been unable to travel there to seek it out.[18]

On 5 July 1923, two of the skins collected by Rogers arrived at the British Museum (Natural History), and were described that same year by Percy Lowe, who named the new species *Atlantisia rogersi*. 'Atlantisia' alludes to the belief by some workers that the Tristan da Cunha islands are remnants of the fabled sunken continent of Atlantis. Previously little-studied, in the 1980s *A. rogersi* was the subject of a detailed field survey by South African researchers Drs M.J. Fraser and W.R.J. Dean, and Dr I.C. Best from Bahrain.[18]

Two pheasant finds in Indo-China

During an expedition to Indo-China in 1923, aviculturalist Dr Jean Delacour rediscovered a previously obscure species of blue pheasant, when, aided by ornithologist Pierre Jabouille, he succeeded in persuading the natives to capture 22 living specimens of Edwards's pheasant *Lophura edwardsi* in the back hills of the Quangtri province. Until then, this species had only been known to science from four skins, sent in 1895 to the Paris Museum from Quangtri by French missionary Père Renauld.[5,19]

Yet even more exciting than his rediscovery of Edwards's pheasant was Delacour's discovery, during the very same expedition, of a completely new pheasant – when a living pair of birds belonging to a totally unknown species was sent to him from the limestone mountains of Donghoi and northern Quangtri, in northern Annam, on the Vietnam-Laos border. These two specimens were transported safely back to France, where they bred, eventually giving rise to a large number since distributed to aviaries and parks worldwide – all of which is very fortunate, because no other living specimens of this species obtained in the wild have ever survived the journey back to the west. (Happily, despite the inevitably high degree of inbreeding, captive collections of this pheasant have not shared the bizarre fate of another notably inbred species, the Queimada Grande viper – see *Reptiles*)[5,19]

Described by Delacour and Jabouille in 1924, it was named *Hierophasis imperialis*, the imperial pheasant, but has since been renamed *Lophura imperialis*, stressing its affinities with the *Lophura* species – known collectively as the gallopheasants ('chicken pheasants'), and including such attractive species as the silver pheasants, firebacks, and kalijs.[5,19]

Up to 30 in long, with a wide tail and short crest, the male imperial pheasant is a dark, midnight coalescence of black and very deep blue, encroached upon only by a bright scarlet, twin-lobed wattle on each side of its face, crimson-coloured legs, pale bill and brown-tipped wings. The latter features are shared by the female, but she lacks the male's blue-black colouration, replacing it with chestnut-brown shades above, becoming lighter below.[5,19]

Baker's 'lost' bowerbird

In 1928, Rollo H. Beck, a bird collector from the American Museum of Natural History, but with little experience of New Guinea's avifauna, struck a decisive blow for gifted amateurs everywhere. Upon his return home from a collecting trip to that island's Mandated Territory, he presented the museum with three specimens of a resplendent, new species of bowerbird. Of comparable shape and size to the common starling, its principally black plumage was set aflame by a fiery-feathered cape flowing over its shoulders, a bright golden-yellow band across each wing, and a vivid scarlet crown above its ebony-plumed face. According to Beck, the three specimens had been collected in the vicinity of Madang, a coastal town in the Adelbert Mountains' Astrolabe Bay.[20]

The following year, their species was officially described, and named *Xanthomelus* [later renamed *Sericulus*] *bakeri*, Baker's regent bowerbird[20] – after which it vanished entirely. For 30 years, searches within its type locality failed to find a single specimen and it became one of the greatest enigmas in modern-day ornithology.

In 1956, however, Prof. Thomas Gilliard, a major authority on bowerbirds and birds of paradise, set out to discover its secret homeland. After establishing that it did not exist near Madang, he learnt from Beck's widow that in actual fact the three specimens collected by him had been obtained at a spot some distance away from Madang, to the west. And sure enough, when Gilliard arrived at that place, he sighted several birds, the first examples of Baker's regent bowerbird seen in the wild by a scientist since the species was first discovered back in 1928.[21]

Return of the relict gull

On 24 April 1929, a single individual of what seemed to be a new subspecies of the Mediterranean gull *Larus melanocephalus* was collected by K.G. Sîderbom at Tsondol on the Etsin River of northern Inner Mongolia. Two years later, it became the type specimen of *L. m. relictus*, the relict gull. For many years afterwards, the Etsin River bird was also its *only* specimen – despite several searches by ornithologists, no other example of this new gull was found. (Ironically, a second specimen had been collected, on 9 April 1935 in China, but remained unrecognised for what it was in the Zoological Institute of Leningrad's Academy of Science until identified in 1971.)[14,22]

As a result, some authorities eventually suggested that the relict gull was not a separate taxonomic form at all, but merely a hybrid between two already-known species – the great black-headed gull *L. ichthyaetus* and the brown-headed gull *L. brunnicephalus*. During the early 1960s, however, this identity was disproven, and the mystery of the relict gull finally solved, when it was rediscovered in small breeding colonies. In 1967, around 100 pairs were found nesting on Baroon Torey

Nor, one of Transbaikalia's series of Torey lakes.[14,22]

Nowadays classed as a full species in its own right, the relict gull has since also been found to breed on Kazakhstan's Lake Alakul, and has been collected from as far afield as its Etsin River type locality, the Yellow Sea's coastlands, and northern Vietnam.[14,22]

Giant pied-billed grebe – how tourism terminated the *poc*

The grebes constitute a family of primitive aquatic birds whose members include such well-known European species as the dabchick and the great-crested grebe. In America, one of the most familiar species is the common pied-billed grebe *Podilymbus podiceps*, and in 1929 ornithologist Ludlow Griscom discovered that it had a giant-sized flightless equivalent peculiar to Lake Atitlan in the southwestern highlands of Guatemala. Accordingly, he named it *P. gigas*. Its holotype had been collected as long ago as 1862, but had not been considered to be anything special, so it had remained undescribed until Griscom had chanced upon it in the Dwight collection of bird specimens at the United States National Museum.[23]

Once numbering up to 100 pairs, since the 1960s the giant pied-billed grebe's story has been one of calamitous, unrelenting decline, its numbers dwindling year by year. This decline is principally due to a voracious species of fish called the large-mouthed bass – introduced into Lake Atitlan to attract angling-inclined tourists, it has wreaked havoc upon the lake's unique ecosystem by devouring its supplies of smaller fishes and crabs, the staple diet of the grebes. Depletion of its reedbeds by native Indians who used the reeds to weave mats for

Giant pied-billed grebe – discovered in 1862, described in 1929, destroyed by 1991. (Dr Anne LaBastille)

the point of no return. In 1991, in her book *Mama Poc*, Dr LaBastille announced that there were no longer any giant pied-bills living. The *poc* was extinct – another species irredeemably lost.[24]

A precious partridge

The year 1932 saw the description of *Arborophila rufipectus*, the Sichuan hill partridge – a small, sturdy bird with a huge, gaudy, fan-like crest. Limited solely to four counties within southwestern China's Sichuan Province, for the next three decades it was known only from its type, a male. However, during the 1960s Prof. Li Guiyan obtained a series of specimens, enabling him to prepare the first scientific account of the female's morphology. Disturbingly, despite being one of China's rarest birds this species has not received formal protection.[25]

another lucrative tourist demand also threatened the grebes (known locally as *pocs*), which nested among the reeds. The outlook for the species' continuing survival seemed grave. Tragically, the reality was even worse.[24]

One of the *poc's* principal researchers and supporters was Dr Anne LaBastille, who recognised that the only way to safeguard its remaining individuals would be to capture them all and transfer them to a safer locality. When her colleague, Dr Lori Hunter, attempted to do this, however, at least a third of the total number flew away – an event that filled her with despair.[24] For the giant pied-bill is indisputably *flightless* – therefore, the specimens that had flown away could not have been genuine *pocs*. Instead, they were nothing more than misidentified common pied-bills. Worse still, when Drs LaBastille and Hunter investigated the lake's entire grebe population, they found that only two or three individuals were giant pied-bills; the rest were the common, flying version, *P. podiceps*. In short, while science had been blissfully consoling itself that at least 30 or so of the the *poc*, *P. gigas*, still existed, this species had actually declined to

Congo peacock – an ornithological detective story

A head-dress belonging to a native tribesman from Zaire (formerly the Belgian Congo), a pair of old, forgotten museum exhibits set aside from the main collection, and the keen, retentive memory of a dedicated scientist. These were the principal components of a complex detective story spanning more than 20 years, but climaxing in the mid-1930s with what is widely acclaimed to be the most important ornithological discovery of the 20th century.

In 1913, Dr James Chapin was in Zaire's Ituri Forest, taking part in an okapi expedition (see p. 16). An ornithologist from the American Museum of Natural

History, he had been collecting bird specimens, and as the region's native hunters wore elaborate head-dresses of feathers he decided to obtain a selection of these too. Most of their feathers were from brilliantly-coloured cuckoo-related birds called touracos, whose species Chapin was readily able to identify. A head-dress from Avakubi, however, contained one particular feather (not two as many books claim) that puzzled him a great deal. A secondary wing-quill of rufous background colour, overlain with regularly-spaced black bars, its texture and form suggested to Chapin that it was from some type of gallinaceous bird (i.e. pheasant, grouse, quail), but he was unable to assign it to any known species from the Ituri region. He was so intrigued by it that he bought the complete head-dress and rigorously investigated its mysterious plume's origin.[26-7]

In Zaire, Chapin learnt that such feathers came from a bird known locally as *mbulu* – but he was unable to discover whether or not this name merely referred to a breed of domestic chicken. Back in America, his assiduous examination of the feather confirmed that it was certainly from a gallinaceous bird, but all attempts at ascertaining the latter's identity met with failure. And so, albeit reluctantly, Chapin carried on with his official work and locked the quill away in a drawer. Fortunately, however, he never forgot about it.[26-7]

By 1936, Chapin's continuing interest in the avifauna of Zaire had ultimately led him to compile a definitive work on the subject, and his researches for it had taken him to the Congo Museum at Tervueren, Belgium. It was here, while browsing through its ornithological collection, that he caught sight of two old and dusty stuffed birds, mounted on a board on top of a tall cabinet, placed aside from the main collection due at least in part to their poor state of preservation. To Chapin, however, they were the answer to a prayer – because even from a distance he could very readily see that one of these birds, more rufous in colour than its darker partner, possessed wing quills identical to the strange plume that he had obtained 23 years earlier.[26-7]

Needless to say, Chapin immediately made full enquiries concerning the origin and identity of the birds, and learnt from the museum's director, Dr Henri Schouteden, that they had been part of a collection of taxiderm specimens kept for some years at the Brussels office of the Kasai Trading Company. According to a faded label attached to their board, these two strange birds were nothing more than imported, immature specimens of *Pavo cristatus*, Asia's familiar blue peacock. However, the merest glance at them was more than sufficient for Chapin to recognise that this identification was totally incorrect, and that in reality they did not resemble any species of bird known to science. In a later study of them, he described the pair as follows:[27]

The blackish individual had large spurs, and was plainly an adult male. Its whole back and rump were blackish, glossed with dull dark green. The base of the neck, chest, lesser wing-coverts, and tips of retrices [tail plumes] had brighter violet reflections. There was an upright crest of narrow black feathers, and just in front of that, in the middle of the crown, a curious patch of short whitish bristles. The rufous bird appeared to be an adult female of the same species, and its back was glossed with brilliant metallic green.

But what could they be? An affinity with pheasants and peacocks seemed most likely from their appearance; but, zoogeographically at least, such a notion must surely be nonsense, as it was well known that pheasants and peacocks did not occur in Africa. Schouteden favoured the possibility that they represented a peacock-chicken hybrid, derived from outside Africa. During lunch with some old Congolese acquaintances a little while later, however, Chapin casually mentioned these puzzling birds and the Avakubi feather, and learnt to his delight that one of his friends knew the *mbulu* well. Furthermore, this friend stressed that it was neither a domestic form nor a hybrid but an elusive species that dwelt deep within the most secluded part of the Ituri Forest.[26-7]

This momentous piece of news galvanised Chapin and Schouteden into speedy action – they contacted ornithologists worldwide, collated all available information regarding the mysterious *mbulu*, and sent out requests to the people of Zaire to send all news of future *mbulu* sightings to the Tervueren Museum. A great deal of fresh data eventually emerged, so that there could no longer be any doubt. The *mbulu* was unquestionably a species new to science, and, in defiance of all previous concepts, a bona fide African pheasant, most closely related to the Asiatic peacocks[26-7]. Consequently, on 20 November 1936 Chapin formally named it *Afropavo congensis* – 'African peacock from the Congo' or, more simply, the Congo peacock – with the Tervueren Museum's male taxiderm specimen as its type. All that now remained for him to accomplish was the acquisition of some specimens from its native habitat, in order to confirm the anecdotal evidence that he had been amassing.[28]

On 19 June 1937, Chapin set off to Africa, and on his arrival at Stanleyville he learnt from local vet Dr T. Els that a pair of these birds had already been obtained at Ayena,

not far from Stanleyville, and were now in his possession, preserved via formalin injection. Chapin also received a letter from one of his correspondents, Dr Pierre Dyleff, who informed him that four specimens were awaiting his arrival at Angumu. Chapin's persistence had paid off – one small, bewildering feather had led to the discovery of a very beautiful, radically new species, now known to science from several specimens.[26-7]

Interestingly, close examination of the new specimens revealed that the male Congo peacock actually bears a vertical tuft of long white bristles, positioned just in front of the small crest of black feathers. In the original, poorly-preserved Tervueren specimen, this tuft had either been worn down or had broken off, leaving behind only the '...curious patch of short whitish bristles' that had puzzled Chapin when he had first seen it.[26-7]

In-depth anatomical studies have confirmed that despite lacking their ocellated train, the Congo peacock is truly most closely allied to the Asiatic peacocks, although it seems to reflect a much more primitive stage in peacock evolution. Unlike many of the reclusive denizens of little-explored jungles, this highly significant species has become a familiar sight in the west over the years, because several have been successfully maintained in various zoos, including those of New York, London, Antwerp, and Rotterdam – a far cry from when its existence was unknown and its ambassadors left to gather dust on top of a museum cabinet.[26]

Cabanis's tanager – the case of the missing cage-bird

The finch-like tanagers of the Americas are among the world's most brilliantly-coloured birds, and hence very popular cage-bird species. With its grey-blue neck and crown, bright azure back and rump, and blue-bordered wings and tail, a particularly attractive representative of this group is Cabanis's tanager *Tangara cabanisi*, a 6-in-long species once lost for over 70 years. It was first described in 1868, by Dr Philip Sclater of London's Zoological Society, from a single skin obtained at Costa Cuca, near Quetzaltenango in western Guatemala. Nothing more was heard of this species until 1937, when it was unexpectedly rediscovered on Mount Ovando, Chiapas, in Mexico, by Florida University bird specialist Dr Pierce Brodkorb. Apart from one other Chiapas sighting in 1943, it vanished again, but during the 1970s small flocks were seen on several occasions at El Triunfo, Chiapas.[12,29]

Zavattariornis – a strange starling, or a curious crow?

In 1938, the Italian ornithologist Dr E. Moltoni described a species of bird destined to become one of ornithology's greatest anomalies.[30] Indeed, in recent years this singular species and the equally extraordinary Congo peacock have been said '...to represent the two most remarkable ornithological discoveries made in Africa this century'.[12]

Named *Zavattariornis stresemanni* by Moltoni (honouring Italian zoologist Prof. E. Zavattari and German bird specialist Dr Erwin Stresemann), it had been discovered only a few months earlier in the thorn-bush and acacia grasslands at Yavello (Javello) in southern Ethiopia's Sidamo Province, where it builds large dome-shaped nests at the tops of acacia.[30] Subsequent investigations have disclosed that it is entirely confined to an area of just over 2300 square miles, but

fortunately it is common within this range, and does not seem to be threatened in any way at present.[12,30-2]

Except for its rather slender bill, *Zavattariornis* is ostensibly crow-like in basic outline, and jackdaw-sized. Its relatively drab plumage – consisting of white underparts and forehead; grey upperparts, chest, and flanks; and blue-black wings and tail – is quite comparable to an American species of crow known as Clarke's nutcracker *Nucifraga colombiana*, but *Zavattariornis* is distinguished by the bright blue patch of bare skin ringing each eye[12,30-2] (as in Rothschild's mynah, p. 107).

Whereas its general appearance, therefore, is quite unremarkable, studies of its finer morphological and anatomical details have provided some fundamental surprises regarding its taxonomic affinities – or lack of them. Although *Zavattariornis* had been classed by Moltoni as a corvid (member of the crow family) and afterwards became known as the Ethiopian bush-crow, it differs markedly from all other corvids in a variety of different ways. Moreover, certain aspects of its behaviour are more reminiscent of starlings (such as the frequently observed emergence of three adult birds from a single nest, indicating assisted rearing of fledglings), as are its parasitic biting lice or mallophagans (and closely-related host species often possess closely-related parasites). Similarly, it has been spied consorting with various species of starling when feeding (on terrestrial insects).[12,30-2]

Inevitably, therefore, *Zavattariornis* has incited much debate regarding its classification, with avian researchers variously supporting a corvid allegiance, favouring its inclusion within the starling family, or even suggesting that it should be housed within a family of its own.[31-3] Today it is usually classed as a highly aberrant corvid – a categorisation openly acknowledged, however, to stem more from considerations of convenience than certainty.

Ribbon-tailed bird of paradise – the tale of a tail

Not all birds of paradise are large, brilliantly-coloured species. Some, particularly the manucodes, are relatively small with dark plumage, and are much less conspicuous and thus more readily overlooked than their bigger, flamboyant relatives. However, the most recently discovered bird of paradise was not of this smaller, less noticeable, drab type, but instead one of the family's longest and most spectacular members. The history of its discovery is no less extraordinary.

In his book *Papuan Wonderland* (1936), J.G. Hides recorded seeing some pairs of a very strange bird of paradise to the west of New Guinea's Mount Hagen. The male form was particularly eyecatching, because its tail comprised just a single pair of long and slender, ribbon-like feathers, 3 ft in length and creamy-white in colour, contrasting sharply with the bird's very much smaller, predominantly dark-plumaged body, and frequently flicked as they trailed behind it in flight. Not recognising the species, Hides instructed one of the police officers accompanying him on his expedition to shoot a male specimen and obtain its exceptional tail feathers for study.[34]

Learning of the sighting, New Guinea explorer-naturalist Frederick Shaw Mayer decided to find out more about this remarkable bird, which did not seem to correspond with any species known at that time. By 1938 he had discovered that it could be found approximately 80-100 miles west of Mount Hagen, and that its amazing tail plumes were often worn in the hair of native tribesmen from this region. In August 1938, a missionary gave him two such feathers obtained from one of the natives, which were subsequently passed to Dr C.R. Stonor who designated them as the type specimen of a brand new species. Officially describing it in 1939, he named it *Astrapia mayeri*, in honour of the man responsible for bringing it to scientific notice. As for its common name, its immensely long tail feathers – 3.5 times the combined length of its head and body – ensured that it would be referred to ever afterwards as the ribbon-tailed bird of paradise.[21,35]

Shortly after Stonor had received the tail feathers, three complete specimens, collected by two explorers in the forests west and northwest of Mount Hagen, were sent to Australian Museum zoologist Dr Roy Kinghorn. The species has since also been recorded from Mount Giluwe, and living examples have been exhibited at Sydney's Taronga Zoo.[21]

Three other new birds of paradise have also been discovered during the 20th century. One, closely related to the ribbon-tail, is the Huon astrapia. It was discovered in the Rawlinson Mountains of New Guinea's Huon Peninsula. Described in 1906 by F. Foerster, who named it *Astrapia rothschildi*, the male of this species, just over 2 ft long, is very beautiful. It has a glossy blue crown; a nape of reddish-copper which transforms into shimmering cerise across the forepart of its back and over the short cape of feathers above its shoulders, and darkens into velvet black overlain with a viridescent sheen upon its back's lower reaches; a transverse band of bronze across its chest, separating its shiny blue-black chin and upper breast from its gleaming green lower breast and abdomen; lustrous black wings; and a very long, broad tail principally black but surfaced with glistening purple.[21,36]

Also native to the Rawlinson Mountains is the Huon parotia, which Lord Rothschild dubbed *Parotia wahnesi* in 1906. It is the most recently revealed species of six-wired bird of paradise – all of which bear a sextet of slender, wire-like feathers, three on each side of their head just behind the eye, and each one terminating in a paddle-shaped racquet.[21,36] And in 1911, a crow-like bird of paradise, with a pair of yellow facial wattles and a smaller pair of blue wattles sprouting from the base of its bill, was described from western New Guinea's Mount Goliath. Due to its very short tail and kinship with an already-known species called the paradigalla, it was named *Paradigalla brevicauda*, the short-tailed paradigalla.[21,37]

Archbold's bowerbird – separated from its crests for eleven years

Named after Richard Archbold (an expert on New Guinea birds), Archbold's bowerbird *Archboldia papuensis*, the only member of its genus, is the bowerbird family's most recently described species. It was discovered in 1939 by Austin Rand within the alpine forests of western New Guinea's Oranje Mountains, and described by him in 1940. The male specimens that he collected were relatively large, principally black-bodied birds with similarly-shaded heads – which made the male specimen obtained from a Mount Hagen native on 12 June 1950 by Prof. Thomas Gilliard very worthy of note. Although apparently belonging to the same species as Rand's birds, it was instantly differentiated by way of its two striking golden crests – one on its forehead, the other on its nape. Obviously, Archbold's bowerbird existed in two manifestly distinct subspecies, so the crestless version represented by Rand's specimen was renamed *A. p. papuensis*, and Gilliard's

double-crested equivalent was christened *A. p. sanfordi*.[21,38]

Prince Ruspoli's touraco and other Ethiopian enigmas

Touracos make up a family of gaudy-plumaged, cuckoo-related birds endemic to the African tropics. Principally green (occasionally blue) in colour, these crow-sized species are most famous for possessing two plumage pigments (turacin and turacoverdin) peculiar to themselves; no other species in the entire animal kingdom produces either of them.

In 1896, a specimen of a very beautiful but wholly unknown species of touraco was uncovered at the Genoa Museum. It had been obtained close to Lake Abaya in southern Ethiopia, and was one of a collection of birds amassed by Prince Ruspoli of Italy. Befitting its royal connection, its plumage was the quintessence of avian grandeur – its pastel-green neck and underparts combining with the deeper green of its back and wing coverts to yield an effective backdrop for its startlingly scarlet crest and wing primaries, its white face and throat, jet-black rump, and vivid purple tail. In honour of its eminent discoverer, the new touraco was named *Touraco ruspoli*[39] – after which it promptly sank back into ornithological obscurity, because for over 40 years nothing more was heard of this beautiful new species.

Happily, however, it proved merely to be elusive rather than extinct, because in 1942 it was rediscovered inhabiting juniper woodland at Arero, about 60 miles east of Yavello, again in southern Ethiopia. Five specimens were collected by C.W. Benson, and since then further sightings have been reported periodically – but as the species appears to be totally restricted to a plot of juniper woods and evergreen foliage covering no more than 10 square miles, its population size is inevitably small.[10]

Other finds made by Benson in southern Ethiopia during that same period included a new species of swallow – the white-tailed swallow *Hirundo megaensis*, whose type specimen was an adult male that he had collected in 1941, 10 miles north of Mega; and three specimens of the Teita falcon *Falco fascinucha*, collected at Yavello – and hence several hundreds of miles north of this species' type locality of Teita, Kenya (where the only two previously recorded specimens of this short-tailed raptor had been obtained in 1895).[31]

Cahow – the seabird resurrected from three centuries of extinction

In the mid-1940s, a small, unassuming species of seabird called the Bermuda petrel or cahow, *Pterodroma cahow*, made what must be the most sensational comeback on record for any animal species during this century. Its saga began more than 300 years earlier, in 1609, when Bermuda witnessed the arrival of the first permanent population of settlers from Great Britain. As with human settlement throughout the world, an unwelcome stowaway soon accompanied them ashore – the black rat. Its presence in this particular instance was even more disastrous than usual, because it multiplied so rapidly on Bermuda that it literally ate the settlers out of house and home, causing a tremendous famine that could have resulted in wholesale starvation. This, however, did not happen, because they discovered a highly valuable native source of food – the affable, ground-dwelling cahow. By 1621, hardly any were left, and even the passing of a specific law to

safeguard the sparse survivors appeared to have come too late. Within a few years, the cahow seemed to have vanished. Almost three centuries were to pass before the first indication of its possible perpetuation emerged.[8,10]

Close to the principal island of Bermuda is a group of tiny islets called the Castle Harbour Islands. While visiting one of these in 1906, L.L. Mowbray collected a petrel that was shown ten years later to be a cahow. This became the species' type specimen – because in spite of its former abundance, the cahow had never been scientifically described or named.[8,10]

Having tantalised ornithologists with this reappearance and thus proof that, against all odds, it had survived the slaughter waged during the 17th century, the cahow abruptly disappeared again. No additional conclusive evidence of its existence surfaced for almost three decades – until on the evening of 8 June 1935 a young bird was taken to biologist Dr William Beebe on Bermuda; it had been sent by the lighthouse keeper. A third cahow, which had killed itself by colliding with a telegraph wire, was obtained on Bermuda in June 1941, but there was still no sign of a breeding colony. The young bird from 1935 was proof enough that breeding was still taking place – but where?[8,10]

The answer came towards the close of World War II, when in March 1945 the cahow's secret breeding locality was discovered in the Castle Harbour region by ornithologist Frederick Hall, who found it by accident, during the construction of a United States Air Force base. This find was followed up in early 1951 by cahow seekers Robert C. Murphy and Louis Mowbray (son of L.L. Mowbray), who noted 18 pairs.[8,10,40]

After 330 years, the cahow had risen like a maritime phoenix, and has received full protection ever since. Its numbers remain vulnerable low – no more than a few dozen – but its breeding chances have been greatly improved by the attachment to its nesting burrows of artificial, cahow-sized entrance holes, permitting ready access to the cahows but preventing entrance by the slightly larger red-tailed tropic birds, thereby saving it from the threat of competition with the latter species for nesting sites.[8,10,14]

Just four years after Hall's rediscovery of the cahow as a breeding species, a previously unknown relative was also revealed. In 1949 Murphy's petrel *P. ultima* was formally described; its type specimen had been collected on the Polynesian island of Oeno.[41] One of the least-known of all seabirds, it is only rarely sighted, and its eggs were spied for the very first time as recently as March 1990. This sighting was during a successful search for the species, led by ornithologist Peter Harrison, on the uninhabited rock tower of Marotiri, in a southeastern Pacific chain of islands called the Australs. Several hundred pairs of Murphy's petrel were discovered on the tower,[42] but the search had an even more exciting sequel. On the following day, the expedition sailed to Rapa, Marotiri's closest island neighbour, and there Harrison discovered a wholly new species of storm petrel. One of the largest known to science, it is currently awaiting official description, but has been provisionally (and aptly) christened 'Fregetta titan'.[42]

Takahe – the New Zealand wanderer's return

The year 1948 closed with the celebration of another spectacular rediscovery – a large flightless bird with multicoloured plumage, native to New Zealand's South Island, and known as the takahe. Its name is of Maori

origin, and translates as 'the wanderer', which is particularly apposite, because the takahe had been wandering in and out of scientific obscurity for more than a century. In 1847, New Zealand naturalist Walter Mantell excavated some bones at Waingongoro and Wanganui in North Island. They proved to be from a sturdy, flightless species of rail, distantly allied to the familiar moorhen and coots, but most closely allied to a collection of larger, brilliantly-coloured species known as purple gallinules (genus *Porphyrio*) with representatives distributed all over the world. Although previously unrecorded by science, Mantell's rail was well known to the Maoris of North Island, who had hunted it in earlier times and referred to it as the *moho*, but stated that it was no longer seen. Its bones were described the following year by British palaeontologist Prof. Richard Owen, who named this new but seemingly extinct species *Notornis mantelli*.

In 1849, *Notornis* reappeared in an unexpected locality and in a most unexpected way. A *living* specimen was captured at Duck Cove on Resolution Island, one of the southwestern islets of South Island, by a dog belonging to a seal hunter. Its skin was purchased by Mantell, and was sent to the British Museum; the remainder supplied the sealer with an unexpected addition to his menu.[8,10,26,44]

It transpired that *Notornis* was known to the South Island Maoris as the *takahe*, and, unlike its North Island counterpart, evidently still survived. Two years later, another South Island specimen was caught, this time in Deas Cove, opposite Secretary Island in Thompson Sound (and now housed in New Zealand's Dominion Museum). After this, however, the takahe vanished for 28 years and was believed extinct, but in December 1879 a rabbit catcher captured one not far from the southernmost end of South Island's Lake Te Anau; it was later purchased by the Dresden Museum (but was 'lost' during World War II).[8,10,26,44]

After making comparisons between specimens of the South Island takahe and the North Island moho, German zoologist Dr Adolf B. Meyer decided that the two were sufficiently distinct for the takahe to merit separate specific status. And so in 1883, with the Dresden example as its type specimen, he named it *N. hochstetteri*, in honour of explorer Ferdinand von Hochstetter who had searched for it in vain during its previous 28-year period of 'extinction'.[45] Later studies, however, overturned Meyer's ruling, demoting the takahe to subspecific level (i.e. as *N. mantelli hochstetteri*), because the only major difference between takahe and moho was the slightly longer length of the moho's legs. Indeed, some researchers nowadays even deny the takahe subspecific distinction.[8]

Although the moho was known to science via skeletal remains, its appearance in life was (and still is) unrecorded, but if it was anything like the takahe it must have been quite magnificent. Standing 1.5 ft high, and of stocky build like a small turkey, the takahe's extremely soft, silky plumage is a rich pageant of colour – dark indigo-violet upon its head, neck and underparts, transforming into shimmering ultramarine over its shoulders and wings, and deep jungle-green across its back, but mellowing into paler, tawny-olive shades upon its rump and its tail (which also has a tuft of pure-white undertail coverts). As a final flourish, its legs and much of its massive beak are coral-pink, ripening into scarlet at its beak's shield-like base.[8,10,26,44]

One might expect that such a visually arresting bird would be difficult to overlook – yet the takahe's history reveals only too readily that it is singularly adept at concealing itself. No fresh conclusive reports of *Notornis* emerged until autumn 1894, when a living specimen was captured on North Island!

This was the one and only time that a moho appears to have been caught since its bones were first uncovered by science in 1847. It was procured by surveyor Norman Carkreek, and its skin and feathers were retained for many years afterwards by Roderick A. McDonald at his homestead in Horowhenua. This historic specimen could have finally provided science with the long-awaited opportunity to document the external appearance of North Island's moho, hitherto believed extinct, but tragically it was lost without any record of its morphology ever having been made.[46] The only moho seen alive by a westerner was gone.

As no other modern-day moho has ever been collected or even sighted, all subsequent *Notornis* reports given here apply solely to its South Island equivalent, the takahe – whose name is generally used nowadays for the entire species.

On 7 August 1898, the moho's southern counterpart re-emerged yet again from obscurity, when a takahe was caught alive by a dog belonging to Donald Ross, on the shore of Middle Sound, Lake Te Anau. For the first time, the entire specimen – skin, skeleton, and internal organs – were preserved, and reached Dunedin's Otago Museum, where it ultimately became known as 'the last of the takahes', because, true to form, the takahe disappeared once more, and for a much longer period than ever before.[8,10,26,44]

By 1948, almost 50 years had passed without a single takahe having been collected. Admittedly, there were rumours of supposed sightings, but these were never confirmed, and so avian researchers finally declared it extinct. Not everyone, however, was fully convinced. Dr Geoffrey Orbell, a medical doctor from Invercargill, was one such person. He collected a great deal of information concerning the takahe's possible existence, including testimony from Maoris inhabiting the area around Lake Te Anau. He learnt from these sources that in the mountains around this lake's eastern shores another large lake existed, whose valley was the traditional homeland of this elusive bird but was currently undocumented by westerners. Such was its connection with the takahe that it was known to the Maoris as *Kohaka-takahea* – 'the takahe's nesting place'.[8,10,26,44,47]

Inspired by this optimistic and stimulating news, Orbell led a small expedition to the newly-revealed lake in April 1948, but although he discovered some signs that indicated the presence of takahes, no birds were seen. Even so, it was promising enough for Orbell to feel justified in leading a second expedition there seven months later.[8,10,26,44,47]

On 20 November 1948, he and his companions were trekking through the valley across a clearing carpeted in snow-grass, when – in what must have seemed to them to be an incongruously casual manner given the occasion's scientific significance – the first takahe conclusively reported for half a century stepped out into view just ahead of them, and straight into the ornithological history books. Once again, *Notornis* had fooled everyone – thriving when it was supposed to be extinct, and frequenting a locality not previously known to exist. By the end of 1948, the team had succeeded in netting two specimens (alive and unharmed), which they meticulously filmed and observed before releasing them

again; they also saw a third, which eluded capture.[10,26,44,47]

In 1949, Orbell led yet another expedition to this valley, and as a result of sightings made during that visit he estimated that at least 20 breeding pairs lived there, with additional takahes in another valley close by. The whole region was declared a protected zone, with all visitors prohibited unless they had received full governmental permission to enter it. More recently, a captive breeding programme has been initiated to ensure that the species survives even if some dire event should overtake the wild stock. For the moment, therefore, the takahe and its known native range, appropriately christened Takahe Valley, seem safe.[10,14,26,44,47] Let us hope that continued preservation will guarantee that the future never witnesses a repeat of the takahe's famed disappearing act, and that New Zealand's wanderer has returned for good.

African bay owl – a zoogeographical enigma

The bay owl *Phodilus badius* is a widely-distributed Asian species whose range extends from northern India to Indonesia. Taxonomically, however, it stands aloof, sufficiently different from even its closest relatives, the barn owls, to require a subfamily all to itself – or at least that was the situation until the early 1950s. One of the most unexpected ornithological discoveries of this century occurred in 1951, when a previously unknown species of bay owl was found not in Asia, but in Africa.

The discovery in Africa of a species belonging to a group traditionally looked upon as exclusively Asian is not new (as already shown with the African green broadbill and the Congo peacock), but is nonetheless very unusual. This case is made even more mysterious by the fact that only one specimen, the type, of this owl has ever been obtained. It was procured at an altitude of 8100 ft in eastern Zaire's Itombwe Mountains, and differed from the Asian bay owl by way of its somewhat darker plumage, smaller feet, and flattened bill. Officially described in 1952, its species was dubbed *P. prigoginei*.[48]

A sighting of an owl that was almost certainly an African bay owl was made in the mid-1970s, at the Rwegura Tea Estate in Burundi, suggesting that the species is not totally confined to Zaire's Itombwe Mountains; but otherwise this bird is no better known scientifically than it was on the day after its discovery, 42 years ago.[12]

The Itombwe Mountains also house a number of other rare and scantily-known species of bird first described this century. These include: the African green broadbill (1907 – see p. 107), the forest ground-thrush *Turdus oberlaenderi* (1914), Chapin's flycatcher *Muscicapa lendu* (1932), Rockefeller's sunbird *Nectarinia rockefelleri* (1932), Schouteden's swift *Schoutedenapus schoutedeni* (1960), and the Albertine owlet *Glaucidium albertinum* (1983).[49]

James's flamingo – out of sight (and reach) for 70 years.
(Lady Philippa Scott)

James's flamingo – out of sight (and reach) for 70 years

During an expedition in 1886 to the salt lakes beyond the Atacama desert within the high, southern Andean mountain range that constitutes the Chile-Bolivia border, its participants not only observed the already-known Andean flamingo *Phoenicoparrus andinus* and Chilean flamingo *Phoenicopterus chilensis* but also discovered a previously unknown member of this family. In honour of the expedition's sponsor, British businessman Berkeley James, it was christened *Phoenicoparrus jamesi*, James's

flamingo. Slightly smaller than the other two species, the new flamingo was further differentiated by its predominantly orange-yellow bill (with only the tip black), the black 'mask' encircling its eyes and extending to the base of its bill, and the rich rosy colour of its legs.

Specimens were collected and sent to many major museums worldwide – after which James's flamingo became a notable enigma. Due to the near inaccessible nature of its type locality, other expeditionary teams declined to look for it there, and searches made elsewhere failed to uncover any evidence of its existence. Furthermore, as the museum specimens began to fade with the passing decades, even references in books to its diagnostic colours became confused and inaccurate. Eventually, many ornithologists feared that it must be extinct; some even dismissed it as an unimportant variety of one of the other two species.[50]

In 1956, however, both of these hypotheses were disproven, when American explorer A.W. Johnson and a bold team of Chileans scaled the southern Andes' hostile peaks to reach the very highest lakes in the range. There they found James's flamingo, corresponding precisely with the original descriptions of the specimens obtained in 1886, thus vindicating its classification as a valid species. In January 1957, and a little further to the north, Johnson and company reached the salt lake of Laguna Colorada ('Red Lake') in southwestern Bolivia, and encountered this species' nesting grounds. Subsequent visits have revealed the presence of several thousand breeding birds there. More recently, it has become a successful breeding species at Berlin Zoo; and there are currently some specimens exhibited at the late Sir Peter Scott's world-renowned Wildfowl and Wetlands Trust at Slimbridge, in Gloucestershire, England.[50]

Some day there may be a momentous sequel to this exotic bird's discovery and rediscovery. The local Andean Indians inhabiting its provenance unhesitatingly distinguish the three species of flamingo living there – referring to the Chilean flamingo as *guaichete*, the Andean as *tococo*, and James's as *chururo*. In addition, they claim that a fourth type of flamingo also exists there, which they refer to as the *jetete*.[51] Could there be an unknown species of flamingo still awaiting discovery in this remote, little-explored region? After all, the nesting grounds of James's flamingo – extensively populated by a species neither small nor inconspicuous – remained undiscovered until less than 40 years ago.

Seychelles scops owl – lost in the mists for half a century

One of the world's least-known owls, the Seychelles scops owl *Otus insularis*, a handsome russet-plumaged species characterised by its lengthy, unfeathered legs, is found only on the tiny island of Mahé. Like so many other indigenous forms of Seychelles wildlife, its numbers fell rapidly following man's increasing interactions with this island group's ecology. Some avian researchers believe that the introduction by man of the South African barn owl onto Mahé provided *O. insularis* with severe competition for food. By the beginning of the 20th century it had become gravely endangered, with what was ultimately thought to be the last record of a living specimen occurring in 1906.[10,12,52]

No further news of the Seychelles scops owl emerged, and it was eventually deemed to be extinct – until 1959, when it was unexpectedly rediscovered by ornithologist Philippe Lalanne amid the remote, mist-shrouded mountains of Mahé's south-central region. At first, only a few pairs were believed to exist, but later searches and estimates led to a revised figure of around 80 pairs in secondary forest across one third of the entire island. Moreover, shortly after its initial rediscovery, scientists learnt that a single specimen had in fact been collected in 1940, but had failed to attract any attention. Happily, the Seychelles scops owl no longer seems to be in decline; and it now appears that its nocturnal and reclusive lifestyle may have been responsible for at least part of its supposedly 'endangered' status.[10,12,52]

123

Less than a year earlier, on 7 September 1958, a new species of scops owl had been discovered, and in another Indian Ocean island chain. This time the locality was La Convalescence, on Grand Comoro of the Comoro Islands, and the species was *Otus pauliani*.[53] This small, mysterious bird is currently known only from its type specimen – a male, collected by the British Ornithologists' Union Centenary Comoro Expedition – but others have been heard calling as recently as 1983.[12,53] And in 1992, another elusive Comoro owl, the whistling Anjouan scops owl *Otus capnodes*, was rediscovered by biologist Dr Roger Safford; it had not been reported since its discovery in 1886.[54]

Puerto Rican whip-poor-will – winging its way from prehistory to present day

A relative of the well-known American whip-poor-will and Britain's elusive nightjar, a type of short-winged whip-poor-will was known to inhabit the forests along Puerto Rico's north and south coasts during the late 19th century and early 20th century. But as it closely resembled the American species, *C. vocifera*, it did not receive any scientific attention. Moreover, after a reliable sighting of some such birds by naturalist Alexander Wetmore, made on 23 December 1911 in the vicinity of the Insular Experimental Station at Rio Pedros, it disappeared and was considered extinct.[8,10,14]

A few years later, Wetmore excavated some fossil whip-poor-will bones, several thousand years old, within the Clara and Catedral Caves near Morovis, Puerto Rico, and recognised that they represented an undescribed species, which in 1919 he dubbed *Setochalcis* [later becoming *Caprimulgus*] *noctitherus*. Shortly afterwards, he studied a dead specimen of the lost modern-day form of Puerto Rican whip-poor-will, and realised that the present-day and the prehistoric types were one and the same.[8,10,14]

As the species appeared to be extinct, however, the matter seemed to be of academic interest only – until March 1961, when a strange call was recorded by Cornell University researcher George B. Reynard during fieldwork on Puerto Rico. Although clearly a whip-poor-will cry, it did not match that of any known type – confirming native Puerto Rican testimony that their whip-poor-will had sounded quite different from other species. Using an amplified version of the recording as a lure, Reynard enticed within collecting range a male whip-poor-will, belonging to the supposedly demised species. Populations have since been located in three different forests within the island's southern section.[8,10,14] *C. noctitherus* is sometimes classed as a subspecies of *C. vocifera*, but its distinctive voice is sufficient for many to treat it as a full species.

Eyrean grasswren – virtuoso of the vanishing act

Within the space of just a few months in 1961, three of Australia's most famous species of 'extinct' bird were sensationally rediscovered.

The Eyrean grasswren *Amytornis goyderi*, an attractive, warbler-related species with a long tail held high in the air, has acquired the reputation of being one of the world's most elusive birds. Roughly 6 in long, with brown upperparts overlain by short white streaks, darker wings and tail, buff underparts, white breast, and a thick sparrow-like bill, this inhabitant of spinifex grasslands was discovered in 1875 by F.W. Andrews, during the Lewis Expedition to South Australia's famous Lake Eyre and its environs. Two specimens were caught, ultimately reaching the British Museum (Natural History), after which it made the first of its celebrated disappearances. No further report occurred for almost half a century – until 1931, when a single pair was sighted in the area where the original couple had been collected. After the 1931 record, however, the species vanished again, this time for 30 years.[55]

On 3 September 1961 it was rediscovered once more, when two adult birds and a nest containing two young were spied at Christmas Waterhole on the Macumba River, near Lake Eyre North, by an ornithological team from Victoria.[56] On 2 August 1966, during the West-East Crossing Expedition to the Simpson Desert, north of Lake Eyre, naturalist Keith Davey saw a pair of grasswrens 37 miles northwest of this desert's Poeppel's Corner. He was sure that they were Eyrean grasswrens – if so, this is its earliest Northern Territory record.[55]

Another surprise came in August 1976, when Ian May discovered that the Eyrean grasswren was actually quite abundant on the sandhills east of Poeppel's Corner and west of Eyre Creek, as well as at the aptly-named Birdsville (just inside eastern Queensland). But when those same areas were visited the very next year the birds had largely vanished, with just a few remaining near Poeppel's Corner. In the hope of establishing a captive breeding programme to safeguard this unpredictable species, a pair was captured in 1977 and maintained thereafter at Sydney's Taronga Zoo.[55]

At the time of the Eyrean grasswren's reappearance in 1961 only seven grasswren species were recognised, but in 1967 Normal Favaloro collected some specimens of a pale-coloured form that proved to be an eighth – described by him a year later and christened *A. barbatus*. Popularly termed the grey grasswren, and inhabiting southwestern Queensland and northwestern New South Wales, it was first reported as long ago as 1921, but no specimen was obtained. In 1942, Favaloro saw one by the Bullvo River, but the form was generally dismissed by other authorities as a pale mutant variety of the western grasswren *A. textilis*. Twenty-five years later, however, Favaloro succeeded in proving them wrong.[57] And just a year after that, a third species of 'lost' grasswren reappeared, when the black grasswren *A. housei* was positively sighted for the first time since its discovery in 1901.[58]

Noisy scrub-bird – sounding out its return

The lyrebirds, with their ornate tails and talent for vocal mimicry, are among the most famous of Australia's diverse avifauna. Less spectacular, and hence less well-known, are their smaller, superficially thrush-like relatives, the scrub-birds. Two species exist – the rufous *Atrichornis rufescens*, and the noisy *A. clamosus*, and it was the latter which staged a famous comeback after almost a century of 'extinction'.

The noisy scrub-bird was officially described in 1844 from Drake's Brook, Waroona (south of Western Australia's capital, Perth), and was later discovered at various localities along the southwestern coast, including Torbay and Albany. A long-tailed, short-winged form, 8.5 in long, with brownish-red upperparts, white chin and underparts, plus a distinctive brown throat-band, it earned its common and scientific names from its extremely loud (albeit melodious) voice. This generally provided would-be observers with their only clue to its presence, because its plumage blended very effectively with the thick swampside foliage in which it usually remained hidden from view.[8]

Although it seemed most common around Albany, the noisy scrub-bird was never an abundant species, as its preference for swampland and running streams limited its population size. By the 1880s it had become exceedingly rare, and after a lone specimen had been collected in Torbay in 1889 by A.J. Campbell, it was believed to have become extinct.[8]

Australian ornithologist Vincent Serventy was quite stunned, therefore, when on Christmas Eve 1961 he received a phone-call from a newspaper reporter asking him to comment upon the noisy scrub-bird's alleged rediscovery just a few days earlier. Serventy learnt that on 17 December naturalist Harley Webster had clearly heard

Noisy scrub-bird – last reported in 1889, its reappearance in 1961 was an ornithological sensation.
(Fortean Picture Library)

its unmistakable call emerging from some thick scrub-land on a small headland close to Mount Gardner at Two Peoples Bay, about 25 miles east of Albany. Moreover, it transpired that just a month earlier, on 5 November, P.J. Fuller and Charles Allen had actually seen a noisy scrub-bird in this same locality, giving them the first conclusive sighting of its species for 72 years. Serventy later journeyed with Webster to this spot, and discovered a small colony of the birds.[59]

Yet no sooner had the species returned to the land of the living than it straight away seemed set to plummet back into extinction, due to some plans to build a small town on the edge of its very limited and only known area of distribution. Thankfully, however, the plans were abandoned – due in no small way to royal intervention in the form of a personal plea by H.R.H. Prince Philip of the U.K. for the area to be left undisturbed. And by 1967, a zone of 13,600 acres, the scrub-bird's entire known distribution range, was declared a reserve, providing added security for this species continued survival.[10,59]

Western bristlebird – another turn-up at Two Peoples Bay

Also making a comeback in 1961, and once again at Two Peoples Bay, was the western bristlebird *Dasyornis longirostris*. 'Dasyornis' ('hairy bird') and 'bristlebird' both refer to the cluster of stiff, hair-like feathers around the bill of all three species belonging to this Antipodean genus of warbler, whose members are predominantly brown-coloured, and roughly 6 in long, with lengthy, broad-ended tails and pale underparts.

The western bristlebird was discovered in 1839 by John Gilbert on the Swan River, near Perth (though none has been recorded from there since), and was described and named in 1840 by John Gould. In the later 1800s it was collected at King George's Sound, and was reported in the early 1900s from Wilson's Inlet – until a fire destroyed this colony in 1914. Except for a single specimen collected in 1945 at Two Peoples Bay, no more was heard of this species for almost half a century. Then in April 1961, small numbers were rediscovered at Two Peoples Bay, and later also at King George's Sound. Now that part of its known range is contained within the noisy scrub-bird's protected zone, it is likely that its numbers will show a healthy increase. Worth noting is that many authorities nowadays class the western bristlebird merely as an occidental subspecies of the common (eastern) bristlebird *D. brachypterus*, from which it differs visually by its chestnut-coloured rump and longer, narrower bill.[8,14]

New and rediscovered owls

The Nduk eagle owl *Bubo vosseleri* (sometimes classed as a well-delineated subspecies of Fraser's eagle owl *B. poensis*) is a large, striking species with bright brown upperparts, silky white underparts overlain by slender brown cross-barring, and an ochre-yellow face with prominent ear-tufts. It was formally described in 1908 by Reichenow, who based his account on an adult specimen obtained at least two years earlier from Amani, in northeastern Tanzania's Usambara Mountains. The species was named after Dr Vosseler of the Biological Institute in Amani, who had obtained a young individual which he sent to the Berlin Museum in 1906. For more than 50 years, these were the only specimens of the Nduk eagle owl available to science. A bird that may have been of this species was sighted near Amani on 20 December 1930, and on 6 September 1931

(flying in the daytime); otherwise, there were no records from the wild either.[12,14,60]

Then on 28 April 1962, Dr G. Pringle, Director of Amani's East African Institute of Malaria, was visited by Gabriel Joseph, who had brought with him a young owl he had found in the high forests nearby. Pringle was fairly sure that it was a Nduk eagle owl, and after caring for it over the next few weeks he passed it on to London Zoo, where his identification was duly confirmed.[60] Since then, other specimens have been obtained – from the late 1970s there have been three more individuals displayed at London Zoo, and a number of confirmed sightings in the field. As far as is known, however, this species is solely confined to the Usambara Mountains, and appears to have declined in numbers as a result of forest destruction within its already restricted habitat.[12]

The 1960s were good years for revealing owls. In 1965, the type specimen of a new species of scops owl was collected at Kenya's Sokoke Forest. Named *Otus ireneae* when described a year later by ornithologist Dr S. Dillon Ripley,[61] the Sokoke scops owl appears to be more common than *B. vosseleri*, but is similarly threatened by forest clearance.[3,12,61] And in 1968, a photograph was taken of a small, short-winged, medium-brown owl with a conspicuous dark brown bar across its throat, sighted near Nagpur in India's Madhya Pradesh. This provides the best evidence obtained in the past 76 years that the forest spotted owlet *Athene blewitti* did not become extinct in 1914, as feared, but has lingered into much more recent times, and may still survive today.[3]

Rufous-headed robin – an eastern enigma

Few species of striking appearance are so elusive that they can even remain hidden from their local human neighbours, let alone the scientific world – which makes the rufous- headed robin rather special. In July 1905, English explorer Alan Owston was travelling through central China when some of his animal collectors working in the Tsin-Ling Mountains of Shensi Province captured and brought to him three specimens of a small but extremely beautiful bird. Although it obviously belonged to the thrush family, it was instantly set apart from all known species by its fiery-coloured head, contrasting markedly with its sombre, slate-grey back, greyish-white underparts, brown wings, and black-bordered pure-white throat.[10,62]

Owston's three examples of this exquisite little thrush were sent to Lord Walter Rothschild's renowned bird collection at Tring Museum, and after studying them, Ernst Hartert named their species *Larvivora ruficeps*. Its highly attractive appearance made it a much sought-after bird by other ornithologists visiting the Tsin-Ling Mountains, but no-one succeeded in obtaining – or even seeing – any other specimens. Even the local people could not help, because they had never seen it before either.[10]

Decades rolled by, with additional studies of the three original examples leading to the species' reclassification as a member of the robin genus, so that it was referred to thereafter as *Erithacus ruficeps*, the rufous-headed robin. Otherwise, it was largely forgotten.[10]

On the evening of 15 March 1963, during a session of bird study and ringing at the peak of Mount Brinchang in west-central Malaya's Cameron Highlands, ornithologist Dr Elliot McClure sent his assistant to inspect the nets, to see if they had captured any birds. When the assistant returned, he was carrying a living specimen of a very small but gorgeous robin-like bird that McClure was unable to identify. Offsetting its drab brown and grey body was the brilliant orange colouration of its head. Recognising its worth, if not its species, but nonetheless unwilling to kill such a beautiful little bird for collection purposes, McClure elected to take some close-up colour photos of it. He also weighed, measured, and ringed it, and afterwards released it back into the wild.[63]

Eager to identify his unexpected find, McClure sent descriptions of it to fellow ornithologists far and wide, its photo appeared in several publications, until its identity was eventually ascertained – it was the elusive *E. ruficeps*, a discovery that was doubly startling. Not only had a near-mythical bird reappeared, but in addition no-one had ever expected it to occur as far away from central China as west-central Malaya (areas separated by more than a thousand miles).[63] Since this discovery, the world has still not uncovered any further information on its lifestyle, behaviour, population size or nest. However, its continuing existence is certain – three specimens were recorded in 1985 at Jiuzhaigou, Sichuan, and six singing males were sighted in 1987.[64]

Vo Quy's pheasant – making a meal of a mystery bird

Vo Quy's pheasant *Lophura hatinhensis* is the most recently discovered and also the least-known of all pheasant species – only two specimens had been recorded prior to the 1990s. The first of these, the species' type, was collected in 1964 by the late Do Ngoc Quang in the vicinity of Son Tung and Ky Thuong, in Vietnam's Nghe Tinh Province. A male, with predominantly royal blue plumage offset by a white crest and long

Kitti's hog-nosed bat is the world's smallest mammal – its body is no bigger than a bumblebee.
(Jeffrey A. McNeely)

Goeldi's monkey – linking the true South American monkeys and the marmosets?
(The Zoological Society of London)

Confined to a single tiny Japanese island, the Iriomote cat was unknown to science until 1965. (Tadaaki Imaizumi/Nature Production, Tokyo)

Escapee Asian jungle cat discovered near Ludlow, Shropshire, in February 1989. (Dr Karl Shuker)

Kellas cat trapped in 1984 at Revack Lodge, northern Scotland.
(Edward Orbell)

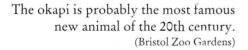

The okapi is probably the most famous new animal of the 20th century.
(Bristol Zoo Gardens)

Kouprey (male) – the grey wild ox of Cambodia, officially described in 1937.
(Helmut Diller/World Wide Fund for Nature)

King cheetah – discounted as a native
myth until 1926.
(Lena and Paul Bottriell)

Despite its striking
colour, the golden
bamboo lemur eluded
discovery until 1985.
(Dr Bernhard Meier)

Taxiderm specimen of male
Vu Quang ox – an important
new mammal found in 1992.
(Dr John MacKinnon/
World Wide Fund for Nature)

Famous statue at
Tongling in China,
depicting five Chinese
river dolphins.
(Prof. Zhou Kaiya)

Scaly-tailed possum – known to Aboriginals as *wyulda*, but unknown to science until 1917.
(Wildlife Photos W.A.)

Opposite: Discovered in 1976, Peru's long-whiskered owlet required a totally new genus.
(Dr John P. O'Neill)

Left: Pacarana – Count Branicki's *'terrible mouse'*, the size of a fox terrier.
(Jürg Klages/Photo und Graphik, Zurich)

Left & below: The world's smallest, living, flightless bird is the Inaccessible Island rail. Was it native to the lost continent of Atlantis?
(Dr Ian Best/Denstone Expeditions Trust, courtesy of Michael Swales)

The type specimen of Vo Quy's
pheasant – discovered in 1964.
(Jonathan C. Eames)

After its discovery in 1923, the
imperial pheasant was not successfully
captured in the wild again until 1990.
(Jean Howman)

Congo peacock (male) – a
single perplexing feather led to
its discovery in 1936.
(Jean Howman)

The takahe's rediscovery in
1948 was a sensational
ornithological triumph.
(J.L.Kendrick/Department of
Conservation, Wellington, New
Zealand)

Pardusco – Peru's unclassifiable *cloud bird*, discovered in 1973.
(Dr John P. O'Neill)

The native homeland of Lear's macaw remained a mystery until 1978.
(Birdland, Bourton-on-the-Water)

Although brilliantly coloured, the Fijian crested iguana remained undetected by science until 1979. (John Gibbons Memorial Trust, courtesy of Dr William Kenchington)

Platypus frog – the first frog known to science that broods its young in its stomach, found in 1973. (Prof. Michael J. Tyler)

Blomberg's giant toad – it can attain a length of 10 in. (Paignton Zoological & Botanical Gardens)

Not a worm, but a bizarre semi-terrestrial catfish from Brazil, discovered in 1984.
(Dr Paul Sterry/Nature Photographers Ltd, Basingstoke)

Neon tetras (top and bottom left) and cardinal tetras (centre) – two of today's most popular aquarium fishes, they have been known to science for less than sixty years.
(Burkhard Kahl)

Opposite: Titan longhorn, the world's largest beetle, rediscovered in 1910 inside a fish's stomach.
(Matthias Forst/Cologne Zoo)

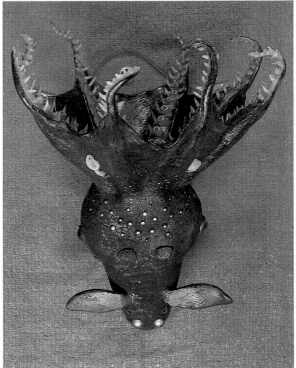

Above: Vampire squid – it resembles an octopus and is referred to as a squid, but is in fact neither.
(Royal Museum of Scotland, courtesy of David Heppell)

Left: Glory of the sea cone – once extremely rare, it is still the world's most coveted species of seashell.
(Royal Museum of Scotland, courtesy of David Heppell)

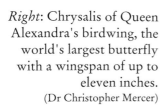

Right: Chrysalis of Queen Alexandra's birdwing, the world's largest butterfly with a wingspan of up to eleven inches.
(Dr Christopher Mercer)

Colony of the giant tubicolous vent worm, *Riftia pachyptila*, on Galapagos sea floor. (Prof. John M. Edmond)

Madagascan long-tongued hawk moth – Darwin predicted its existence 51 years before its discovery. (Marcel Lecoufle)

white tail feathers and also by a bright red area of bare skin around each eye, it was preserved as a mounted taxiderm exhibit, and is currently held at Hanoi's Institute of Ecology and Biological Resources. The second specimen, another male, was obtained close by in 1974, by Troung Van La; sadly, however, it was not preserved. Others were spied in nearby valleys, but none was collected. In 1975, this species was formally described (in Vietnamese) by biologist Prof. Vo Quy of Hanoi University, who had encountered it in the wild during his youth, and now perceived it to be a species awaiting scientific recognition.[65]

For quite a time, however, it seemed as if such recognition would be of little practical worth, because after an absence of confirmed sightings for several years, zoologists began to suspect that Vo Quy's pheasant had died out. Then in February 1990, a team of Vietnamese ornithologists made a startling discovery. Far from being extinct, *L. hatinhensis* was being regularly trapped and eaten by local farmers! The scientists immediately requested the farmers to bring them alive and uninjured any future specimens that came their way, and soon afterwards two males and one female (the first time that a female, brown in plumage, had been seen by zoologists) were duly handed over. These were sent to Hanoi Zoo, where they are currently on public display.[65] Interestingly, a single male imperial pheasant *L. imperialis* was also caught alive – the first seen for many years – but tragically died the following day.[65] (see also p. 110).

Despite the relatively recent date of the Vo Quy's pheasant's 'official' discovery, at least one notable western scientist may have encountered it many years earlier. In 1920, Prof. Jacques Berlioz (at that time director of the Laboratory of Ornithology at Paris's National Museum of Natural History) saw a pheasant in Vietnam that he could not identify with any species previously recorded by science.[66] Could it have been a Vo Quy's pheasant? If not, it must have been an imperial pheasant (as this species was not formally discovered until 1923) – unless, of course, there is a further species of Vietnamese pheasant still awaiting detection.

Greater yellow-headed vulture – a belated bird of prey

Not all new birds come to light in the field. The year 1964 saw the scientific debut of a new species of American bird of prey, when the greater yellow-headed vulture *Cathartes melambrotus* received its long-overdue official description, based upon a specimen originating from Kartabo in Guyana. Ironically, this 'new' vulture had actually been known to ornithologists for many years, and was already well-represented in museums all over the world, but unfortunately it had been confused in the past with the *urubitinga* subspecies of *C. burrovianus* (nowadays termed the lesser yellow-headed vulture), so that its true identity as a valid species in its own right had not previously been realised.[67]

A duo of doomed rails – living yet effectively extinct

Whereas most animal rediscoveries provide a measure of hope for the long-term continuation of the species, in the case of two recently rediscovered rails their revivals seem likely to be at best only very temporary ones.

Sometimes treated as a distinctive subspecies of the slate-breasted rail *Rallus pectoralis* rather than as a separate species, for a long time the Auckland

Island rail *R. muelleri* was known only from its type specimen, described in 1893. Then in 1966, a single individual was captured alive near a rubbish dump on Adams Island, a member of the Auckland group, by the southern party of the joint Dominion Museum-D.S.I.R. expedition visiting these islands from 14 January to 14 February. It was taken to the New Zealand Wildlife Division's Native Bird Reserve and aviary at Mount Bruce, near Masterton, and was later observed and photographed there by naturalist Anthony Whitten during work for his Churchill Fellowship. A small chestnut-coloured rail whose underparts are boldly striped in transverse black and white bands, it is currently the only confirmed representative of its species on record since 1893; similar birds had been sighted on Adams Island during the 1940s, and on nearby Ewing Island during the 1940s and 1960s, but none was captured.[8,68]

Similarly, in 1973 a single specimen of the Fijian barred-wing rail *Nesoclopeus (Rallina) poeciloptera* was unexpectedly encountered on Viti Levu's Nadrau Plateau. Prior to this, ornithologists had believed that this large brown-and-grey species had been exterminated on its island homes of Viti Levu and Ovalau some time before 1890, by cats, rats, and mongooses – all introduced there in earlier days by man.[8,14]

Unless further specimens also turn out to exist, these solitary representatives of their two species cannot save them. In short, although each has a living representative, the Auckland Island rail and the Fijian barred-wing rail are both *effectively extinct*. When employed precisely, this term describes any species whose last surviving examples are, for various reasons, unable to perpetuate it by reproduction. Such reasons can include: the existence of just one single living specimen (as with *R. muelleri* and *N. poeciloptera*), or the existence of several specimens all of the same sex; or the existence of specimens of both sexes but too old or diseased to mate and/or to produce viable offspring.

A once-common species that has suffered a devastating decline via persecution at the hands of man and at the jaws of his canine, feline, and rodentine entourage, is New Zealand's famous owl parrot or kakapo *Strigops habroptilus*. In the late 1970s, only 12 kakapos were known to exist, all of them male. Happily, however, the species was rescued from the limbo of effective extinction in 1981, when a female was found on Stewart Island, followed later by others.[69]

Aldabran warbler – tiny bird, tiny distribution

Discovered in 1968, and described a year later, the Aldabran warbler *Nesillas aldabranus* has one of the tiniest distribution ranges of any bird species – about 24 acres of

Kakapo – for several years, this species was alive yet effectively extinct, because all known living specimens were male (happily, a female was discovered in 1981).

coastal vegetation on the Seychelles atoll of Aldabra.[70] As an inevitable consequence, it is also one of the rarest bird species. Indeed, by 1988 no more than two individuals were known to exist, but as this warbler's terrain – profusely pitted with razor-edged cracks and crevices in the underlying coral – is not conducive to easy exploration, others may exist undetected.[14]

Pardusco – a conundrum from the clouds

In June 1973, two male specimens of a small, warbler-like bird were collected in Peru's Carpish Mountains during an ornithological field exploration organised by the American Museum of Natural History. Some additional specimens of this species, one that proved to be new to science, were obtained there during 1974-5. It is known to the locals as the pardusco; and to ornithologists as a paradox. With mostly plain brown upperparts and tawny-olive to tawny-ochraceous underparts, the pardusco superficially resembles the wood warblers or parulids, an exclusively New World family of songbirds. However, it exhibits two primitive, highly perplexing features that complicate this classification.[71]

One of these is the presence of the hypoglossus anterior, a muscle that all ostensibly similar birds (i.e. those that possess nine primary wing feathers) lack. The other is its unusual ceratohyoideus muscle, which, unexpectedly, takes its origin not only from the lateral, but also from the medial, surface of this bird's ceratobrachiale bone. When its anatomical characteristics were assessed *in toto*, the resulting combination was so bewildering that its researchers, Drs George Lowery and Dan Tallman, were quite unable to assign the pardusco with comfort to any existing family of birds. In July 1976, they christened it *Nephelornis oneilli* ('O'Neill's bird of the clouds') – in honour of Dr John P. O'Neill, an expert on Peruvian birds, and in recognition of the pardusco's habitat, consisting of cloud-covered forests[71] – but its taxonomic affinities to other birds remain a mystery even today.

Po'o-uli – what was that masked bird?

Deep within a remote forest on the northeastern slope of Haleakala, a volcanic peak on the Hawaiian island of Maui, a species of bird hitherto unknown to science was discovered by ecology students Jim Jacobi and Tonnie L.C. Casey in July 1973. If external appearances were anything to go by, measuring a mere 5.25 in, with nondescript brown upperparts, cream underparts, a black face mask, and a short pointed bill for pecking tree bark in search of insects, it hardly seemed a likely candidate for stirring up great excitement within ornithological circles. Yet no assumption could have been further from the truth, because this new species, soon named *Melamprosops phaeosoma* ('brown-bodied black-face') and known locally as the *po'o–uli*, proved to be a member of one of the world's most extraordinary bird families – Drepanididae, the Hawaiian honeycreepers.[72]

Apparently descended from a single, generalised finch-like species, the Hawaiian honeycreepers comprise more than 30 modern-day species, each with its own characteristic bill shape for use within its own, exclusive ecological niche. Thus, there are certain species with sharp bills or sickle-shaped ones for various insect-capturing techniques, some with parrot-shaped bills for seed-eating, and others with long slender bills for nectar-sipping. Collectively, these remarkable birds, endemic to the Hawaiian archipelago, probably constitute the world's most spectacular example of adaptive radiation – the evolutionary development and divergence of many species, from a single ancestral one, to occupy many ecological niches. This special scientific significance makes it all the more tragic that, within the last 100 years, at least a third of all honeycreeper species have become extinct – due to over-hunting by natives for their plumes, predation by introduced vermin, and their vulnerability to diseases carried by introduced bird species, not to mention over-collection of specimens for museums by excessively zealous bird collectors.[72]

In the wake of such extinctions, the unexpected detection of a totally new species (so distinctive that it required a new genus) was therefore extremely exciting, a most welcome addition to a family more associated with decimation than discovery. Unhappily, however, the po'o–uli is itself rare, seemingly confined to the upper Koolau Forest Reserve on Haleakala, and of small population size. It is currently protected by U.S. federal law from disturbance, capture, and killing, so it may at least escape the threat of bird collectors, but whether it can avoid the equally menacing presence of tree-climbing rats and exotic avian diseases is very much a matter for conjecture.[8,14]

Kabylian nuthatch – an Algerian surprise

No less endangered than the po'o–uli is the Kabylian nuthatch *Sitta ledanti*, a small dainty species of tree-dwelling bird first made known to science as recently as 1975 – when one very small population was discovered in a relict group of conifers on the summit ridge of Djebel Babor, in Algeria's Little Kabylie range. With only 20 or so pairs in total, the species was in a very vulnerable position, especially as its only known habitat, the surrounding forest, was threatened by summertime overbrowsing by cattle and goats. Due to appreciable ornithological concern for this newly-disclosed species' survival, however, the entire Djebel Babor area has been declared a national park. And in June 1989 a second population was found – comprising 350 birds in Algeria's fully-protected Taza National Park, at Jijel.[14,73]

Xenoglaux and *Xenonetta* – a strange owl and a stranger duck

On 23 August 1976, trekking through cloud forest on the Andes' eastern slopes in northern Peru, Louisiana State University Museum ornithologists Drs John P. O'Neill and Gary P. Graves saw a tiny brown owl that was unlike any previously documented species. What made it distinct were its long and fragile facial filaments, which extended beyond the edge of its head in a delicate feathery fringe, and the very long and striking bristles at its bill's base that grew upwards to yield a fan-like crest between its eyes. The owl became known as the long-whiskered owlet, and comparative studies confirmed that it was indeed new to science. Weighing no more than 2 oz, it seemed most closely related to those comparably minute species the pygmy owls (genus *Glaucidium*) and (like them) lacked ear-tufts, but it also lacked feathers on its tarsi and feet. It was thus allocated a genus to itself, *Xenoglaux* ('strange owl'), and its full scientific name, *X. loweryi*, honours Dr George H. Lowery, director of the Louisiana State University Museum.[74]

From strange owls to stranger ducks, the

Campbell Island flightless teal *Xenonetta nesiotis* was not formally described until 1935, and by 1944 it was presumed extinct. There was an unconfirmed report in 1958, but nothing more until 1976 – when this brown-plumaged, yellow-billed duck with reduced wings was positively identified on Campbell Island (about 380 miles south of New Zealand) by the New Zealand Wildlife Service. Nowadays, it is deemed to be nothing more than a well-marked subspecies of the New Zealand flightless teal (a slightly larger, darker-billed bird); thus it has been renamed *Anas aucklandica nesiotis*.[75]

White-winged guan – right bird, wrong habitat

The white-winged guan *Penelope albipennis* is a large pheasant-like bird, whose type specimen was obtained on 18 December 1878 on northern Peru's Countess Island – an area ringed coastally with mangroves but bearing tall dry forests at its centre. Two more were procured a short time later, again from northern coastal regions of Peru – after which nothing else was heard of this species. As mangrove forests predominated in the provenances of all three specimens, such areas were scoured meticulously over the years that followed, but to no avail.[76]

Then in the mid-1970s, a local inhabitant of northwestern Peru informed his neighbour Gustavo del Solar (an agriculturalist and longtime guan seeker) that he knew of a concealed locality in which this 'vanished species' still survived. But this locality consisted of a deep pass on the western Andes' foothills – very different from the white-winged guan's alleged coastal habitat. Nonetheless, accompanied by Peruvian avifauna expert Dr John P. O'Neill, del Solar elected to investigate this secluded area.[76]

And on 13 September 1977 (just a few months short of a century after the species' original discovery) their perseverance was rewarded by a conclusive sighting there of a white-winged guan. Shortly afterwards, its hideaway was visited by Peruvian zoologist Dr Hernando de Macedo-Ruiz, in the company of del Solar, and also bird photographer Heinz Plenge who succeeded in taking the first pictures of living white-winged guans in their natural habitat. This proved not to be coastal mangrove vegetation at all, but the thickets of the dry, interior forests.[76]

It was this confusion that had been the prime reason for the guan's previous successes at evading detection – its would-be detectors had been looking in the wrong habitat. (As pheasant expert Dr Jesus Estudillo Lopez later commented: 'It was as ridiculous as looking for camels in the Arctic.') Also, based upon conversations with the local people, Dr O'Neill later estimated that this species may number in the several hundreds, so extreme rarity could not be offered as an explanation for its evanescence.[76]

Magenta petrel and Chatham Island taiko – two birds in one

The rediscovery of the magenta petrel *Pterodroma magentae* was cause for double celebration by zoologists, because it solved not one but two ornithological mysteries.

Until 1978 it was known only from a specimen taken at sea just south of Pitcairn Island in the south Pacific in 1867. Several years later, some geologically-recent skeletal remains discovered on Chatham Island (500 miles west of Pitcairn) were shown to be from a petrel species not recorded before by science, which became known as the Chatham Island taiko. No living specimen was taken, and according to the islanders' testimony the taiko had died out around 1914 (although unconfirmed sightings had continued into the 1940s).[8,14]

The two petrels unexpectedly became one in 1964, when, after comparative studies of the taiko remains and the single specimen of magenta petrel, Dr W.R.F. Bourne declared that these two lost forms belonged to one and the same species – though it would naturally be desirable to have some more magenta petrels to hand for further comparisons to check this conclusion. And in 1978, 111 years after the latter's sole representative had been acquired, two more magenta petrels were indeed obtained (with a third merely observed), not on Pitcairn Island, but from the taiko's homeland, Chatham Island.[8,14,77]

Photographs and measurements taken of the two captured specimens fully confirmed Bourne's belief – 'magenta petrel' and 'Chatham Island taiko' were two different names for the same single species. Afterwards, the birds were released back onto Chatham and into the dense bush forest in which they had been captured.[8,14,77]

Lear's macaw – everyone knew of it, but no-one knew where it came from

Another mysterious species rediscovered in 1978 was Lear's macaw *Anodorhynchus leari*, a smaller, turquoise-headed relative of the spectacular hyacinth macaw *A. hyacinthinus*. Its existence first became known to science in 1831, when Victorian bird painter and nonsense-rhymes writer Edward Lear painted a macaw of unrecorded origin that he believed to be a hyacinth macaw. It was later recognised to be a separate species, and was named in

honour of him (though some authorities also refer to it as the indigo macaw). Despite having been represented in aviaries worldwide since 1831, it remained a major conundrum to ornithologists for over a century – because no-one knew where these captive specimens had actually been caught. Not even their country of origin, much less their precise provenance, was known. As far as science knew, the species might even have been extinct in the wild – always assuming that it was a valid species, and not a hybrid of the hyacinth macaw and the closely-related glaucous macaw *A. glaucus* (see p. 143), as some researchers were beginning to suggest.[78]

In 1964, the late Dr Helmut Sick, a German-born Brazilian ornithologist, began an intensive programme of searches for the missing macaw in a bid to solve its riddles once and for all. It was a programme that would take 14 years to succeed. On 31 December 1978 he spied three Lear's macaws in a little-explored area of Brazil's northeastern Bahia region, the Raso de Catarina. And in January 1979 he sighted a flock of about 20, proving that it was not a hybrid form.[78]

In 1990, a single specimen of Spix's macaw *Cyanopsitta spixii* was also spotted in Bahia (in the north) by an ornithological expedition sponsored by the International Council for Bird Preservation (ICBP). This small, grey-headed, blue-bodied species was first discovered as long ago as 1819 by Austrian naturalist Johan Baptist von Spix, but it remains one of the world's least-known parrots. Spix's macaw had hitherto been written off as extinct in the wild (though if only one specimen exists, it is still effectively extinct there), and only about a dozen specimens exist in captivity – most in private collections.[14,79]

A flutter of flightless birds

In 1965, the Japanese Ryukyu Islands' southernmost member, Iriomote, offered up to science a previously unknown species of cat, plus a new form of pig in 1975 (see *Mammals*). In 1981, it was the turn of the Ryukyus' principal member, Okinawa, to provide a zoological surprise – this time comprising the scientific description of a new flightless rail.

Christened *Rallus okinawae*, inhabiting the island's northernmost reaches, and roughly equal in size to an adult chicken, it is a particularly attractive, colourful species, thus making its late zoological detection all the more surprising (needless to say, it is well known to the local people of this area, who call it *yanbaru kuina*). Its olive-brown wings provide a subtle backdrop for its dark blue underparts, handsomely barred with white, and for its light orange legs and long slender bill. Its throat and face are black, decorated with a broad white stripe running backwards towards the neck from the rear edge of each of its red eyes, and brightened by its head's bluish-grey crown.[80]

An unconfirmed sighting of the New Caledonian woodrail *Tricholimnas lafresnayanus* occurred in 1984. This species was believed until then to have become extinct in the 1930s, but judging by local testimony it now seems likely that small numbers do exist here[81] (this may also be true of the New Caledonian lorikeet *Charmosyna diadema*, currently known only from two specimens obtained prior to the 1860s[81]).

A second interesting flightless bird described in 1981 was the white-headed steamer duck *Tachyeres leucocephalus*. Native to the coast of Chubut, Argentina, like other steamer ducks it derives its name from the steamship-like sound that it makes when swimming.[82]

Yellow-fronted gardener bowerbird – never before sighted in the wild by a westerner

The yellow-fronted gardener bowerbird *Amblyornis flavifrons* is a species that has attained near-legendary status within ornithological circles as the ultimate 'lost bird'. Its plumage is principally rufous-brown except for its immense crest which is gleaming gold and billows over its shoulders to stunning effect – or at least this would be the effect if anyone were ever fortunate enough to observe a living specimen, a feat that ornithologists have been inordinately unsuccessful at achieving.[21]

To begin with, its official scientific discovery did not take place in its native New Guinea homeland; instead, it became known by way of three (possibly four) dead specimens bought, for scientific study, at various of the major plume markets of Europe. Its striking appearance not only warranted its classification as a distinct new species (described in 1895 by Lord Walter Rothschild), it also inspired at least a dozen scientific expeditions in search of living examples – but none was obtained.[21] In fact, the species was not even sighted – a sorry saga of failure that seemed destined never to end in success, until 1981.

Following a previous visit in 1979, in January 1981 California University zoologist Dr Jared Diamond was exploring the uninhabited Foja (Gauttier) Mountains in Irian Jaya (the western, Indonesian half of New Guinea) when he became the first (and currently the only) westerner to see a living yellow-fronted gardener. Indeed, he saw not just one but about 22 of them, and estimated that up to a few thousand birds may exist there.[83]

He even observed its courtship, involving the building of an elaborate turret-like bower by the male, who decorated it with fruit and flowers before attempting (unsuccessfully) to entice a female into it for mating, offering her a large blue fruit in return for her favours.[83]

All in all, the yellow-fronted gardeners' history of mystery seemed finally to be at an end. And Dr Diamond lost no time in taking plenty of photographs of them, and of their mating ritual and bowers – only to lose all his evidence, film and camera, when his boat later capsized in a river. Except for the memory of his observations, all that he had left were some tape-recordings he had made of their calls, which ranged from noises similar to the sounds of chopping wood and paper rustling to a motley cacophony of screeches, clicks, whistles and croaks.[83] Bearing in mind Diamond's misfortune, could they have been the bowerbird equivalent of laughter?

Owls and o-os

In 1981, the cloud-forest screech owl *Otus marshalli* – an attractive new species with long white eyebrows – was described from the Peruvian mountains.[84] Also in 1981, there was a probable sighting of the laughing owl *Sceloglaux albifacies*, one of New Zealand's only two species of true owl, last recorded in 1914, when a confirmed sighting was made in the Mount Richmond State Forest Park. Yet in spite of extensive searches initiated by the 1981 report, no fresh evidence has emerged so far in support of this species' survival.[85]

A much more tangible ornithological event in 1981 was the reappearance of an oddly-named bird. Based upon their call (and pronounced 'oh-oh'), 'o-o' is the common name for a quartet of birds belonging to the honeyeater family, and confined solely to the Hawaiian Islands.

With velvety-black plumage decorated by elegant epaulettes of primrose-yellow and similar flourishes upon their long forked tails (and also along the edges of their wings in some species), the o-os were among the most ornate members of this archipelago's avifauna. Tragically, however, their plumes were prized by the native Polynesians, their habitats were swiftly invaded and destroyed by western species introduced by man, and their skins were looked upon as valuable additions to museum collections.

Originally, each major island had its own unique species of o-o, but one by one they disappeared – the Oahu o-o *Moho apicalis* by 1837, Bishop's o-o *M. bishopi* of Molokai by 1904, the exceptionally beautiful Hawaiian *M. nobilis* by 1934, and the Kauai *M. braccatus* (also called the o-o-aa) shortly afterwards. Happily, the last-mentioned of these was rediscovered in 1960, at Kauai's Alakai Swamp (though with only a couple of pairs at the very most existing today, its respite from extinction sadly cannot last much longer).[86]

In addition to these species, there is a single recorded sighting of an o-o bird on Maui, made by bird collector Harry Henshaw in June 1901.[87] But when no other reports were forthcoming, it was eventually dismissed as a misidentification. In 1981, however, Henshaw's opinion was finally vindicated, when an American ornithologist called Mountainspring had a clear sighting of an o-o on the northeastern slope of Maui's extinct volcano Haleakala, during an autumn survey of bird migration in the Hawaiian Islands. Moreover, the newly-revealed o-o turned out not to be a new species, unique to Maui, but seemed instead to be a representative of the Molokai species, *M. bishopi* – the first time that a single species of o-o has been recorded from two separate islands.[88]

An albatross from Amsterdam Island

Amsterdam Island is an extremely small, subtropical island, one of the French Southern and Antarctic Territories, sited midway between South Australia and South Africa in the Indian Ocean's southern reaches. It is also the only known breeding ground of a large, white-faced, dark-bodied species of albatross officially described by science in 1983. Distinguished from other species by their striped, black-tipped bills, the first specimens were discovered there in 1978. When ornithologists ascertained that the total population consisted of only 30-50 birds, they decided not to take any for formal description, delaying the latter task until a specimen could become available via natural causes. This occurred in 1982, when a dead albatross was found on the island and became the type specimen of the new species – *Diomedea amsterdamensis*, the Amsterdam albatross.[89]

MacGillivray's petrel – literally heading for rediscovery

Prior to the 1980s, MacGillivray's petrel *Pterodroma macgillivrayi* was one of the world's most mysterious seabirds, a small dark-grey species known only from a single fledgling collected on the Fijian island of Ngau in October 1855. Its preserved remains are now in the British Museum (Natural History). In 1983, 128 years after its discovery, naturalist and Fijian resident Dick Watling began what was to become a year-long pursuit of this 'lost' species. One evening in May 1984, his quest came to a successful end when he rediscovered it in an unexpected manner.[90]

He had been seeking petrels by day and at night, using powerful flashlights to lure onto the ground any that may be flying nearby. That evening, one petrel had apparently become so dazzled by the lights that it crashlanded – right on top of Watling's head. And so it was that a dazzled petrel and a dazed Dick Watling restored another missing species to life. After carefully examining the bird – which seemed none the worse for its collision – and confirming it was a MacGillivray's petrel, Watling released it. He has since been engaged in estimating the likely population size of this species on the island.[90]

Red Sea cliff swallow – losing the lost

Also of ornithological note during 1984 was the discovery of a new species of swallow – the Red Sea cliff swallow. It was aptly christened *Hirundo perdita* ('lost swallow'), as the locality of its breeding grounds is unknown. Moreover, its type specimen (found dead on an islet off Port Sudan on 9 May) seemed to have been an off-course individual that had somehow been caught up in a widescale emigration of Palaearctic bird species.[91] No other specimen of *H. perdita* has been recorded, so for the time being the lost swallow is once again lost.

Cryptic parrots from South America

Until 1985, the last time that a new species of parrot had been identified in the western hemisphere was in 1914. In 1985, two were revealed within weeks of one another.

During a field trip to the mountain forests of Ecuador's El Oro Province in 1980, ornithologist Robert Ridgely caught sight of a green parakeet that was clearly a member of the genus *Pyrrhura* ('fire-tailed'), an event that he was quick to recognise as being distinctly odd for two important reasons. Firstly, *Pyrrhura* parakeets were not supposed to exist in this area; secondly, its combination of red and blue wing-patches, red crown, and maroon tail distinguished it from all species of *Pyrrhura*, regardless of locality. He was unable to follow up his unexpected sighting until 1985, when a return expedition succeeded in obtaining a series of specimens for formal study. Moreover, he learnt that a single specimen of identical appearance was actually contained within the British Museum's collection of birds at Tring; it had been procured in 1939, but had never been classified or described. In 1988, this species was christened *P. orcesi,* and is popularly known as the El Oro parakeet.[92]

The second new South American parrot from 1985 was the Amazonian parrotlet – spied for the first time by Charles Munn, in eastern Peru's Manu National Park. A particularly small species with a powder-blue crown, but otherwise predominantly grass-green in colour, it proved to be a member of the genus *Nannopsittaca* (occupied until then by one species only). When it was formally described in April 1991 it was christened *N. dachilleae,* in memory of a famous environmental journalist, the late Barbara D'Achille.[93]

Jerdon's courser – absent-without-leave for 85 years

Not since 1961 had there been such a momentous year for the reappearance of long-lost birds – within just a few weeks in 1986, two of the world's 'classic' extinct birds were rediscovered, followed by the restoration of a third missing species.

The first species to re-emerge was Jerdon's courser *Cursorius bitorquatus,* a dainty, long-legged plover-like bird with buff plumage and two characteristic bands of white – one lying like a necklace around its throat, the other located a little lower, extending down from its shoulders to lie across its breast. First recorded in 1848 by Dr T.C. Jerdon, it appeared to be restricted to the Pennar and Godavari river valleys in India's Andhra Pradesh state, and was very rarely seen at the best of times; but after a reliable sighting made in 1900 by Howard Campbell near Anantpur, it seemed to have vanished completely. Several subsequent searches failed to find any sign of it at all, so Jerdon's courser ultimately appeared to have joined the all-too-long list of extinct modern-day birds.[8,86,94]

In the 1960s, the Indian ornithologist Dr Salim Ali of the Bombay Natural History Society headed what would prove to be another unsuccessful quest for this species, and a further expedition by the society in the mid-1970s fared no better. Yet even in the face of continuing failure Dr Ali was reluctant to accept that Jerdon's courser was extinct – if only because there seemed no good reason at all why it should be. It had not been persecuted by man, its habitat had not been disrupted, and it seemed to have few if any serious predators.[94]

And so in summer 1985, concentrating their efforts upon the Pennar Valley, Dr Ali and the Bombay Natural History Society launched yet another search, cross-examining the local people in depth, and distributing coloured paintings of the species in poster form. Eventually, the party received its first ray of hope; three different shikaris (native hunter guides) each informed Ali and colleagues that he had recently seen just such a bird.[94]

On 12 January 1986, more than eight decades of pursuit ended in success. One of the three shikaris who had reported the species obtained unequivocal support for his claim – a living specimen of Jerdon's courser, captured that same evening in scrub jungle near his home in Cuddash District. On 15 January it was examined by a member of the Bombay Natural History Society, who confirmed its identity. The society hoped that the courser could be successfully maintained alive in captivity, but sadly it died just four days later. However, its skin was preserved, and other living specimens were soon discovered, but none was captured. Instead, the society recommended that the area containing them should become a protected zone, and the Andhra Pradesh forest department agreed, thereby safeguarding the future of the species. News of the rediscovery was afterwards hailed by Dr Nigel Collar, research director of the International Council for Bird Preservation (ICBP), as being 'the bird conservation highspot of the 1980s.'[94]

Ivory-billed woodpecker – reviving the Van Dyck of birds

With a total length of 20 in, and striking black-and-white plumage highlighted in the male by a brilliant scarlet crest (black in the female), the ivory-billed woodpecker *Campephilus principalis* is a magnificent sight, one that inspired the celebrated bird painter John James Audubon to hail it as the 'Van Dyck of birds'. It exists in two subspecies – North America's *C. p. principalis* and Cuba's *C. p. bairdii*.[8]

Although widely distributed throughout its range in the forests of the southeastern United States during the 19th century, the American ivory-bill was never a common bird in any given area, due to the specificity of its habitat requirements. Only extremely mature forests were suitable, and each breeding pair of birds required a territory of at least 2000 acres. As a consequence, the clearance of huge expanses of woodland by the developing timber industries towards the end of the 1800s sounded the death-knell for this vulnerable bird – the destruction of its habitat driving it inexorably towards extinction. By the late 1930s, the total population of the entire American subspecies was estimated to number less than two dozen individuals.[8]

Since then, quite a number of eyewitness reports have been documented, but due to the superficial similarity of the ivory-bill to the slightly smaller but much more common pileated woodpecker *Dryocopus pileatus* the chances are that few were valid. Of these latter few, however, two are particularly noteworthy. John V. Dennis, a woodpecker expert in the U.S., sighted an ivory-bill in the forests of Texas's Neches River valley on 10 December 1966 (the first positive Texas record since 1904), and again on 19 February 1967 (this time in the company of fellow ornithologist Armand Yramategui). Subsequent forays convinced Denis that a few pairs (perhaps as many as ten) existed in the area.[95] Two years later, on 4 April and again on 15 April 1969, animal sculptor-artist Frank Shields sighted an ivory-bill in a tree in his forest at Interlachen, Florida. The 15 April sighting was made at a distance of no more than 80 ft, and Shields, familiar with the species' distinguishing markings from his professional studies of animal colouration, unhesitatingly identified the bird as an ivory-bill – but the best evidence was yet to come. On 11 June, once again on his land, Shields discovered a single, striking black-and-white feather. From its precise size, shape, and markings, he was able to identify it as an ivory-bill's wing feather – specifically, one of the smaller, inner primaries adjoining the secondaries.[95] Since these encounters, however, no additional conclusive evidence for ivory- bill survival in the U.S.A. has been forthcoming.

Meanwhile, its Cuban counterpart had been suffering a similar fate, due again to habitat destruction, so that by the 1970s the continued existence of this subspecies was equally open to question – which in turn meant that the entire species could well be extinct. To the delight of ornithologists, however, this dismal prospect was triumphantly repudiated on 16 April 1986, when, after weeks of unconfirmed reports and all-too-fleeting glimpses of what might have been an ivory-bill, a confirmed sighting of a male specimen in flight was recorded at a distance of only 18 ft. The eyewitness responsible was another woodpecker expert – Dr Lester L. Short, from the American Museum of Natural History, who had been participating in a Cuban-led search for the ivory-bill in the island's northeastern Guantanamo province.[96]

The rediscovery of the Cuban subspecies has raised hope that undetected specimens of its American equivalent may also exist; but with both forms, total numbers must surely be extremely small, placing the ivory-bill's long-term survival very much in doubt.

Gurney's pitta – unseen for 34 years

Gurney's pitta *Pitta gurneyi* is a beautiful ground-dwelling species with a multicoloured plumage elegantly combining brown wings, barred yellow underparts, and a bright turquoise tail, with a black-and-gold face, and a shimmering blue crown. Once common in the lowland forests of southern Thailand and Burma, its habitat has suffered such longstanding and wide-ranging devastation at the hands of farming and human settlement that the species had not been positively sighted since 1952, and at the end of 1985 it was formally classed as extinct. Happily, in June 1986, four years of persistent searches by Uthai Treesucon and Philip Round (from Bangkok's Mahidol University Wildlife Research Centre) paid off handsomely, when they succeeded not only in observing, but also in photographing, Gurney's missing pitta. They even discovered a nest with fledglings. Since then, its two rediscoverers have been attempting to persuade the Thai government to declare the section of forest in which their pitta sightings were made a protected area, to secure the birds' safety from the combined threat of farming, logging, and trapping for the animal trade market.[97]

Ivory-billed woodpecker – believed extinct for several decades, this handsome 'Van Dyck of birds' was rediscovered in Cuba in 1986. (Fortean Picture Library)

Just two years later, in 1988, Schneider's pitta *P. schneideri,* exclusive to Sumatra, was rediscovered in rainforest on Gunung Kerinci, the island's highest mountain. Its last previous sighting had been in 1977.[98]

Returning to 1986, this year continued its record for avian comebacks by welcoming back the golden-naped weaver *Ploceus aureinucha.* Last reported in 1926, several specimens were sighted in Zaire's Ituri Forest by three zoologists studying the okapi.[99]

Helmeted woodpeckers and hooded antwrens

In February 1987, one of Brazil's most striking birds reappeared, via a confirmed sighting of a female helmeted woodpecker *Dryocopus galeatus* in western São Paulo. Not too dissimilar from its famous relative the ivory-bill, but easily differentiated by its smaller size and heavily barred underparts, this species has also been reported spasmodically from eastern Paraguay, but with less conviction, thereby making the São Paulo sighting – by an ornithologist called Edwin – the first reliable record of the helmeted woodpecker for several decades.[100]

Another bird from Brazil made headlines in 1987, when a pair of black-hooded antwrens *Myrmotherula erythronotos* was observed in September by members of the Rio de Janeiro Birdwatchers Club, at a secret locality within the remains of what had once been an extensive forest in Rio de Janeiro State. A small, ebony-headed, chestnut-backed member of an exclusively New World family of birds, it had previously been known only from museum specimens collected a century earlier from a region of tropical forest between Rio de Janeiro and Campos that was largely destroyed in later years – thus making this species' rediscovery all the more unexpected and important.[100]

Madagascan serpent-eagle

Summer 1988 saw the rediscovery of the Madagascan serpent-eagle *Eutriorchis astur,* when Drs B.C. Sheldon and J.W. Duckworth, two members of an expedition from Cambridge University, England, spotted a very distinctive bird hunting along a river valley beneath the canopy of Madagascar's dense, humid, northeastern forests. During their 45-minute period of observation, they could clearly discern the bird's curious hood-like crest of feathers – a crest that succinctly distinguishes *Eutriorchis* from all other birds of prey on the island. Moreover, on 23 February 1990 herpetologist Dr Chris Raxworthy found the decomposed body of a *Eutriorchis* by a trail running between the villages of Iampirano and Ranomena II in the Ambatovaky Special Reserve's rainforests. He collected its skull and three primaries, which were formally identified by ornithologist Peter Colston of Tring Museum.[101-2]

Fairly small, measuring no more than 23-26 in (much of which comprises its very long tail), and with heavily barred underparts, the Madagascan serpent-eagle was last recorded conclusively in 1930, and the 1990 skull is the first intact example in any museum.[101]

Summer 1988 also witnessed the refinding of São Thomé's dwarf ibis *Lampribis bocagei* (last seen in 1928), following a visit to this island shortly before by an ICBP team.[102]

Night parrot – brought back to life by a dead specimen

Not only nocturnal but also virtually flightless, the night parrot *Geopsittacus occidentalis* is a very unusual, ground-dwelling species that was common in arid areas throughout Australia in the 1800s.

During the 20th century, however, sightings have been very scarce, most during its early years, and substantiated by the collection of just one specimen – in 1912 at Western Australia's Nichol Spring. Consequently – yet with surprising disregard for the fact that four specimens were reliably spied at Cooper's Creek in South Australia's far northeastern section in 1979 – the night parrot has been considered by most authorities to be one of this continent's *former* inhabitants. However, in October 1990, during a drive along a road near Queensland's Mount Isa, Australian Museum ornithologist Walter Boles stepped out of his vehicle to observe a rare bird, and discovered an even rarer one lying dead at his feet. It was a recently-killed night parrot that had clearly met its death in a collision with a vehicle. A veterinary pathologist from Sydney, who later examined this find, verified that it had been dead for no longer than a year at the most, and quite probably for as little as three months.[103]

A fortuitous discovery had thus restored the night parrot back onto the list of living Antipodean fauna. It may also provide Walter Boles with an unexpected bonus of £20,000 – the prize on offer since April 1990 by the *Australian Geographic* journal to anyone who could obtain conclusive proof of this species' continuing existence.[103]

São Thomé grosbeak – a major rediscovery on a minor island

Hot on the heels of their success in uncovering its dwarf ibis in 1988 (p.141), ICBP ornithologists revisiting the tiny West African island of São Thomé in 1991 scored an even greater triumph when they observed a pair of small finch-like birds in a forest. The birds belonged to this island's endemic species of grosbeak, last seen alive in 1890.

The São Thomé grosbeak *Neospiza concolor* is one of the world's least-known birds. It was discovered in 1888, when Francisco Newton collected two specimens in forests near Angolares on the Rio Quija, on the island's eastern coast. It was next reported two years afterwards, but despite several specific searches for it since then, it had never been spotted again, until its unexpected rediscovery 91 years later by David Sargeant and Tom Gullick. Following São Thomé's settlement by the Portugese in 1483, great expanses of lowland forest were destroyed to make way for coffee plantations, giving rise to the commonly-held belief that habitat loss was the principal reason for this species' apparent extinction. Clearly, however, in spite of such desecration the grosbeak has managed to survive, though the total population has remained a very small one, and must be very vulnerable to any further dangers.[104]

The early 1990s saw a number of other noteworthy resurrections within the bird world. Hitherto known only from its type specimen, collected in 1937, the Cocha antshrike *Thamnophilus praecox* was refound in 1990 when a team from Philadelphia's Academy of Natural Sciences observed three pairs on the shores of Imuya Cocha, in Ecuador's Rio Lagarto drainage. In August 1991, the Santo Martin starling *Aplonis santovestris*, endemic to Vanuatu's Espiritu Santo and not seen by any of the expeditions that have visited this island since 1961, was spotted in cloud-forest on Mount Santo. A drake netted alive on 29 August 1991 by a fisherman at Lake Alaotra, in northeastern Madagascar, proved to be a Madagascan pochard *Aythya innotata*, a species of duck restricted almost entirely to this lake and not spied since 1960. And in 1993, the four-coloured flowerpecker *Dicaeum quadricolor* was rediscovered, on the

Philippine island of Cebu where it was last seen 80 years ago.[105]

Glaucous macàw – the bird world's sea-green scarlet pimpernel

Having brought the mammal section of this book to a close with an account of the thylacine, it seemed appropriate to end the bird section with a species that is in many ways the thylacine's avian counterpart, namely a leading contender for the title of the world's most common extinct bird. The species in question is the glaucous macaw *Anodorhynchus glaucus* – related to the recently rediscovered Lear's macaw *A. leari* (p. 134), but even more mysterious.

Both in size and colour, the three species of blue macaw (genus *Anodorhynchus*) exhibit an interesting gradation. The largest of this trio is the hyacinth macaw *A. hyacinthinus*, named after its magnificent, exclusively blue plumage. Next in line is the middle-sized Lear's macaw, in which much of the hyacinth macaw's vivid cobalt shading has been replaced by subdued turquoise. And then comes the glaucous macaw, slightly smaller than Lear's, with a plumage incorporating (as its name stresses) a subtle range of greenish-blue and sea-green hues – particularly upon its head, belly, and the upper surface of its tail feathers. In addition, its throat is brownish-grey, and the feathers around the lower portion of its face are sooty in colour.[106]

The scientific debut of this species took place in 1818, when it was formally described by Vieillot. Its distribution at that time appeared to encompass southern Brazil, central and southern Paraguay, northeastern Argentina, and northern Uruguay, but by the end of the 19th century this once-common species had seemingly disappeared throughout its entire range. The

reasons for this astonishing disappearance are still unknown, because the glaucous macaw had rarely been studied in the wild. Over the years, a few specimens had been captured alive and had been exhibited in various of the world's major zoos – one of these was received by London Zoo in 1886, and a well-known example lived at Paris's Jardin d'Acclimation from 1895 until 1905. Indeed, it is often claimed that this Paris specimen was the very last glaucous macaw. Conversely, some authorities confer that sombre distinction upon an individual which arrived at Buenos Aires Zoo in the 1920s and was still alive there in 1936, but there are others who believe that this was actually a Lear's macaw.[14,106]

Yet even if it was a genuine glaucous macaw, there is no certainty that it really was the last one. On the contrary, the published literature dealing with this species contains an appreciable number of reports alleging the much more recent existence of glaucous macaws, both in captivity and in the wild. Some of these are very vague, little more than rumours; but certain others are compelling enough to have stimulated cautious expectation within ornithological circles that this controversial bird's formal rediscovery is not very far away.

For instance, parrot specialist Rosemary Low recently revealed that in 1970 the late Rossi dalla Riva of Brazil, an occasional breeder of rare parrots and very knowledgeable regarding his local region's avifauna, claimed that glaucous macaws nested there, but he would not name the precise locality, fearing that local collectors would send their hunters to trap them. Low also noted that in 1988, after spending some months in the field (she did not name the area), a very experienced bird trapper came back home and announced that he had spied glaucous macaws, but had not been able to photograph or capture any of them.[106]

Dieter Hoppe heard tell that during the 1970s a glaucous macaw had apparently been exhibited in a bird park either in Belgium or the Netherlands, and that another supposed specimen had been alive somewhere in Australia in or around 1960. In 1985, Hoppe also documented a much more tangible, firsthand encounter. Several years earlier, he had visited an animal dealer who had shown him two very strange hyacinth macaws, much smaller than normal and with atypical sea-green plumage;[106] Hoppe now believes that these were glaucous macaws. In addition, he has published[106] a photo of an odd-looking macaw assumed by the photographer, Tony Silva, to have been a Lear's macaw, but which was principally sea-green in colour instead of deep turquoise – another incognito specimen of *A. glaucus*? Certainly, there is a very real possibility that there are currently a number of unrecognised specimens of this scarcely-known species 'undercover' in captivity, i.e. erroneously labelled as hyacinth or Lear's macaws.[106]

In 1982, Dr A.E. Decoteau claimed to be in regular correspondence with a European aviculturalist (no name or country of abode given) who is actually breeding a flock of glaucous macaws, from a tame pair that he has owned for several years.[106] However, I have yet to see any mention elsewhere of this sensational programme of captive breeding.

Perhaps the most promising of the glaucous macaw's many reputed reappearances in recent years took place in February 1992, following the arrival at British customs of a pair of Lear's macaws imported by parrot breeder Harry Sissen on loan from Mulhouse Zoo, near Strasbourg,

France. When he came to customs to inspect them, Sissens was amazed to find that the female seemed to be a glaucous macaw. On 31 March, London's *The Mail on Sunday* newspaper contained a full-page account of this remarkable episode, and included an excellent colour photograph that clearly portrayed the sea-green colour of the bird's breast and head, with indications of brown markings present upon its throat. Since its arrival in Britain, this extraordinary specimen has been scrutinised by two leading parrot experts, Robin Pickering and Joseph Cuddy, who are among the very few people alive today to have examined every one of the eight preserved skins known to be from genuine glaucous macaws, housed in various of the major museums across the globe. Neither of them has any doubt regarding the bird's identity as a bona fide *A. glaucus*. Peter Colston, scientific officer at the British Museum's ornithological department at Tring, was shown photos of the bird by *The Mail on Sunday* and he agreed that its head was reminiscent of the glaucous macaw's. However, he also pointed out that it did not seem to possess this species' sooty facial feathers.[107]

At present, therefore, Sissen's import remains unidentified. It may yet prove to be nothing more than a Lear's macaw (albeit an aberrant, green-tinged one) – but if it really is a glaucous macaw and can be demonstrably shown to be one (perhaps by DNA hybridisation tests), and if other incognito specimens can also be found and unmasked, then the only species of South American bird believed to have become extinct since this continent's western colonisation will be extinct no longer, and the search for the sea-green scarlet pimpernel of the bird world will finally be at an end.

Goliath frog and common frog (Jordi Sabater Pi)

REPTILES AND AMPHIBIANS

Hairy Frogs and Dragons of Komodo

I sat and gazed at them as though they had been beings from another world. Their casual identification of the picture, coming so unexpectedly, had quite startled me, for the drawing depicted a creature that I had long wanted to get hold of, perhaps the most remarkable amphibian in the world, known to scientists as Trichobatrachus robustus, *and to everyone else as the Hairy Frog.*

GERALD DURRELL – THE BAFUT BEAGLES

There was a rustle of dry leaves a little way up the shady ravine and then, without further warning, a prehistoric monster stepped out into the sun. No photograph or film can capture the threat of a dragon in the flesh, in search of food. He stood with his broad head held high, tasting the air with a forked yellow tongue, looking it seemed directly at me with a dark cold basilisk eye.

DR LYALL WATSON (DESCRIBING HIS FIRST SIGHTING OF AN ADULT KOMODO DRAGON) – EARTHWORKS

Frogs with filamentous 'fur' and dragon-like lizards sometimes exceeding 10 ft in length are just two of the species listed on the roll-call of extraordinary reptiles and amphibians that first entered the zoological catalogue, or achieved notable re-entries in it, during the

145

course of the 20th century. This select company of herpetological history-makers also includes: a frog as large as certain African antelopes, and another that hatches its eggs within its own stomach; a legendary New Zealand lizard on public display for more than a century before it was recognised to be a new species undescribed by science; a tragic snake that bred itself into extinction; the world's longest toad and its most venomous frog; and a zoologically heretical tortoise – unnervingly fleet of foot, with a shell as flat and flexible as a pancake.

Hairy frogs and golden frogs

At the end of the 19th century, missionary-naturalist George Latimer Bates was stationed in Rio Muni (now Equatorial Guinea) on the Benito River, north of western Africa's

Gaboon River, amassing a collection of animal specimens for the British Museum (Natural History). Among those that he obtained from the Benito River itself were some very peculiar frogs. Approximately 4 in long, and greenish-brown in colour with black markings, they superficially resembled ordinary pond frogs – except for one extraordinary feature. Their flanks and thighs seemed to be covered with hair![1-2]

Closer observations revealed this 'hair' to be a mass of fine skin filaments, richly supplied with blood vessels, which drifted loosely when the frogs were submerged in water but clung against their bodies like matted fur when they were on land. Inevitably, this new species became known as the hairy frog, a soubriquet mirrored in its scientific name – describing it in 1900, George Boulenger dubbed it *Trichobatrachus robustus* ('sturdy hairy frog').[1-2]

This species has since been found elsewhere in western Africa, and scientists have learnt that only males have 'hair', and only during the breeding season. During this season, the male needs to take in more oxygen than usual, in order to fuel its concomitant increase in physiological activity, but this need cannot be met by its lungs alone, because they are only poorly developed. However, frogs are also able to absorb oxygen directly through their skin, and in the hairy frog the success of this process is greatly increased by its 'hair', because the total surface area of these filaments equals that of the frog's entire body, i.e. they provide it with twice as much surface area of skin through which to absorb oxygen. Hence its lungs' inadequacy is compensated for by the effective performance of its 'hair' as accessory gills.[2]

Hairy frog (male) – its 'hair' comprises filaments of skin utilised as accessory respiratory structures. (Dr Jordi Sabater Pi)

Pancake tortoise – uncharacteristically, this species is relatively swift-footed, and has an extremely flexible shell.
(Frankfurt Zoological Garden)

Also worthy of note are the long claws present on the second, third, and fourth toes of each foot. These are not ordinary claws, instead, each actually comprises the tip of its toe's skeleton, protruding through the toe's skin (though it can be retracted back if need be). They enable the frog to cling to rocks, but can also be used very productively in self-defence, as many animal collectors have discovered to their cost (see, for example, Gerald Durrell's delightful book *The Bafut Beagles).*[2]

A second distinctive frog described in 1900 was *Mantella aurantiaca,* Madagascar's golden frog. One of the most beautiful amphibians in the world, this 2-3-in-long species has an iridescent golden-yellow skin, bestowing upon it the guise of a living gem when seen squatting upon the rich green foliage of its forest habitat.[3] It is also one of the very few species of frog to practise internal fertilisation; with most other frogs, the eggs are fertilised externally as soon as they are ejected by the female.

Temple turtles and pancake tortoises

The year 1903 witnessed the scientific description of the yellow-headed temple turtle *Hieremys annandalli,* requiring the creation of a new genus. Since time immemorial, this freshwater species has been greatly revered in Thailand, so much so that specially-erected, pool-encompassing temples exist here to house it – making western science's ignorance of it until the 20th century all the more surprising.[4-5]

Also described in 1903 was a most unusual species of tortoise, unexpectedly fleet-footed and the sole member of another new genus. Inhabiting rocky regions of Tanzania and Kenya at altitudes exceeding 3300 ft, *Malacochersus tornieri i*s aptly called the pancake tortoise, because its shell is almost flat, and is also surprisingly pliable, unlike the hard, rigid carapace of other tortoises. The shell's shape and flexibility enable its owner to make good use of low rocks and very narrow crevices in which to hide when threatened by predators, thereby exploiting a means of escape unavailable to related species.[4,6]

Goliath frog – world's longest frog

The hairy frog was not the only distinctive new frog discovered by George Latimer Bates during his West African forays at the turn of the century. At Efulen, in Cameroon, he captured a specimen of what proved to be the world's longest frog. Measuring 10 in in length, olive-brown in colour on top (with small dark spots on the body and irregular cross-bars on the limbs), yellowish-white underneath, and with a notably flattened head, it became the type specimen of what is nowadays known as the goliath frog. In 1906, the species was officially named *Rana goliath* by herpetologist George Boulenger, but later studies showed that it was sufficiently different from other *Rana* frogs not just in

147

Goliath frog – weighing up to 8 lb, this enormous species, discovered in 1906, is as large as some antelopes.
(Dr Jordi Sabater Pi)

as these would have an appetite for sizeable prey. However, as confirmed by goliath frog specialist Dr Jordi Sabater Pi, although this species will indeed eat small rodents and amphibians its principal prey consists of insects.[9]

The dragons of Komodo

Among the most notable new lizard finds from the early years of the 20th century was the web-footed gecko *Palmatogecko rangei* – a semi-transparent consumer of termites, indigenous to southwestern Africa's Namib Desert. The only member of its genus, it was described in 1908.[4,10] Another discovery was Weber's sailing lizard *Hydrosaurus weberi* – a large, basilisk-like species of aquatic agama native to the Moluccan islands of Halmahera and Ternate, and described in 1911 by Thomas Barbour.[4,11] None, however, could compare with the reptilian revelation that was about to take place on a hitherto-obscure Indonesian island called Komodo.

Once upon a time, giant reptiles were thought of as creatures of the distant past. Dinosaurs were long extinct, and dragons existed only in ancient myths – or so everyone thought, until science announced the discovery of a real-life dragon of sorts, one that was every bit as mighty and monstrous in appearance as its mythological namesakes. Just eastwards of Java and Bali is a collection of much smaller Indonesian islands known as the Lesser Sundas. One of these is Komodo, composed of volcanic rock and covered in dense tropical forests. A very small island, less than 25 miles long and no more than 240 square miles in total area, Komodo may not

size but also in anatomy to warrant its own genus, so it was renamed *Conraua goliath*.[7]

Since the discovery of its type specimen, even larger individuals have been recorded. According to the *Guinness Book of Records* for 1992, an enormous specimen was caught in Cameroon's River Sanaga during April 1989; it measured 14.5 in and weighed 8 lb – thus comparable in size to dik-diks and certain other small antelopes![8] One might expect that frogs of such extraordinary dimensions be everyone's initial concept of a likely home for a population of giant reptiles – which only goes to show how wrong first impressions can be.

Originally uninhabited by man, in the early 19th century Komodo had become of great use to the sultan of the neighbouring island of Sumbawa, who used it as a 'Devil's Island' on which to maroon convicts and political opponents. It was also visited from time to time, by native hunters and pearl-seekers from Sumbawa, Flores, and other parts of Indonesia, and once back home again they often spoke of what they had learnt about Komodo from the island's enforced residents, and of their own experiences there.

They told of huge, frightening monsters, of a type somewhat akin to a crocodile in appearance, but which lived on the land, and thought nothing of devouring pigs,

deer – and humans. This giant form became known as the *boeaja darat* ('land crocodile'), reports of which soon attracted so much attention that even the scientific world, usually so sceptical of native tales and testimony, began to take notice.[12-13]

One authority who found the Komodo 'land crocodile' rumours intriguing was Major P.A. Ouwens, director of Java's Botanical Gardens, at Buitenzorg (Jakarta). In 1910, in an effort to learn something conclusive regarding this matter, he contacted J.K.H. van Steyn van Hensbroek – at that time Governor of the island of Flores, Komodo's much larger, eastward neighbour. By good fortune, the governor was a keen amateur naturalist, who

Komodo dragons – discovered in 1912, this is the world's largest lizard, occasionally exceeding 10 ft in length.

promised to find out whatever he could for Ouwens when he next visited Komodo. Meanwhile, Ouwens's interest was heightened by a report received from an airman, who had recently made a forced landing on this island, only to discover to his alarm that it was populated by 'horrible dragons'.[12-13]

In 1912, van Steyn van Hensbroek finally arrived on Komodo and met up with two Dutch pearl-seekers, Kock and Aldegon (members of a Dutch pearl fleet), who recounted many a hair-raising tale of their encounters with the terrifying *boeaja darat*, and declared that it could attain a length of up to 23 ft! Disentangling fact from fiction whenever possible, examining the skin of an unusually large lizard discovered in one of the resident's huts, and following the tracks of what was said by some Sumbaya exiles to be a genuine *boeaja darat* (but failing to observe the tracks' originator), the Flores governor ascertained that the maximum length reached by Komodo's 'land crocodile' was appreciably less than the figure claimed by his companions. Moreover, he concluded that it was not a crocodile at all, but most probably an extra-large member of the monitor lizard (varanid) family. Eventually, he succeeded in shooting a fair-sized specimen, measuring 7 ft 4 in long, and sent its skin and a photo of the corpse to Ouwens in Java.[12-14]

It was indeed a varanid, much bulkier than the familiar monitors known from Africa, Asia, and Australasia, but otherwise quite comparable. Although some monitor species are small, others can attain lengths of several feet, but almost all are characterised by their elongate, mobile necks, extremely long tongues and tails, and principally carnivorous lifestyles.

Not long afterwards, the Buitenzorg Botanical Gardens sent a collector to Komodo to procure some living specimens of this new lizard. Four were brought back to Java, including an adult that measured no less than 9.5 ft.[14] More recently, specimens up to 10 ft 2 in long have been recorded, thereby making this giant monitor the largest of all lizard species – but not (as many books mistakenly allege) the longest.

Salvadori's monitor *Varanus salvadorii* of New Guinea quite often exceeds 10 ft in length (Komodo equivalents are much rarer). However, whereas the tail of this and all other species of large monitor comprises at least two thirds of their total length, that of the Komodo species only comprises about half of its total length, so it is far sturdier and heavier than other monitors of comparable length, and thus a much more formidable predator.[15-16]

Later in 1912 Ouwens published a scientific description of this new, giant lizard, which he named *V. komodoensis*. As for its common name – its huge size and impressive appearance, coupled with the fire-spurting illusion created by its long, bright-yellow tongue's flickering, flame-like movements, were sufficient inspiration for it to be referred to thereafter as the Komodo dragon. This name was first committed to print towards the end of the 1920s, by dragon-stalking American naturalist W. Douglas Burden.[17]

Van Steyn van Hensbroek learnt much from the pearl-fisher Aldegon, and others on the island, regarding the Komodo dragon's behaviour and lifestyle (functioning both as an active predator and, especially, as a prodigious devourer of carrion), and passed on this information to Ouwens to be incorporated within his formal description of the species. The accuracy of most of that information has since been confirmed by herpetological

researchers, including the following excerpts, in which Ouwens noted that the dragons live:[14]

London Zoo's first Komodo dragon, photographed during the late 1920s.

...on land, where they make great holes under the stones and rocks, in which they always remain at night. Their feet are fairly long, and in spite of their awkward build, they can move with great rapidity...The neck is rather long and extraordinarily mobile. The animal can move its head in every direction, and so it can see everything: this is of great use to the creature, as it seems to be remarkably deaf. Mr. Aldegon says, that, if only care is taken, that the animal does not see the hunter, the latter may make as much noise as he pleases, without the animal being aware of his presence...They live either singly or in troops. Their food is exclusively of animal nature. If Mr. Aldegon shot wild pigs or birds and left them on the ground, they were eaten by the Boeaja darat, which sometimes fought desperately for the prey.

The widespread interest initially generated by the Komodo dragon's discovery was inevitably eclipsed in the west by the all-consuming events of World War I. But it was revived in 1926 by W. Douglas Burden, when he succeeded in bringing to New York's Bronx Zoo the very first living specimens of Komodo dragon ever seen outside Asia. Others have since been exhibited at other zoos, including London Zoo, and Indonesia's own Jakarta Zoo.

Our knowledge of its recorded range in the wild state has also increased, because it has since been found not only on Komodo but also on the even smaller neighbouring islands of Rintja and Padar, as well as in the southeastern coastal areas of Flores.[18]

Over 80 years have passed since the Komodo dragon made its scientific debut in Ouwens's paper, but there are still many

151

mysteries relating to it that await a satisfactory solution. One concerns its present-day location. According to Floridan herpetologist Dr James M. Kern, fossil evidence suggests that its ancestors evolved neither on Komodo nor on other members of the Lesser Sundas, but instead in Australia many millions of years before the Lesser Sundas rose up out of the sea. Yet Australia is separated from these islands by at least 500 miles of notoriously turbulent waters, and the Komodo dragon is far from being a masterly swimmer. So how did it reach Komodo?[18]

Equally perplexing is why it should have attained such colossal proportions. Physiologist Dr Jared Diamond from California University recently noted that in earlier days Flores and certain other southeast Asian islands housed two species of small stegodont elephant, and suggested that the dragon evolved as a specific predator of these pygmy pachyderms. However, MacQuarie University palaeontologist Dr P.B. Mitchell challenged this hypothesis by recalling that the stegodonts were not the only medium-sized herbivores available as prey, so the concept of a predator evolving to feed exclusively on these two species is unlikely.[19]

Finally, it is worth mentioning that as recently as the early 1980s an unconfirmed report was recorded that suggests that Komodo dragons may also exist on the island of Sumbaya.[20] Clearly this spectacular species has quite a few surprises still in store.

Tail-wagging frogs without tails

The most primitive species of modern-day frog comprise the trio belonging to the genus *Leiopelma* (originally spelt *'Liopelma'*), confined exclusively to New Zealand – home of so many other 'living fossils' on account of its many millions of years of isolation from all other land masses. Together with their only close relative – an American species, *Ascaphus truei* – their vertebrae have two concave faces (the amphicoelous condition), like those of most fishes but unlike those of any other frog. They lack eardrums and vocal sacs, but possess tail-twitching muscles – even though they do not possess a tail. (Ancestral frogs were tailed, but the tail disappeared during subsequent evolution.)[4,21]

Prior to this century, the only known *Leiopelma* frog was Hochstetter's frog *L. hochstetteri*, inhabiting mountainous regions of North Island. Then in September 1916, Harold Hamilton of Wellington's Dominion Museum collected some specimens of a similar but hitherto unrecorded frog on Stephens Island, a tiny dot of land in the Cook Strait, close to the northernmost tip of South Island. This was described in 1919, and given the name *L. hamiltoni* in honour of its discoverer. Although Hamilton's frog was later believed to have become extinct, it was rediscovered in January 1950, and some years afterwards a population was also found on nearby Maud Island. Even so, it nowadays exists in such small numbers that it lays claim to the dubious privilege of being New Zealand's rarest species of frog.[22]

In 1942, a third *Leiopelma* species was described. Christened *L. archeyi*, its scientific recognition was somewhat belated. S.P. Smith had discovered some small, greenish-golden frogs now known to be of this 'new' species as long ago as June 1862, high in the Coromandel Peninsula's Tokatea Ridge, North Island, but these had simply been considered to be a variety of Hochstetter's frog, and thus had attracted little attention.[23]

The extraordinary case of Queimada Grande's vanishing vipers

One of the world's most venomous species of snake was officially described in 1921. Less than 50 years later it had apparently died out in the wild, via what must surely be one of the most bizarre causes of extinction on record. Named *Lachesis* [now *Bothrops*] *insularis* by its discoverer Dr A. Amaral, it is (or was) a 3-4-ft-long species of lance-headed pit viper, predominantly pale brown with widely-spaced transverse stripes. It was restricted to a miniscule uninhabited islet called Queimada Grande – a rocky chunk of steep slopes interspersed with scattered patches of tropical foliage, located on the coast of Brazil's São Paulo State, roughly 40 miles southwest of the Bay of Santos.[24]

On such a tiny outcrop of rock as Queimada Grande (with scarcely 0.75 miles of surface area above sea level), suitable prey for this species was, hardly surprisingly, something of a rarity. Only one notable source existed – birds, flitting back and forth from the mainland. Thus, for the viper to survive it had to be inordinately adept at obtaining prey.

Compelled to subsist upon creatures that could readily fly safely away from the island – the Queimada Grande viper could not afford to make mistakes. The means that it had evolved to reduce such mistakes to a minimum were twofold. Firstly, unlike its larger, principally ground-living relatives on the mainland, this viper was arboreal, with a partially prehensile tail, so it could pursue birds perching on the islet's foliage as well as upon the ground. Secondly, and most devastatingly, its venom was extraordinarily potent – far more so than that of other pit vipers – and capable of paralysing prey almost instantaneously. This ensured that

once a viper actually caught a bird, its meal was guaranteed, because its venom's rapid action prevented the bird from flying away before the poison took effect.[4,24-5]

It seemed a very efficient, successful arrangement for the viper; and as there appeared to be 3000-4000 specimens on Queimada Grande at the beginning of the 1920s, there seemed little chance that it would ever become an endangered species. However, in 1930, when a scientific survey took a closer look at these snakes on their islet home, it found that whereas 50% of the total number were male, only 10% were female. The remaining 40% were intersexual specimens, predominantly female in anatomy but with male copulatory organs – and hence sterile.[4,25-6]

The production of intersexes is not an uncommon occurrence within highly inbred populations in many animal species – and it would be difficult under natural conditions to obtain a more inbred population than from a species wholly confined to an island of less than a square mile in area. And the longer an inbred population inbreeds, the greater the probability that its offspring will be intersexual. On Queimada Grande by 1955,

Queimada Grande viper – described in 1921, has it bred itself into extinction on its island home?

there were far fewer specimens, and only 3% were female, with 70% of the remainder comprising intersexes. Clearly, this could only end in one way; there would ultimately come a time when every viper born would be an intersex, after which – as intersexes are usually infertile – the species would become extinct.[4,25-6]

The viper's only hope lay in the possibility that more specimens would be discovered beyond Queimada Grande. These could then be introduced onto the island for interbreeding with its own population, which in turn would increase the genetic variability of the species there and thus reduce its tendency to yield intersexual specimens. Such a hope, however, was never fulfilled, because the species was never discovered elsewhere.[4,25-6]

No vipers were discovered on a two-day visit to this islet in 1965. A year later, Butantan herpetologist R. Hoge captured seven of them;[4,25] but, as far as I am aware, none has been reported here since (though there may be specimens in captivity around the world). Apparently, the Queimada Grande viper has bred itself into extinction.

Rediscovering the taipan – Australia's largest venomous snake

Sometimes more than 10 ft long, the taipan *Oxyuranus scutellatus* is Australia's largest venomous snake. But following its type specimen's procurement in 1867 near Cooktown, Queensland, this slender, brown-scaled species nevertheless succeeded in eluding science for 56 years – until two more were collected in 1923, on Queensland's Cape York Peninsula. By that time, however, the Cooktown specimen had been forgotten, so these two were thought to represent a hitherto-undescribed species, which was promptly christened *Oxyuranus maclennani* and referred to as the giant brown snake. The interest generated by this 'new' species inspired the search for other specimens of it, and eventually quite a number were obtained – whereupon comparisons duly disclosed that these, the two from Cape York, and the Cooktown example all belonged to the same species.[27]

Until very recently, the taipan was also deemed to be Australia's most venomous snake (probably exceeded worldwide only by the sea snakes, king cobra and black mamba), and its large poison fangs are indeed capable of inflicting an often fatal bite. But fortunately human fatalities are rare – on account of its relatively restricted range along Queensland's coasts and also the coasts of southern New Guinea, and its generally elusive nature. In 1976, however, Drs J. Covacevich and J. Wombey revealed that its western, inland contingent actually comprised a wholly distinct species – now known as the small-scaled snake *P. textilis microlepidota* – whose venom is believed to be four times as potent as that of the taipan.[27]

Taipan - prior to 1923, Australia's largest venomous snake had eluded science for 56 years.
(New York Zoological Society)

Crocodile lizard

Known to the local Chinese people as 'the lizard of great sleepiness' as a result of its tendency to fall asleep while sunning itself on boughs overhanging mountain streams and rivers in Kwangsi Province, the Chinese crocodile lizard *Shinisaurus crocodilurus* is an unusual species. It was first made known to science in 1928, when specimens were collected during an expedition to Canton by researchers from Sun Yat-sen University.[4,28]

Named after the crocodile-like double row of horny scales that it bears on the upper surface of its tail (with a single row running down the middle of its back), this pale-brown species is the sole member of its genus. It seems to be most closely related to an equally obscure group of lizards termed xenosaurs (see p. 158), even though they live many thousands of miles further east – in Mexico and Guatemala. Indeed, some herpetologists nowadays refer to it as the Chinese xenosaur. Unlike the flattened skulls of the New World species, however, that of *Shinisaurus* is compressed, yielding a high, narrow outline.[4,28]

...And the genuine articles

In 1929 herpetologist Dr Karl Schmidt, from Chicago's Field Museum, described and named a new species of crocodile – *Crocodylus novaeguineae* – from the Sulu Archipelago, various other Philippine islands, and New Guinea. Measuring 10 ft in total length, it is characterised by a long snout.[29]

The following year, Schmidt received three specimens of a small crocodile form from the Philippine island of Mindanao. He expected them to belong either to the saltwater crocodile *C. porosus* (that island's most common crocodile), or to his newly-described New Guinea species. Instead, they proved to be distinct from both, evidently representing another new species, which Schmidt described on 15 May 1935, naming it *C. mindorensis*. Although most closely related to the New Guinea crocodile, it was readily distinguished by several morphological features, such a proportionately heavier, broader skull with a greater degree of pitting, more pronounced ridges around the eyesockets, and a larger eustachian tube (the internal connection between the ear and the back of the throat).[30]

Just a few years earlier, in 1923, a team from the Chicago Natural History Museum found Morelet's crocodile *C. moreleti* alive and well in a swamp inland from Belize in what was then British Honduras. Until that find, it had been known solely from some skins brought to the Paris Museum in 1851 by French traveller Morelet.[31] It is also known to exist in Tabasco, Mexico, but is one of the world's most endangered species of reptile.

Lafrentz caecilian – a discovery in dung

Caecilians are legless, worm-like amphibians of the African, Asian, and American tropics and subtropics, whose discovery is often due more to luck than to intention. This was certainly true for the Lafrentz caecilian *Dermophis oaxacae* from Mexico. Scientifically described in 1930 (when it was initially classed merely as a subspecies of *Gymnophis multiplicata*), it had been discovered by K. Lafrentz on a coffee plantation in Oaxaca State. Lafrentz had been digging through a pile of donkey dung, when suddenly a throng of blue-black caecilians emerged from it. Measuring 1-1.5 ft in total length, this creature was well-known to the local

Indians, who referred to it as *metlapil* (and were convinced, mistakenly, that it was poisonous), but comprised a species previously unknown to science.[4,32]

Golden frogs and black toads

The existence of one of Panama's most popular, if unusual, tourist attractions only gained zoological attention at the relatively late date of 1933 – for that was when E.R. Dunn formally described the golden frog of Panama's El Valle de Anton, naming it *Atelopus varius zeteki* (after James Zetek, who had collected its type specimen in 1929).[33]

Not normally more than 2.25 in long, these engaging amphibians have black-dappled, orange skin. Over the years, scores have visited their mountain-encircled, oval-shaped valley, eager to espy its most famous inhabitants reposing like tiny droplets of molten gold upon the rocks and lush green foliage fringing the streams of El Valle de Anton. Inevitably, however, harmless observation of these delightful little creatures has not been sufficient to satisfy some tourists, who have been unable to resist the temptation to collect some of the frogs and attempt (unsuccessfully) to bring them back home alive as exotic, living souvenirs.[34]

As a result, the total population size of *A. v. zeteki* (sometimes classed as a species in its own right) has fallen calamitously, to such an extent in fact that today this frog is virtually extinct – tourists are fortunate to see even a single specimen. Destroyed through greed and lack of consideration just like the goose that laid the golden eggs in Aesop's fable, El Valle de Anton's unique golden gathering may soon be gone, forever.

Only a year after the description of *A. v. zeteki* was published, herpetologists learnt of a second species of endangered, distinctly-coloured, valley-confined batrachian new to science. In September 1934, zoologist Dr Carl L. Hubbs visited Deep Springs Valley – an isolated depression within the desert mountains of northeastern Inyo County, California – in search of some cyprinodont-like fishes seen there by Prof. G.F. Ferris of the Stanford Natural History Museum, in case they were new to science. He was unable to find any, but he did obtain some unusual black toads, whose dark skins were decorated with delicate white spots and fine tracings. In 1936 he showed these amphibians to Dr George S. Myers at the University of Michigan, who recognised that they were distinct from all known toads.[35]

In March 1937, Prof. Ferris brought back five living black toads from Deep Springs Valley. Their species was officially described by Myers in 1942, naming it *Bufo exsul* and allying it with the northern toad *B. boreas*.[35]

Endemic to this single locality, the black toad is naturally vulnerable to outside interference, and when various draining and irrigation work was later carried out in its valley, a great number of juvenile toads were killed, endangering the species' longterm survival.[34] It is to be hoped, therefore, that future work will recognise the importance of preserving this toad, and act accordingly.

Georgia blind salamander – a subterranean surprise

North America is home to several species of cave-dwelling salamander, but its most extraordinary example remained unknown to science until 19 May 1939. This was the day on which an air-lift pump operating in a 200-ft-deep Artesian well at Albany, in Georgia's Dougherty County, brought to the surface a pallid, shovel-headed, eel-like creature that was unlike any species seen before. Measuring 3 in long and with bright pink plume-like gills, it also possessed two pairs of spindly limbs that betrayed its allegiance to the amphibian (rather than to the anguilline – eel) lineage. It was sent to arachnologist Dr Howard W. Wallace, who in turn submitted it for identification and study to U.S. herpetologist Dr A.F. Carr.[36]

In superficial outward appearance it recalled the olm *Proteus anguinus* (a bizarre Yugoslavian relative of the American mudpuppies that was once thought to be the larva of a mountain-dwelling dragon). However, x-ray examinations of the living animal revealed that it was in reality a morphologically degenerate member of a quite different family, consisting of the plethodontid salamanders. Of these, the species that it most closely resembled was the Texas blind salamander *Typhlomolge rathbuni*, but whereas the latter had a prominently pointed snout, the entire head of the new species was strikingly spatulate. Moreover, its skull was more simple in construction, and it lacked external eyes, intimating that this salamander was of even greater spelaean (cave-dwelling) persuasion than *Typhlomolge*.[36]

In July 1939, Carr formally named it *Haideotriton wallacei*, desigating it as the sole member of a new genus. An aquatic species with a finned, laterally compressed tail to augment its propulsion through underground water sources via fish-like undulations of its slender body, its lack of pigmentation bestows upon it an opalescent, semi-transparent appearance. This enabled Carr to perceive that its type specimen was a gravid female – her eggs could be readily discerned through her body's wall. *Haideotriton* is highly adapted for life in total darkness, bearing along the sides of its head

and lower jaw a very pronounced lateral line system, comprising numerous finger-like projections that detect water currents and thereby reveal the presence of potential prey swimming nearby.[36]

By 1954, *Haideotriton wallacei* was still known only from its type specimen (though others have since been recorded), but during that year another new species of plethodontid cave salamander came to notice, when Dr Edward McCrady formally described *Gyrinophilus palleucus*. Once again, it was virtually unpigmented, but unlike *Haideotriton* it had well-developed limbs and readily visible eyes. *G. palleucus* was a major herpetological find, as it proved to be America's largest species of cave-dwelling salamander, with a total length sometimes exceeding 6 in. Its type specimen, an adult female, was obtained in 1944 from Sinking Cove Cave in Tennessee's Franklin County, and others were later procured from four more limestone caves in this same county.[37]

Palestinian painted frog – a victim of human conflict

The year 1940 saw the discovery of the Palestinian painted frog *Discoglossus nigroventer*, an attractive ochre-coloured species bearing red blotches and spots on its limbs and upperparts, and with dark underparts. Today, it is considered to be the world's rarest amphibian – assuming that it still survives at all. The first specimens collected were two tadpoles and two sub-adults, from the swamps of Hula Lake's eastern shore, situated directly upon the Israeli-Syrian border – the scene of intense fighting for many years. Needless to say, the continuing existence of any species living in such a disrupted location is so uncertain a matter that few would care to speculate optimistically regarding it.[8,38]

In 1955, one other specimen was obtained, this time an adult female, which lived for quite a time in a well-cared-for terrarium owned by its collector, M. Costa. He recorded that it was only active at night, spending most of the daytime buried in the sand with just its head protruding above the water – indicating, as noted by David Day in his own coverage of this species, a specialised existence within shallow swamps. No additional specimen has been recorded; and as the swamps have since disappeared, it is unlikely that this important frog (the only *Discoglossus* species native to the Mediterranean's eastern side) will ever be seen again – an innocent victim of human conflict.[39]

Xenosaurs – reptilian recluses from the New World

The xenosaurs ('strange lizards') are inconspicuous, brown-scaled lizards from Mexico and Guatemala, fairly small (less than 1 ft long) but powerfully built, and sufficiently different from all others to merit their own genus – *Xenosaurus*. Reclusive forest dwellers, remaining hidden during daylight hours beneath tree roots or within crevices, until the 1940s only one species – *X. grandis* – was known. Then in 1941, *X. rackhami*, with brilliant red eye-irises, was officially described from Finca Volcán, east of Cobán in Guatemala. This was followed in 1949 by *X. newmanorum*, from the Xilitla region of Mexico's San Luis Potosi State. A fourth species, *X. platyceps*, from Tamaulipas, Mexico, was described in 1968.[40]

Most closely allied to the Chinese crocodile lizard (see p. 155) and the limbless lizards known as anguids (e.g. the slow worm *Anguis fragilis*), morphological characteristics of the xenosaurs include their cylindrical teeth (small in size but numerous in number), non-linked osteoderms (in most reptiles possessing them, these hard bony plates beneath the body's epidermal scales are closely connected together), and flattened skulls.[4,40] In view of their secretive lifestyle, there may well be species of xenosaur still awaiting scientific detection.

Blomberg's giant toad

In 1951, 45 years after the world's largest species of frog had been officially described, the world's longest species of toad hopped onto the scientific stage.

Its story began a year earlier, while Dr John Funkhouser from Stanford University's Natural History Museum was visiting his friend Rolf Blomberg in Quito, Ecuador. He learnt from Blomberg that a giant form of toad supposedly existed in the area of Nachao, in southwestern Colombia's Nariño Province. Spurred by Funkhouser's interest, Blomberg set out to discover more concerning this mysterious creature, and in August 1950 he travelled to Nachao in search of specimens.[41]

A month later, he returned to Quito with the exciting news that this titan of the toad world was not a myth but a genuine creature – verified by the spectacular example that he had captured on 11 September and had brought back with him. This became the type specimen of *Bufo blombergi*, described in 1951. Its head-and-body length was 207 mm (8.28 in), and it weighed 1 kg (2.2 lb) when captured.[41]

Moreover, Blomberg had been informed by Nachao locals that even larger specimens existed, and that the species was most plentiful during the area's wet season (he had arrived there during the height of its dry season). Accordingly, in May 1951, during the rainy period, Blomberg returned to Nachao, and succeeded in capturing three living specimens, which were maintained thereafter at New York's Bronx Zoo.[41] These were indeed bigger than the species' type, but probably the biggest of all captive specimens on record is one that was exhibited more recently at Germany's Ruhr Zoo, with a head-and-body length of 250 mm (10 in), and a weight of 1.125 kg (2.475 lb).[16]

Not only is this species notable for its great size, it is also very handsome in colour, with a thick black stripe separating the copper glow of its upperparts from the brownish-purple hue of its underparts. Although the world's longest toad species, Blomberg's giant toad is not its largest. That title is claimed by the cane toad *B. marinus* – for even though the latter is slightly shorter than *B. blombergi*, it is more massively-built and somewhat heavier.[16,41]

Due to its impressive appearance, Blomberg's giant toad soon became very much in demand as a zoo exhibit and in particular among private collectors of herpetological creatures – to such an extent that it is now listed by the IUCN as an endangered species. Yet, disturbingly, it can still be purchased from herpetological dealers, with the continuing collection of specimens from the wild threatening its longterm future.[41]

The snake-neck without a snake-neck

The snake-necked tortoises earn their name from their long, slender neck, which, when extended out of the shell, can appear rather like an emerging snake. This makes Australia's western snake-neck *Pseudemydora umbrina* something of an anomaly, because its neck is very short, not snake-like at all. Its type specimen was obtained as long ago

as 1839, but no other example was discovered until 1907. After that, this odd species disappeared again, but in 1953 a third specimen was located, in swampland near Perth.[42]

Since then, others have been found here (where they undergo a form of summertime hibernation termed aestivation – as do certain lungfishes). Nevertheless, it is sufficiently uncommon to be classed as the world's rarest species of tortoise. By the late 1970s, less than 100 were known to exist in the wild, but a small population is maintained at Perth Zoo, which may assist in sustaining numbers of this unusual reptile.[16]

Bolson tortoise – overlooked for 71 years

It may seem difficult to overlook the largest species of terrestrial reptile in North America, but for 71 years this is precisely what happened to the Bolson tortoise. Although it was first scientifically documented in 1888, by A. Duges, it was not formally described, and for much of the time thereafter was thought to be one and the same as the Florida gopher tortoise *Gopherus polyphemus*. Only when specimens were found in north-central Mexico in the late 1950s did the Bolson tortoise regain scientific interest – whereupon it was recognised to be a wholly distinct species. In 1959, it received its much-belated formal description, penned by J.M. Legler, who dubbed this rediscovered reptile *Gopherus flavomarginatus*.[43-4]

Fossil finds have since shown that the Bolson tortoise was once distributed as far north as Oklahoma, but it is nowadays confined exclusively to the Bolson de Mapini in Mexico's famous Chihuahua desert. Tragically, despite its status as an endangered species, it is still hunted by the local populace; if stringent protection measures are not enforced, in the very near future this significant species could truly become extinct, with no second comeback.[44]

Agak (carn-pnag) – a formidable frog from New Guinea

In December 1960, news emerged concerning the discovery of what was said to be an exceptionally large form of frog in New Guinea. Known locally as the agak or carn-pnag, it supposedly measured up to 15 in from snout to vent (anal opening), thereby rivalling the West African goliath (see p. 147) for the title of the world's longest frog, and allegedly weighed more than 6 lb. Three years later, however, this would-be usurper of the goliath frog's record was exposed as a charlatan, when it was officially described by Prof. Michael Tyler. Naming it *Rana jimiensis* – its precise provenance was Manjim, on the Jimi River Valley's Ganza River in New Guinea's Western Highlands province – Tyler revealed that the first reports had been exaggerated. The maximum authenticated length on record for the agak comprised a rather more modest 160 mm (just under 6.5 in). Even so, this still makes it the second largest species of frog in New Guinea – exceeded only by the Arfak Mountains frog *R. arfaki*, whose females can attain a snout-vent length of 8 in.[45]

One-toed amphiuma – an 'eel' with legs

Also known as Congo eels, amphiumas are neither eels nor from the Congo (nor should they be confused with conger eels). Admittedly, their long slender bodies are distinctly anguilline, especially as their vestigeal, non-functional limbs are rarely noticed on first glance. Zoologically, however, these highly unusual creatures are amphibians (large aquatic salamanders, to be precise), which inhabit swamps in the southeastern U.S.A. Prior to the early 1960s, only two species had been documented, whose major external differences from one another centred upon their number of toes: *Amphiuma means* has two toes on each foot, whereas *A. tridactylum* has three. However, this situation was soon to change, thanks to an accidental find that had occurred more than a decade earlier, on the evening of 8 September 1950.[46]

This was when herpetologist Dr Wilfred T. Neill had collected two stranger-than-usual amphiumas in an area between Otter Creek and Cedar Keys in Florida's Levy County. Amphiumas normally bury themselves in the murky soil at the bottom of their swamps, but this area had recently been flooded by torrential rain, so the pond and stream beds had been washed away, exposing their reclusive fauna, including the amphiumas.[46]

Following subsequent laboratory examination of his captures, Neill had recognised that they were conspicuously different from both of the known species – and when, 13 years later, he discovered three more specimens of this new type, he prepared a formal description of it, published in 1964, in which he named it *Amphiuma pholeter*.[46]

The most pronounced distinguishing features of *A. pholeter* were the presence of just one toe on each foot, limbs even tinier than those of the other two species, reduced eyes, and a shortened, simple-shaped head. Its body also exhibited an unusual colour scheme, whereby its upperparts were lighter than its underparts (the reverse is true with other amphiumas), and it measured no more than 271 mm (just under 11 in) in total length – much smaller than either *A. tridactylum* or *A. means*, which can attain lengths in excess of 3 ft.[46]

Evidently, *A. pholeter* is a dwarf species, and the most morphologically degenerate of the three known amphiumas, seemingly adapted for an extensively secretive, fossorial (burrowing) lifestyle.[46]

Abingdon Island tortoise – adept at concealment, despite its size

The South American Galapagos archipelago is named after its giant tortoise *Geochelone elephantopus* ('galapagar' is Spanish for 'a place where tortoises thrive'). An imposing sight, weighing in at a hefty 330-440 lb, and with a burly carapace (shell) at least 3.5 ft long, it once existed on no fewer than 11 of the islands, and occurred in so great a variety of shell shapes that it was once split into at least 15 different species. On some islands the carapace was domed (as in smaller tortoises), on others it was flattened like a saddle. The largest island, Albemarle (also called Isabella), had five species, and ten other islands each had one; but nowadays these are all treated merely as distinctive subspecies of a single species.[34,44]

Regardless of their shell shapes, however, all of the islands' giant tortoises were united by at least one shared feature – a feature that proved to be their undoing. Their flesh was extremely tasty, and this prompted their slaughter *en masse* during the early 19th century by visiting sailors, whalers and other seafarers, until several subspecies were exterminated.[34,44]

One of the most distinctive was the saddle-shelled form on Abingdon (Pinta) Island, *G. e. abingdoni*, whose carapace was unusually thin. By the 20th century's opening years, its population had virtually disappeared, and during expeditions to Abingdon in the 1930s and 1950s not a single specimen was observed. To make matters worse, goats were introduced onto the island in the late 1950s, and their insatiable appetites rapidly converted its all-too-small covering of foliage into an arid wilderness. Not surprisingly, the Abingdon Island tortoise was written off as extinct, but in 1964 no fewer than 28 dead specimens were discovered there. They appeared to have died about five years before, which meant that they must have been alive, but concealed, during the earlier searches. Even so, 28 dead specimens could hardly resurrect the subspecies from extinction.[34,39,44,47]

Nevertheless, it *was* resurrected in March 1972, when – to the astonishment of herpetologists everywhere – a living specimen was encountered on Abingdon. Furthermore, tracks indicating the presence of others were also sighted. The living tortoise, a male (later christened Lonesome George), was transferred to the Charles Darwin Research Station for security. No more specimens have been found on

Abingdon Island giant tortoise – in 1972 a single living specimen was recorded, the only one for several decades.

Abingdon, but in view of the tracks observed, it seems possible that specimens do still survive here – a possibility reinforced in 1981 by the discovery of some tortoise faecal droppings that appear to be no more than a few years old.[44,47]

Even more mysterious than the current status of Abingdon's giant tortoise is that of *G. e. phantastica* – the subspecies of Galapagos giant tortoise endemic to Narborough Island. It is presently known only from a single specimen, obtained there in 1906 by Rollo H. Beck, leader of an expedition from the California Academy of Sciences. Yet in 1964, several fresh faecal droppings were found by J. Hendrickson on Narborough's southern slopes, implying that this is another subspecies skilled in the art of eluding scientific searches.[34,44]

Golden death from the forests of Colombia

The brightly-coloured arrow-poison frogs of tropical Central and South America possess granular glands in their skin that secrete highly toxic compounds. The common name of these frogs refers to the utilisation of their secretions by Indian tribes to coat the tips of arrows or blow-darts and thereby ensure hunting success. When shot into the body of an animal, the projectile's deadly coating immediately paralyses it, with death ensuing rapidly.

Already ranked among the world's most poisonous animals, the arrow-poison frogs gained even further toxicological prestige in 1973, when a previously unknown species, later named *Phyllobates terribilis*, was discovered in the rainforests of Colombia. For this species, whose secretions are used by the Embera Indians to coat darts, proved to be the most toxic arrow-poison frog ever recorded by science. Its appearance, however, belies its deadly status, as it is a rather small, attractive form, golden-yellow in colour.[48]

Gastric-brooding frogs – the female's eggs hatch in her stomach!

The year 1973 also marked the scientific debut of one of the most bizarre frogs known to mankind, discovered in a mountain creek in southeastern Queensland, Australia. It resembled a snub-nosed form of African clawed toad *Xenopus*, and on account of its large flat feet it became known as the platypus frog ('platypus' actually means 'flat foot'), and was christened *Rheobatrachus silus*. As the first wholly aquatic frog to be recorded from Australia it was already a significant species, but just a few months later it divulged the extraordinary secret of its brooding behaviour. On 23 November 1973, 19 days after having been collected from the wild, a captive laboratory specimen suddenly opened its mouth and disgorged into its aquarium a handful of fully-formed young![49]

Later studies uncovered more about the species' secret. After laying her eggs, the female proceeds to swallow them. They enter her stomach, where they hatch into tadpoles and undergo their entire development, after which they make a most unceremonious debut into the outside world, by being vomited up and spat out by their mother. By that time, she is undoubtedly very hungry. It seems that the tadpoles release a substance that inhibits the secretion of her gastric juices, thereby preventing her from digesting her offspring – but also preventing her from digesting any food either.[49]

One of the greatest zoological tragedies of recent times was staged just seven years later – when, in 1980, searches for more specimens of this species in its native homeland met with failure. Thus it seemed that, less than a decade after its scientific discovery, the world's only known gastric-brooding frog had died out in the wild. Even worse, in November 1983 the last captive specimen died – *R. silus* was lost, forever.[49]

By an exceptional fluke, however, the phenomenon itself was not lost, because less than two months later a second gastric-brooding species of frog was discovered, at Eungella, Queensland. It was of similar form to the first one. Named *R. vitellinus*, it became the subject of renewed studies relative to gastric brooding (and also to possible applications of its underlying principles – the inhibition of acidic gastric secretions – in the treatment of human stomach ulcers). But as its known distribution range is extremely small it is imperative that this species is not over-collected. Yet these words may already be too late – no wild specimen has been found since 1985.[50]

The platypus frog might have been saved from extinction if it had been discovered by science at an earlier date, when it was presumably still common. Ironically, there is now evidence to suggest that it had indeed become known to science earlier, but had promptly been forgotten again. In 1991, Dr Glen Ingram of the Queensland Museum disclosed that as long ago as 1915 the museum had received a specimen of *R. silus*, obtained at Montville by Heber A. Longman; sadly, however, it had not been recognised to be a new species, and had been overlooked until Ingram brought its existence to attention 76 years later.[51]

Gray's monitor – the lost is found, on Luzon

Until 1976, one of the world's largest lizards, Gray's monitor *Varanus grayi* (related to the Komodo dragon and now known to attain a length of around 6.5 ft in some adults), was represented by just three museum specimens, and was dismissed by many zoologists as extinct. Formally described in 1845, its type specimen was a juvenile collected from an unknown locality somewhere in the Philippines, and housed in the British Museum (Natural History). The other two representatives comprised a skull (from the Philippine island of Luzon), discovered in 1942 by noted herpetologist Dr Robert Mertens in the Berlin Museum; and a stuffed adult found in 1976 by Walter Auffenberg, in the U.S. National Museum.[52]

This last specimen was of particular significance, because it carried a data tag recording a precise provenance – Pasacao, Luzon. Following up that vital clue, Auffenberg travelled there to ascertain

A platypus frog regurgitating her young into the outside world from the security of her stomach, where she has been brooding them since swallowing them as eggs. (Prof. Michael Tyler)

163

whether this little-known species still survived. To his surprise he found not only that it was still in existence but also that it was widely distributed, especially in the forested areas of southern Luzon's Bicol region, where it is known locally as *butaan*. Of interest is that it feeds regularly on fruit and other plant material (unlike all other monitors), although it does also take birds, birds' eggs, and rodents.[52]

A bronzeback comeback

In 1978, a deceptively serpentine species of legless lizard called the bronzeback *Ophidiocephalus taeniatus* was rediscovered. Ten were collected in soil and leaf litter during early January by herpetologists Dean Metcalf and Harold Ehrmann at Charlotte Waters, near Alice Springs, South Australia. Until then, this species had been known only from its type specimen, caught in the 1890s by P.M. Byrne at Charlotte Waters and described in 1897.[53]

Brachylophus and *Brachyaspis* – each gained a new species in 1979

In January 1979, Dr John Gibbons, of the University of the South Pacific, found a new and very beautiful iguana on the Fijian island of Yadua Taba. Its bulky, pale green body striped with white bands, the crest of spines along its back, and its conspicuous dewlap all distinguished it from the more slender, darker, crestless, and dewlap-lacking banded iguana *Brachylophus fasciatus*. Until that time, the latter was the only Fijian iguana known, and was already recorded from Yadua Taba as well as from the principal Fijian islands.[16,54]

Shortly after its discovery, the Fijian crested iguana entered the record books, by becoming the first species to be bred in captivity even before receiving a scientific name. This occurred when a female specimen, given to Ivy Watkins of the Fijian Cultural Centre on Orchid Island, promptly laid three eggs, which were successfully incubated at Mrs Watkins's home. The species itself was eventually named *B. vitiensis*; and to secure its protection on Yadua Taba, in 1980 the World Wildlife Fund helped engineer the island's designation as the first Fijian wildlife reserve.[16,54]

Australia has the somewhat dubious distinction (at least as far as Antipodean ophiophobes – those frightened of snakes – are concerned) of being the only continent to house more species of venomous than non-venomous snake. This unique reptilian ratio was further emphasised on 6 October 1979, when two specimens belonging to a species of venomous snake not previously known to science were collected by P. Griffin and G. Barron in open eucalyptus woodland at Lake Cronin, Western Australia. Both specimens measured less than 18 in long, and had a striking black head, large eyes, a narrow neck, and a slender body dark brown in colour above, reddish-brown below. Their species was described in 1980 by herpetologist Dr G.M. Storr from the Western Australian Museum, who named it *Brachyaspis atriceps*.[55]

One of the few new species of snake found in recent times, it belongs to the elapid family – one of the largest snake families which includes famous, highly venomous types such as the mambas, cobras, kraits, coral snakes, and about 80% of all Australian snake species.[55]

Mallorcan midwife toad – first made known to science as a fossil

The discovery in 1980 of the Mallorcan midwife toad *Alytes muletensis* was a big surprise for two quite separate reasons. To begin with, it is a rare event indeed for a new species of vertebrate (backboned animal) to be found in Europe – even on small bodies of land like the Balearic Islands. As it turned out, however, the Mallorcan midwife toad was not exactly new. It had first become known to science three years earlier, in 1977 – as a fossil, its second surprise for scientists. The age of those remains had suggested that their species was long extinct, but the living specimens recorded in 1980 succinctly disproved this. Instead, studies disclosed that the toad's success in avoiding earlier scientific discovery lay in its chosen habitat – it lives in colonies hidden from sight within inaccessible crevices in the island's steep limestone cliffs.[56]

Indian cave turtle – its rediscovery was a gift

During a visit in mid-1982 to the Anaimalai Hills in India's Cochin region, Indian zoologist J. Vijaya was presented with an unusual gift that proved to be of substantial scientific importance. Given to her by a native from a village sited on the upper Chalakudi River, it was a living specimen of the Indian cave turtle *Heosemys silvatica*. This was a species known until then only from its type specimen, which was obtained in 1911 from some Kadar natives who captured it on the Anaimalai Hills' northwestern slopes, and from one additional specimen collected in the same locality shortly afterwards. Subsequent searches for it had always been in vain.[57]

Although a relatively small, unimpressive-looking species, it is noteworthy for its terrestrial lifestyle, contrasting markedly with the primarily aquatic mode of existence practised by most of its closest relatives. Following Vijaya's unexpected present, a short field survey seeking more evidence for its current survival took place between 26 October and 5 November 1982, led by one of her colleagues, Dr B. Groombridge; and he succeeded in obtaining a number of specimens at various localities in the Chalakudi valley. This implies that the species is not as rare as traditionally believed – its apparent scarcity more a manifestation of its capability for concealment than a genuine reflection of its numbers.[57]

Couresse – how to rediscover an extinct species the easy way

Until fairly recently, the couresse *Liophis (Dromicus) ornatus* was held to be the world's rarest species of snake. Indeed, for a number of years it was feared to be extinct. Limited to the larger of two tiny specks of land called the Maria Islands, just offshore from the West Indian island of St. Lucia, this non-poisonous species was rediscovered in April 1984 by Dr David Corke, an ecology lecturer at the North East London Polytechnic, who was visiting the Marias in search of this secretive serpent and of the Maria Island ground lizard *Cnemidophorus vanzoi*.[58]

As it happened, Corke did not have to do very much to rediscover the couresse – one morning, a surprisingly bold specimen glided through a forest's leaf litter directly towards him. Startled, but prepared, he promptly captured it, measured, weighed, and photographed it, and then called in some other scientists on the island to verify the record – after which he released his welcome visitor back into the forest.[58]

When the couresse was first discovered, a century ago, it also inhabited St. Lucia, along with the highly venomous fer-de-lance. In an attempt to exterminate the latter snake on this island, man subsequently introduced mongooses – which for the most part duly ignored the fer-de-lances and killed all of the couresses instead![58]

Two giant geckos – is one a living legend?

Geckos are well known to tourists in southern Europe (especially Greece) and further eastwards into Asia, as those small lizards with suction-pad toes that emerge at night to stalk insects across the ceilings of hotel bedrooms. In 1984, however, the zoological world learnt of two species of gecko that are unlikely ever to be seen engaging in activities of this nature – due to their notably large size, which sets them apart from all other geckos.

In July 1984, during the Iran-Iraq war, a shell landed on Fakke, Khouzistan, in southwestern Iran. As it exploded, it disturbed a large lizard which was spotted by Iranian zoologist Mohammed Reza Ensaf, who was serving there as a corporal and medical orderly. He succeeded in capturing it, after which it was passed on to Tehran's Faculty of Sciences, where M. Baloutch considered it to represent a new species of gecko. In 1986, this species was formally described by Baloutch and French scientist Michel Thireau (from Paris's National Museum of Natural History), who named it *Eublepharis ensafi*, in honour of its discoverer (tragically, Ensaf was killed during the Iran-Iraq war).[59]

Richly patterned with dark stripes and spots, *E. ensafi* is currently known only from its type specimen. Its status as a valid species was recently challenged, when in 1989, herpetologist Dr L. Lee Grismer from San Diego Natural History Museum put forward a detailed case for believing it to be merely an unusually large specimen of *E. angramainyu* (described by Drs S.C. Anderson and A.L. Leviton in 1966). Furthermore, although frequently alleged to measure 16 in (even by Baloutch and Thireau), in reality this specimen measures just under 11.5 in, thereby diminishing its claim as a giant gecko.[60]

By a remarkable coincidence, within weeks of this giant gecko's discovery, science finally became aware of another, even larger species – one whose 'history' had begun sometime between 1833 and 1869.

This was the period during which France's Marseilles Natural History Museum had received a specimen of an unusual lizard from an unrecorded locality. As a mounted taxiderm exhibit, it was subsequently put on open display at the museum, where, for many years, it remained in full view of countless numbers of visitors, not to mention generations of scientists. Yet, never once in all that time did anyone realise, or even suspect, that it belonged to a dramatically new species – one that had never been recorded by science.[61]

The decades rolled by, but still the lizard's true identity remained undisclosed and uninvestigated, until 1979, when this strange specimen attracted the curiosity of the museum's current herpetology curator, Alain Delcourt. Eager to learn more about it, Delcourt took some photographs, and along with the specimen's measurements, sent them for identification to a number of reptile experts around the world.[61]

They ultimately reached Canadian biologist Dr Anthony P. Russell, who in turn showed them to Villanova University herpetologist Dr Aaron M. Bauer. Russell and Bauer recognised that the specimen was clearly a gecko, but of grotesquely gigantic proportions, measuring fractionally over 2 ft in total length – twice as long as the newly-discovered *E. ensafi*. It was a

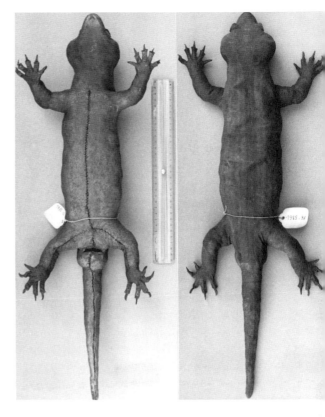

short-headed, bulky-bodied creature, with sturdy legs and a long pointed tail, and was handsomely marked along its back with dark reddish-brown, longitudinal stripes overlying its yellowish-brown background colouration. Its overall appearance compared fairly closely with that of geckos within the genus *Hoplodactylus*, except, once again, for its huge size.[61]

Its existence finally became known to the world at large in 1984, when Bauer's investigations of its possible origin led him to New Zealand; and in 1986 its species was formally described by Bauer and Russell, who named it *Hoplodactylus delcourti* – in recognition of Delcourt's laudable action in rescuing this long-neglected form from more than a century's worth of zoological obscurity.[61]

Its identification as a *Hoplodactylus* species had provided an important indication to its likely origin, because this genus's species are mostly limited to New Zealand, thus implying very strongly that this was also the home of the giant *H. delcourti*. Extra support for this conclusion came from Bauer's investigations here, because he learnt that Maori legends spoke of a strange New Zealand creature called the *kawekaweau* or *kaweau*. No one had previously succeeded in identifying this mysterious animal with any known species inhabiting New Zealand, but various reports from the 19th century described alleged encounters with such creatures. One of the most detailed of these accounts, documented in 1873 by W. Mair, reported the killing of a *kaweau* three years

earlier in North Island's Waimana Valley by a Urewera Maori chief. The chief told Mair that it was a large forest-dwelling lizard about 2 ft long, as thick as a man's wrist, and brown in colour with red longitudinal stripes, and this description is a near-perfect match with that of Delcourt's giant gecko.[62]

Consequently, Bauer and Russell believe that the *kaweau* and *H. delcourti* may indeed be one and the same. Sadly, however, there seems little hope that this can ever be conclusively tested, because it is almost certain that *H. delcourti* has been extinct for many years.

Or has it really vanished? Wellington's *Dominion* newspaper reported on 11 September 1984 that resident Dave Smith allegedly saw one on the western portion of North Island in the 1960s. Also, following a New Zealand radio programme broadcast on

Yemen monitor – viewing a TV programme in 1985 yielded this herpetological newcomer.
(Dr Wolfgang Böhme)

Yemen monitor – viewing a TV programme in 1985 yielded this herpetological newcomer.
(Dr Wolfgang Böhme)

23 March 1990 in which this species' history was recounted by James Mack, assistant curator of New Zealand's National Museum, the museum was contacted by several people who claimed to have spied living specimens of *H. delcourti* in recent times. These eyewitness accounts included three independent, reliable sightings all made at the same locality near Gisborne, on North Island's eastern coast. These, and various other reports, were followed up by herpetologist Anthony Whittaker and government scientist Bruce Thomas, but without success. Nevertheless, Whittaker believes that the species might still survive in the remote East Cape Forests.[63] Perhaps, after all, there will come a time when Delcourt's giant gecko will be known from more than just a single, long-forgotten taxiderm exhibit.

Yet another gecko milestone from the 1980s was the rediscovery in 1986 of a beautiful species known as the golden gecko *Calodactylodes aureus*. Discovered in India in 1870 but never seen again, its continuing existence 116 years later was confirmed by J.C. Daniel, a member of the Flora and Fauna Preservation Society, who encountered it in residence on Tirumalai Hill, one of southern India's most sacred Hindu sites.[64]

Tale of the tv monitor – of the reptilian variety

In February 1987, Dr Wolfgang Böhme and two colleagues documented a new monitor lizard, native to North Yemen. Officially described and christened *Varanus yemenensis* two years later, it seems to be most closely related to *V. albigularis*, a South African species.[65]

Its existence had first become known to science in an unusual manner. One evening in 1985, Dr Böhme was at home watching a television documentary about North Yemen when the programme screened a piece of film featuring a large tree-climbing monitor apparently indigenous to that area. This was of great interest to Böhme, because he knew that there was no known species of monitor native to North Yemen. Moreover, as he was unable to identify the monitor with any known species, he concluded that it must be new to science, and he urged herpetologists planning to visit Yemen in the future to look out for it. In October 1986, eight of these mysterious monitors were caught in Yemen's As Sokhna region during a herpetological field-trip from Zurich's Zoological Museum. Six were given to Zurich Zoo, the other two were sent to Böhme for observation in the living state.[65]

St. Vincent whipsnake – overlooked by science for 93 years

In November 1987, a snake received by Wisconsin's Milwaukee Public Museum from St. Vincent's Department of Forestry proved to be a St. Vincent whipsnake *Chironius vincenti*. This species is related to the familiar grass snake *Natrix natrix*, but wholly confined to this small West Indian island, where it had last been reported as long ago as 1894. The specimen sent to

Milwaukee had been captured earlier in 1987 within a somewhat inaccessible forest, which may explain its success in eluding science for almost a century. Since its discovery, enquiries have ascertained that it is familiar to the local people.[66]

A tuatara turnabout

The last of the 1980s' noteworthy reptilian rediscoveries was nothing if not unusual – because, technically, the species in question was never actually lost.

One of the world's most remarkable reptiles is New Zealand's famous tuatara *Sphenodon punctatus*. Although outwardly lizard-like, it is in reality the only modern-day representative of a once-mighty lineage of dinosaur contemporaries called rhynchocephalians ('beak-heads'). During most of the 20th century, only a single living species of tuatara has been recognised. Yet back in 1877 the eminent New Zealand naturalist Sir Walter Buller described a second species – almost a third

smaller in size and of brighter colouration than *S. punctatus*, but confined solely to two tiny Cook Island islets (North Brother Island and East Island). Buller named this species *S. guntheri*, Gunther's tuatara,[44,67] but other researchers subsequently discounted this classification, deeming it instead to be nothing more than a morphologically distinctive representative of *S. punctatus* (and even denying it separate subspecific status).

However, in December 1989, biologist Dr Charles Daugherty and colleagues from Wellington's Victoria Museum, working in conjunction with Dr M.B. Thompson from Sydney University, publicly released the first details concerning the results obtained from their recent morphological and genetic comparisons of several separate, isolated tuatara populations. These comparisons were published in full a year later, and revealed that the North Brother tuataras

Tuatara – a taxonomic turnabout in 1989 led to the restoration of a second species.
(Fortean Picture Library)

(those of East Island have died out) were sufficiently different from the others to warrant classification as a completely distinct species after all. Thus, in their paper, Daugherty and his colleagues have reinstated *S. guntheri* as a valid, second species of tuatara – official acceptance for one of this century's most important if unexpected reptilian revivals.[68] However, as *S. guntheri* is nowadays wholly restricted to a single tiny islet (just under 10 acres in total area), it urgently requires full, specific protection straight away – otherwise it may not be long before this 'long-lost' species is finally really lost.

Pink snakes, harlequin frogs, and Jamaican iguanas

Madagascar, already renowned as a treasure trove of endemics scarcely studied by science, may have quite a few more secretive species still awaiting formal recognition. During a three-month expedition to this island 'mini-continent' led by Dr Chris Raxworthy in early 1990, at least four herpetological forms were found that could not be readily identified with known species. Two were *Boophis* tree frogs – one with white skin ornamented by brown harlequinesque blotches, the other a bright emerald species with yellow eyes and red feet. The two remaining forms were a species of skink (a short-limbed lizard), and a nocturnal, dark-headed snake, whose pink-scaled body bore a series of longitudinal dark-brown stripes. The snake ultimately proved merely to be a rare colour variant of a species already documented, but the other three are indeed new to science and now await description.[69] And in June 1990, a specimen of the Jamaican iguana *Cyclura collei* was obtained by a hunter in southern Jamaica's Hellshire Hills. Until

then, the last specimen on record was one that had been killed by a hunter's dog in 1969.[70]

Electric frogs and skunk frogs

In 1975, Chris Corben (currently working for the Queensland Forest Service) encountered a tree frog at west-central Queensland's Polygammon Creek that closely resembled a species already known to science (*Litoria rubella*) – until it opened its mouth to emit its mating call. For the sound that emerged was truly extraordinary, a wavering cry reminiscent of the sound produced by a high-voltage, long-duration electric arc. When the frog was captured, studies showed that it also differed a little from *L. rubella* externally, via brown and yellow blotches on its thighs, and chocolate-brown bands on its upperparts. Other specimens were obtained in 1981, near Cloncurry (again in west-central Queensland) by Queensland Museum herpetologist Dr Glen Ingram. In 1990, Ingram and Corben described this species, and christened it *L. electrica* – a fitting tribute to the unique nature of its vocal outpourings.[71]

No less extraordinary was the yellow-patterned, green-skinned species of arrow-poison frog discovered in 1981, within the Andean cloud-forests of the extreme northeastern corner of Trujillo, northwestern Venezuala, by Venezuelan biologist Dr Alfredo Paolillo O. To begin with, in stark contrast to other such species, this particular frog was nocturnal (rather than diurnal), principally aquatic (rather than terrestrial), and was unexpectedly large (for an arrow-poison frog). Its most distinctive characteristic, however, which has earned it its English name, was revealed when scientists attempted to handle it – it swiftly registered its disapproval by secreting a liquid whose smell was not only foul, but actually resembled the infamous odour of the anal liquid ejected by threatened skunks. So far removed taxonomically from other arrow-poison frogs that it required a new genus, the Venezuelan skunk frog was described in March 1991, and as a reminder of two of its most characteristic features was named *Aromobates nocturnus*.[72]

Arnold's giant tortoise – indigenous to the Seychelles, incognito on Mauritius?

The Galapagos giant tortoises were once rivalled for size by huge species inhabiting the Indian Ocean's Seychelles and Mascarenes. Of these, only the Aldabran *Geochelone gigantea* is still certainly alive today, the remainder having been totally wiped out during the 18th and 19th centuries – or so everyone thought, until the coming of Arnold's giant tortoise.

There has been much debate concerning the precise number of giant tortoise species formerly inhabiting the Seychelles, and in September 1982 a new species was described by Dr Roger Bour of France's National Museum of Natural History, who based his description upon three old taxiderm specimens with long, flat-backed shells (two at the above museum, the third at the British Museum). He named it *Dipsochelys arnoldi* (though others prefer to call it *Geochelone arnoldi*, as it is clearly allied to the Aldabran and Galapagos species); and as there are no giant tortoises (other than Aldabra's) in the Seychelles today, he naturally assumed it to be extinct.[73]

Imagine, then, his surprise when, while still preparing his paper, Bour was shown some photos, taken in August 1981 by film producer Claud Pavard, which depicted two living giant tortoises that seemed to belong to his supposedly extinct species *G. arnoldi*. Nor was this the only surprise. The tortoises, males and very old, were living in semi-captivity at a sugar estate, not in the Seychelles, but on Mauritius. Naturally, Bour hoped to visit Mauritius to ascertain conclusively these potentially significant specimens' identity.[73]

And this is where this most promising saga seemed to come to an abrupt end. During my preparation of this book, I was initially unable to locate a single publication carrying any further news regarding this species, and none of my zoological colleagues and correspondents had any details either (sadly, I never succeeded in eliciting a reply from Dr Bour himself). Happily, however, the mystery was finally solved in May 1992, when I learnt from British Museum herpetologist Dr Nick Arnold (after whom *G. arnoldi* had been named) that Dr Bour had indeed visited the two Mauritius specimens, but had found that they were not representatives of *G. arnoldi* after all. Moreover, Dr Ian Swingland, Founding and Research Director of the Durrell Institute of Conservation and Ecology (DICE), informed me that giant tortoises reared in captivity sometimes have shells that have become distorted in shape, due to the way in which these animals have been fed.[74] In some cases, therefore, it is possible that they may even resemble the shells of quite unrelated species, and this is presumably what had happened in the case of the two Mauritius specimens, which were probably individuals originating from Aldabra. Captivity-induced distortion of shell shape can cause problems for tortoise taxonomists too, especially if they are dealing with specimens whose life histories are unknown (and which, therefore, may have been reared in captivity). Thus, as pointed out to me by Dr Arnold, with only three very old specimens on record one cannot even say with absolute certainty that *G. arnoldi* itself is a genuinely distinct species, and it is not listed as such in major herpetological works.[74]

Of course, one objection that could immediately have been raised in relation to this entire episode is the fact that supposed specimens of *G. arnoldi* were discovered not in the Seychelles, but instead in Mauritius. As it happens, however, this objection can be effectively countered – because a number of giant tortoises from the Seychelles are known to have been introduced in Mauritius after that island's own indigenous species had been exterminated during the 1700s. In particular, the French explorer Marion de Fresne transported five such specimens in 1776 from the Seychelles to his military barracks on Mauritius. What was assumed to be the last of this quintet died there in 1918,[73] but there may have been others too, whose records have failed to survive to the present day.

In any event, what is clear is that none of the lost species of Seychelles giant tortoise has been resurrected after all. However, the *G. arnoldi* saga raises the tantalising possibility that there may just be one or two very old specimens of giant tortoise somewhere in the world that really do constitute surviving representatives of this archipelago's former range of chelonians – but how could such specimens be conclusively unmasked? Where shell shape analysis has failed in the past, DNA hybridisation studies may succeed in the future.

Linophryne arborifera *anglerfish*

FISHES

Coelacanths, Megamouths and More

I stood as if stricken to stone. Yes, there was not a shadow of doubt, scale by scale, bone by bone, fin by fin, it was a true Coelacanth. It could have been one of those creatures of 200 million years ago come alive again. I forgot everything else and just looked, and then almost fearfully went close up and touched and stroked...it was true, it was unquestionably a Coelacanth. Not even I could doubt any more.

PROF. J.L.B. SMITH – OLD FOURLEGS: THE STORY OF THE COELACANTH

The discovery of megamouth does one thing. It reaffirms science's suspicion that there are still all kinds of things – very large things – living in our oceans that we still don't know about. And that's very exciting.

DR LEIGHTON R. TAYLOR – WAIKIKI BEACH PRESS

The lobe-finned coelacanth resurrecting its lineage from millions of years of supposed extinction, and the megamouth, adding an entirely new family to the world catalogue of modern-day sharks, are certainly the most celebrated ichthyological finds of the 20th century, but they are very far from being the only notable such finds since 1900. Others include: the formal recognition of the Siamese fighting fish as a species in its own right, and the discovery of another species so pugnacious that it was named after a famous boxer; a spookfish with six eyes, and an eyeless catfish called *Satan;* a fish with fur, and a fish with teeth on top of its head; the first deepwater stingray, and a land-living catfish that actually dislikes water; the world's largest species of freshwater fish, and one of the world's most popular species of tropical aquarium fish; plus the identification of a goblin unicorn from the deep, the rediscovery of a lost species in a sulphur-polluted cattle trough, the finding of a living fish-trap with built-in illumination on the sea bottom, and the enigma of Denmark's bottled sea serpent.

Goblin shark – a nightmarish unicorn from the ocean depths

The beginning of the 20th century was a time of great excitement in ichthyological circles – due to the debut of one of the most grotesque fishes ever seen by man. Up to 14 ft long and generally living at depths of about 1500 ft (but occasionally also in more shallow localities, such as Tokyo's Sagami Bay), the aptly-named goblin shark was first found in Japanese waters, but would not look out of place in a painting by Salvador Dali or Hieronymus Bosch. Its fairly slender, grey-pink body is rather nondescript, bearing two rounded dorsal fins, a pair of similarly-rounded pectorals, plus a pair of larger, straight-edged pelvics, and a single anal fin just in front of the tail. In contrast, the tail fin is very odd, with a long but extremely low ventral half, and little more than a terminal bob for the dorsal half. Most bizarre of all, however, is its head.[1-2]

Extending forward from the top of the head like a fixed, horizontally-held spear is a long, shovel-shaped horn, which overhangs the fish's jaws and provides this surrealistic shark with a disturbingly menacing, malevolent expression. Interestingly, its peculiar protuberance is totally separate from its mouth; by comparison, the 'sword' of swordfishes and marlins, the 'saw' of sawfishes and sawsharks, and the corresponding structures of other fishes similarly endowed all take the form of a greatly enlarged upper jaw. As for its mouth, this is rather odd too – terminally-sited (in most sharks it is placed ventrally), highly protrusible (it is fixed in other sharks), and crammed with diagnostically-shaped teeth that occupy a central role in this species' curious history.[1-2]

During the mid-19th century, fossil shark teeth of a distinctive, thorn-like shape with smooth edges were found in Lower Cretaceous rocks (i.e. dating back 140 million years) in several widely separated localities, including Syria, New Zealand, England and India. They did not correspond with any living shark known at that time –

Rare photo of a preserved goblin shark, whose identity as a genuine living fossil was revealed at the onset of the 20th century.

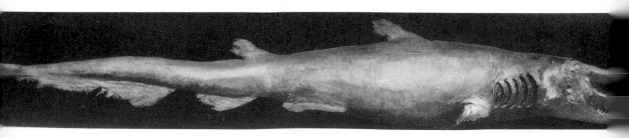

nor did their owner, a remarkable creature bearing a long, horizontal, shovel-like projection on its forehead. This strange shark was thus deemed to be a once widely-distributed species that had ultimately died out entirely, leaving no modern-day descendant. In 1889, this seemingly defunct experiment in shark evolution was formally named *Scapanorhynchus* ('shovel-beak'), and was afterwards largely forgotten – until its astonishing resurrection in 1897.[1-2]

This was when some Japanese fishermen, working in deep waters near Yokohama, hauled up an extraordinary-looking shark – the very first goblin shark ever recorded by science – whose weird, nightmarish appearance instantly distinguished it from all other modern-day species of known fish. Fortunately, after having been rescued by Yokohama-based naturalist Alan Owston, it came to the attention of Japanese ichthyologist Prof. Kakichi Mitsukari. After examining it, Mitsukari was so impressed by its form that in 1898 he transported it personally to the U.S.A., where it was studied by Leland Stamford University researcher Dr David Storr Jordan, an internationally-renowned expert on Japanese fishes. Later that year, Jordan officially described Mitsukari's mystery shark, and in honour of the two men who had brought it to scientific attention, he named it *Mitsukarina owstoni*.[1-2]

The advent of the 20th century witnessed Jordan's paper attracting very appreciable zoological attention worldwide. Yet whereas students of present-day fishes were primarily intrigued with the goblin shark's most readily visible morphological attributes, palaeontologists were becoming equally interested in certain less conspicuous features – namely, its teeth. They had recognised that these were identical in form to those of the supposedly long-extinct shark genus *Scapanorhynchus*.[1-2]

Accordingly, the newly-discovered, modern-day goblin shark was rechristened *Scapanorhynchus owstoni*, but nowadays it is considered to be sufficiently different from its fossil counterpart to require its own genus, so that '*Mitsukarina*' has been restored to use.

Sadly, despite its unique appearance and history the goblin shark is almost as mysterious today as when first brought to science's attention nearly a century ago. Even the function of its characteristic shovel-horn is unknown. However, some researchers have suggested that this species is a sea-bottom feeder, so perhaps it uses its shovel to stir up the sea-bottom's ooze and sediment in order to dislodge the creatures living there, which it can then engulf within its extensible jaws. Its distribution range is also uncertain; specimens have been caught off Japan, South Africa, and possibly Portugal.[1-2]

Thanks once again to its unmistakable teeth, there is also now evidence to indicate its presence in the Indian Ocean.[1-2] At a depth of 4500 feet a submarine cable unexpectedly malfunctioned, so it was brought back to the surface for examination. This revealed the presence of a broken shark's tooth embedded between the cable's strands of wire – implying that a shark had been feeding on organisms that had settled upon the wire. As for the tooth itself, its smooth-edged, thorn-shaped form was immediately recognisable – it was the tooth of a goblin shark. As with everything else associated with this creature, a significant new piece of information concerning it had been obtained by accident.[2]

Macristium chavesi and other infants incognito

In 1903, an extremely strange fish, caught severely injured off the Azores, was described by British Museum ichthyologist

C. Tate Regan, and the hitherto unknown species that it seemed to represent was dubbed *Macristium chavesi*.[3] Totally unlike anything ever recorded before, it eventually found itself housed within a completely new taxonomic order – Ctenothrissiformes – as the only modern-day member amongst a series of fossil species.

Measuring 11 cm (about 4.5 in) from head to tail base, its slender body was grey in colour and somewhat herring-like in overall shape, but was laterally flattened and scaleless. Its most striking features, however, were its very large, prolonged body fins. The dorsal fin, for example, had a very broad base, occupying almost half the length of the fish's back, and contained several extremely long rays. The pectoral fins were also long, and just behind these were the very elongate pelvic fins, which extended back towards the tail fin. Also present was a single, median anal fin, containing 12 rays and positioned just behind and beneath the rear end of the dorsal fin (but on the fish's undersurface).[3-5]

The head of *Macristium* was rather small, and it only had a weak dentition, comprising a set of small sharp teeth on its lower jaw and tongue, as well as on a nasal-related bone termed the vomer, but its diet was unknown. In fact, apart from its deepsea origin, nothing whatsoever was on record concerning this strange species.[3-5] Even its type specimen remained unique for several decades – no other specimen was recorded until 1961, this time from the Bay of Biscay. Obtained by N.B. Marshall, it only measured 3.3 cm (less than 1.5 in), and appeared to be a younger individual than Regan's specimen.[3-5]

In 1967, Drs F.H. Berry and C.R. Robins described a second modern-day member of this order, a short-finned species that they named *Macristiella perlucens*, based upon a young specimen procured in the Gulf of Mexico.[5] By now, the long-neglected ctenothrissids, living and fossil, were engaging the interest of several ichthyologists; but from their studies (especially those of Dr D.E. Rosen), evidence emerged that the *Macristium* and *Macristiella* specimens were nothing more than immature individuals of some already-known deepsea fishes (genus *Bathysaurus*), rather than separate species in their own right. Although still controversial to some extent, this identification is nowadays accepted by many experts, and Ctenothrissiformes is looked upon as a wholly extinct order, its former modern-day representatives demoted to incongruous infants.[5]

Also likely to be an infant incognito is *Korsogaster nanus,* a peculiar fish whose body is covered with small prickles instead of scales. The sole member of its family, it is currently known only from two specimens. Its type was caught near the Bahamas on 26 February 1927, and a second was captured in the central equatorial Pacific by the Scripps Institution of Oceanography's 'Styx' expedition in August 1968. Researchers now believe that these are merely juveniles of a fish known, somewhat unappealingly, as a slimehead (genus *Hoplostethus*), which is related to the squirrelfishes.[6] And *Rosaura rotunda*, a tiny 8.4-mm-long fish known only from its type specimen, caught in the Atlantic off northeastern Brazil during the 'Rosaura' expedition and described in 1954, is now thought by some to be an aberrant immature giganturid. These are grotesque deepsea fishes with huge bulging eyes, distantly related to salmon.[7]

Pugnacious pisceans – the Siamese fighting fish

Notorious for the aggressive behaviour of males in close proximity to one another, the fighting fishes (genus *Betta* – translating as 'warrior') are among the most familiar stars of tropical freshwater aquaria, which makes it all the more ironic that their most famous representative was among the very last to be recognised by science.

The first to attract ichthyological attention were the Sumatran fighting fish *B. brederi*, the Javan *B. picta*, and the Malayan *B. pugnax*, all of which had been described by the mid-1800s. A somewhat rarer species, *B. bellica*, had also been described by the 19th century's close, but it was not until 1909, following C. Tate Regan's studies of these flamboyant fishes, that another three species were distinguished. Two of those, the banded fighting fish *B. fasciata* (another rare form) and the Bornean *B. taeniata*, received little attention afterwards. The third, conversely, was not only one of its country's most well-known animals, but had already gained fame among European aquarists too – and all long before its separate specific status had been recognised by science. For this species, which gained from Regan the formal name *Betta splendens,* was none other than the Siamese fighting fish.[4,8]

Introduced into France as early as 1893, followed three years later by its German debut, Thailand's *B. splendens* is undoubtedly the most beautiful of all fighting fishes, and occurs in a varied range of vivid colours in the wild state, with northern males tending towards greenish hues and southern males exhibiting the brilliant red shades that are so popular in aquaria. Additionally, careful selective breeding has created an even greater spectrum of colours, including deep blues and mauves, as well as spectacularly transforming the wild strain's short dorsal and anal fins into greatly enlarged, diaphanous veils that recall the

An early example of an aquarium-bred variety of the Siamese fighting fish.

ostentatiously-elaborate sleeves and lace cuffs of the Victorian dandy.[4]

Based upon outward appearances, therefore, the male Siamese fighting fish may seem to have been emasculated, rendered harmless – but this illusion can be quickly dispelled. All that we need do is place a mirror inside a tank containing one of these piscean popinjays and the fop instantly becomes the fighter. It opens its mouth and gill covers wide, and spreads its fins as far apart as possible as it prepares to do battle with the equally formidable, belligerent rival that in reality is nothing more than its own reflection.[4]

And a fish called Jack Dempsey

In the same year that he unmasked the Siamese fighting fish, C. Tate Regan[9] also described another pugnacious species nowadays very popular in aquaria – a species that could very accurately be referred to as an Amazonian boxing fish. Indeed, so close are this species' behavioural links with the much-revered sport of pugilism that it was soon named after a

Jack Dempsey – a pugilistic cichlid appropriately named after a famous boxer.

famous world heavyweight boxing champion – Jack Dempsey.

Scientifically christened *Cichlasoma biocellatum*, the Jack Dempsey is a tropical freshwater cichlid from South America's Amazon and Rio Negro, and when adult, it is an outstandingly beautiful fish, whose dark flanks, fins, and tail bear an iridescent mosaic of brilliant green spots. Almost nothing is known of its habits or lifestyle, however, except for its famous territorial behaviour, readily observed in aquaria. If one male enters the territory of another during the breeding season, the two circle one another and raise their fins to make themselves appear bigger and more ferocious. If neither fish gives ground then they begin to 'spar', by butting each other with their jaws in a manner that has all the appearance of a genuine boxing match. Nonetheless, it is a largely ritualistic 'bout', as serious injuries are rarely inflicted upon one another, and usually ends with the territory's owner chasing away the invader – rather than with a straight knockout.[4]

Tsuranagakobitozame – Japan's diminutive shark with the long face

In 1912, the world's smallest species of shark was described – a cigar-shaped pygmy known as the spiny-finned dwarf shark *Squaliolus laticaudus,* and referred to by the Japanese as *tsuranagakobitozame* – 'dwarf shark with long face'. Its type specimen, a slender, mouse-sized male measuring a mere 5.75 in, was caught along with a comparably-sized female on 8 June 1908, at a depth of around 600 ft in Batangas Bay, Luzon (one of the principal islands of the Philippines). Inky black with white fins, for the next 49 years these remained the only known specimens of this Lilliputian shark on record – until 2 June 1961, when some Japanese fishermen caught five more, in Honshu's Suruga Bay.[2,10]

Gregoryina and *Indostomus* – fishes that defy classification

We owe our entire knowledge (such that it is) of an extraordinary little fish called *Gregoryina gygis* to the fortuitous find of a Hawaiian seabird. In 1923, the Pacific islands west of Hawaii were visited by the Tanager Expedition, and during their voyage its scientists landed on Laysan, one of the Hawaiian Islands' northwestern members. There they encountered the nest of a white tern that contained a small but most unusual fish, which the bird had recently captured to eat. Measuring just 2 in long, with a small mouth, a keeled undersurface, and a very distinctive complement of rays and spines in its dorsal and anal fins, this fish was wholly different from any species recorded by science, and became the type specimen of *Gregoryina gygas*, formally described the following year. No other specimen has ever been obtained to shed additional light on this mysterious species – so mysterious, in fact, that many ichthyologists place it within an entire family of its own, most closely allied to the flagfishes and morwongs.[11-12]

Perhaps it is time to seek out some more terns' nests.

Even more problematical, however, is *Indostomus paradoxus*, discovered in 1926. The first specimens were caught in Lake Indawgyi, a shallow expanse of water in Upper Burma's Myitkyina District, but 30 years later some were also recorded from a stream running to the lake from neighbouring Thailand. A relatively inactive creature and only 3 cm (just over 1 in) long, with a very slender, spindle-shaped body, and the unusual ability (for a fish) to move its head up and down, this species has often been outwardly likened to a composite of pipefish (syngnathid) and stickleback. Certainly its large tail fin, overall shape of head, and the external plates encircling its body are reminiscent of the former type of fish, whereas its general body shape and the series of isolated spines running along its back are characteristic of the latter. Due to its mixed morphology, fish taxonomists have proposed many different classifications for *Indostomus*, aligning it variously with sticklebacks, pipefishes, and, most recently, the cling fishes (gobiescoids).[11,13]

Anatomically, however, it possesses a number of features peculiar to itself, including a near-absence of muscles in its posterior body region (even the tail fin is operated by a collection of extra-long tendons originating in the body's anterior half), and a lower jaw whose total length is twenty times that of the upper one, stretching back a considerable distance along the fish's underside. Due to its unique overall anatomy, in 1970 Dr K.E. Banister placed *Indostomus* in its very own taxonomic order – Indostomiformes – a classification still adhered to, for the sake of convenience if nothing else, while its precise relationship to other fishes remains a subject open to speculation.[11,13]

Pa beuk – the world's largest freshwater fish

Also called the Mekong giant catfish and the pla buk, and inhabiting the Mekong River's deep waters (flowing through Laos, Thailand, Cambodia, Vietnam, and China), the pa beuk is currently deemed to be the largest species of fish that spends its entire life in freshwater. Surprisingly, it was not described until 1930, whereupon it was formally named *Pangasianodon gigas*. Up to 8 ft long, its huge size sets it well apart from other catfishes, but so too does its diet – whereas the great majority of catfishes are carnivorous, *P. gigas* is exclusively vegetarian (indeed, older specimens are often totally toothless). Unhappily, this impressive creature is nowadays an endangered species, because for many years it has been caught in great numbers during the rainy season, when it migrates upstream for spawning in China's Lake Tali.[4,14-15]

Bathysphaera – an 'untouchable' deepsea riddle

One of this century's most mysterious ichthyological discoveries is a remarkable deepsea fish that was officially described and named in 1932, yet which has never been examined in the flesh and has no representative in any of the world's museums.[16]

On 22 November 1932, Bermuda-based zoologist Dr William Beebe was 2100 ft beneath the surface of the sea in a bathysphere, sited 5 miles southeast of Bermuda's Nonsuch Island. While he was observing the denizens of the deep passing by the bathysphere's windows, two very unusual fishes became illuminated in the craft's electric beam of light as they twice swam past it, no more than 8 ft away. Their

Pa beuk – despite being the world's largest freshwater fish, this enormous species of catfish remained undescribed by science until 1930.
(Neg. No. 121812/Courtesy Department Library Services, American Museum of Natural History)

long slender bodies, with strongly undershot jaws housing numerous teeth, reminded Beebe of barracudas, but running along either side of each fish was a single, laterally-sited, horizontal row of luminous organs (photophores), little short of twenty in total, every one emitting a powerful pale blue light.[16]

Equally striking were the two twitching, tentacle-like structures that hung down beneath each fish – one arising from its lower jaw, the other from the beginning of its short anal fin. Once again, each of these structures emitted light, by virtue of a pair of organs at its tip; the organ attached directly to the tentacle shone red, the other one (attached to the red organ) shone blue. Also noteworthy was their vertical dorsal fin, positioned well back towards the tail-

end of the body. Beebe was unable to discern any pectoral fins or pelvic fins.[16]

From these fishes' general morphology, Beebe concluded that their species was most probably allied to the melanostomiatids, popularly known as the scaleless black dragon fishes. However, its single line of lateral photophores, not to mention its pair of ventral tentacles with light-emitting terminal organs, unequivocally distinguished it from any known species within that family. As a result, Beebe christened his mystifying discovery *Bathysphaera intacta* ('untouchable bathysphere fish'), sole member of a new genus.[16]

Bathysphaera was not the only hitherto unknown species of deepsea fish that Beebe discovered and named, but was unable to capture, during his Bermudan bathysphere observations in the early 1930s. He also spied a mysterious, 2-ft-long, torpedo-shaped fish at depths of 1500 ft and 2500 ft, and named this grey-coloured species the pallid sailfin *Bathyembrix istiophasma*. He described the three-starred angler fish *Bathyceratias trilynchus,* a 6-in-long species sighted at 2470 ft, bearing three 'fishing rod' structures (illicia) on its head, and clearly allied to the deepsea angler fishes (ceratioids – see p. 188); and the five-lined constellation fish *Bathysidus pentagrammus,* spotted at a depth of 1900 ft and resembling a *Chaetodon* butterfly fish or an *Acanthurus* surgeon fish, but exquisitely decorated with five glowing lines of yellow and purple photophores on each side of its roundish body.[16]

Equally beautiful was a long-beaked multicoloured fish with scarlet head, blue body, and yellow tail that Beebe informally named the abyssal rainbow gar – four of which he observed swimming together in a stiff, almost upright posture at 2500 ft.[16]

No specimens of any of these 'untouchable' species have so far been obtained – as with *Bathysphaera,* they are secrets of the sea that were revealed to man only briefly before disappearing back into its depths.[16]

A trilogy of tetras

In 1936, just six years after the reappearance of the golden hamster (see *Mammals*), another future favourite of western pet-owners hit the headlines – by accident.

Canoeing in the Rio Putumayo, one of the Amazon's countless tributaries, A. Rabaut, a French animal collector, noticed a shoal of tiny but exquisitely-coloured fishes, swimming nearby, so he scooped up a handful to examine them more closely. Measuring just under 2 in long, each had a greyish back, colourless fins, and silver belly; the front half of each flank's lower

portion was also silvery, whereas the rear half of each was red. The feature that attracted most attention, however, was the horizontal iridescent stripe running backwards along each flank's upper portion, from just behind the fish's eye to a point a little in front of its tail's base, and separating its grey back from its silver-and-red lower flanks. This stripe continually flickered from brilliant blue to glittering green, according to the angle at which it was viewed, and closely resembled a fluorescent strip of neon lighting.[17]

The species represented by these beautiful little fishes was unknown to science, so Rabaut collected a selection of live specimens, which were passed on to Chicago's John G. Shield Aquarium. The species belonged to the characin family – comprising tiny, carp-like forms – and later in 1936 it was formally described. It was originally christened *Hyphessobrycon innesi,* in honour of William T. Innes, a leading American aquarist;[18] more recently, its generic name has been changed to *Paracheirodon.* Its English name, conversely, has remained the same, and is known to fish-fanciers worldwide – the neon tetra.[17]

It attracted so much attention in Chicago, with aquarists clamouring for specimens

Mexican cave fish – discovered in 1936, this blind tetra is probably more common nowadays in pet aquaria than in its native underground streams. (Dr Jürgen Schramme, courtesy of Dr Thomas Teyke)

and journalists praising it as the most beautiful aquarium fish known to man, that others were swiftly sought in its native Amazon homeland. One German collector brought back at least two thousand, captured at the mouth of the River Nanay just inside Peru, with the assistance of the Javaro Indians. Specimens were also again obtained from the Rio Putumayo.[17]

Unfortunately, the neon tetra initially proved very difficult to maintain and breed in captivity, but by the end of World War II, attempts were proving more successful, thanks to the discovery that soft, slightly acidic water at a temperature of up to 24°C and the presence of water plants in the tank were favoured by it for spawning. Nowadays, the neon tetra is more commonly bred and is one of the most widely available of all tropical freshwater fishes, known to every fish-lover from the lowliest schoolboy to the most learned ichthyologist.[17]

In 1956, a closely related species was discovered, adorned with a somewhat wider 'electric' stripe on each flank, and further distinguished from the neon tetra by its entirely red lower flanks. This species, first called *H. cardinalis* but later renamed *Cheirodon axelrodi* (after fish collector-discoverer Dr Harold Axelrod), is popularly known as the cardinal tetra, and was first found within forest pools in the Rio Negro's upper waters, but is also known from the Orinoco's tributaries. It too soon became extremely popular worldwide as an aquarium species.[19]

The same is true of the Mexican blind cave fish, a curious 3-in-long species discovered in 1936 and shortly afterwards named *Anoptichthys jordani* ('Jordan's eyeless fish'), in honour of its finder, Basil Jordan, who recorded it from Mexico's Cueva Chica. Although related to the neon

tetra, *A. jordani* is radically different from it in appearance, thanks to certain morphological specialisations symptomatic of a cave-dwelling (spelaeic) existence.[20]

As it is never exposed to sunlight and therefore has no need of body pigmentation to protect it from ultraviolet radiation, *A. jordani* has none. Thus its body is translucent, with the red colour of its blood, coursing through the vessels beneath its skin's surface, affording it a pale pink hue. And as it never encounters light, it does not need eyes either; hence they are covered by a layer of skin. Nevertheless, it is still capable of detecting short wavelengths in the visible spectrum (i.e. violet, indigo, and blue light), so it is not totally blind.[20-1]

Although its unpigmented body seems similar to those of freak albino specimens of fishes, the Mexican blind cave fish is not incapable of producing pigment. Individuals kept in aquaria exposed to sunlight will gradually darken. Hence its normal lack of pigmentation is not an irreversible, genetically-induced phenomenon like that of genuine albinos, but is merely an environmentally-determined feature capable of reversion under correct conditions.[21]

In recent years, its scientific name has changed from *A. jordani* to *Astyanax hubbsi*. Due to its strange, somewhat eerie appearance, this species has become very popular among fish fanciers, especially in America, to the extent that today there are probably more specimens in pet aquaria than in its native Mexican cave streams.[21]

Normanichthys – a scaly scaleless fish

The bullheads and sculpins comprise a mostly marine family (Cottidae) housing a diverse range of species, but all were traditionally united by at least one important characteristic – they were all scaleless. In 1937, however, this orderly classification was disrupted with the description of *Normanichthys crockeri,* native to fairly shallow waters off the coasts of Chile, and discovered during the Templeton-Crocker Expedition of 1934-35. Measuring 4.5 in long, although it seems to be most closely allied to the bullheads and sculpins, it is set apart from all of them by its shining array of scales, covering not only its entire body but much of its head too. Equally distinctive is the many-spined composition of its first dorsal fin (it has two). Due to these discrepancies from the basic cottid configuration, *Normanichthys* was placed in a family of its own, of which it remains the only member.[22]

'Old Fourlegs' – the incredible coelacanth (Part 1)

If the okapi constitutes the most significant new species of terrestrial animal to be discovered this century, then its aquatic counterpart must surely be the coelacanth.

Towards mid-day on 22 December 1938, Marjorie Courtenay-Latimer, the curator of the then small and little-known East London Museum at South Africa's southernmost tip, received a phone call from the manager of a local commercial fishing company called Irwin and Johnson, informing her that their trawler *Nerine* had brought in a pile of fishes that she might like to examine. This was nothing new – anxious to acquire specimens of local wildlife for the museum, Miss Courtenay-Latimer had encouraged everyone connected in some way with wildlife to contact her if any specimens came to hand that might be of importance to the museum. As a result, Irwin and Johnson had permitted Captain Hendrik Goosen, skipper

of the *Nerine,* to collect fishes for the museum during trawling excursions, and had informed her on many previous occasions of the arrival of fishes, which she had always inspected for anything suitable for exhibition and preservation at the museum. So, although this latest phone call was most welcome, she did not attach any significance to it, and simply made her way to the wharf with an assistant to examine the fishes, just as she had done so many times before. Little did she realise, it was probably the most important phone call that she would ever receive in the whole of her life.[23-4]

When she arrived at the wharf and saw the pile of fishes waiting for her, she recognised that they were principally sharks – but then she noticed something very different, almost hidden beneath them. Upon her request, the fish that she had spotted was disentangled from the others and stretched out for her to observe it properly. It was the most extraordinary specimen that she had ever seen, and although she was not a trained ichthyologist she realised straight away that this could well be something important. Mauve-blue in colour, faintly flecked with white spots, it was 5 ft long, weighed 127 lb, and had thick bony scales that gave it an armour-plated appearance; but what particularly attracted her attention was its set of very remarkable fins. It possessed quite a number – two separate dorsal fins, a pair of pectorals and a pair of pelvics, a single anal, and a unique type of tail fin.[23-4]

Like the body fins of most other modern-day fishes, the first dorsal fin was borne directly upon the fish's body, and contained rays that arose from the very base of the fin, thereby yielding a fan-like structure. Conversely, each of its remaining body fins was borne upon a muscular lobe (surrounding a complex skeleton), from which the rays arose, and which gave these fins the appearance of stumpy legs.[23-4]

If its body fins were remarkable, this curious creature's tail fin was even more so. In most fishes, the backbone ends at the base of the tail fin, which in turn comprises two distinct lobes – the upper one directed upwards and backwards, the lower one directed downwards and backwards. In contrast, the tail fin of Courtenay-Latimer's fish was pointed, with the fish's backbone running right through it into its very tip, thereby completely separating the fin's upper lobe from its lower one. This compares with the structure of the tail fin in eels and lungfishes – but unlike theirs (and indeed, unlike that of any other modern-day fish known to science), the tail fin of Courtenay-Latimer's fish had a third lobe, sandwiched between its upper and lower lobes, and arising from the very tip of its backbone, thus yielding a tripartite or three-lobed tail.[23-5] Also of note was this fish's excessive oiliness – later found to be caused by a layer of oil-secreting cells below the surface of its skin.[24]

Courtenay-Latimer learnt that this strange creature had been caught at the mouth of the River Chalumna, and that it had snapped at Captain Goosen's hand when it had been hauled aboard. None of the men had ever seen a fish like it before, even though some had been fishing there for the past 30 years.[23-5]

Naturally, she was acutely aware of the importance of preserving this unique specimen for formal identification by a fish specialist, so with the help of her assistant and a very reluctant taxi driver (who needed a lot of persuading before finally agreeing to transport a large, oil-secreting fish), she succeeded in bringing it back to the museum, where she made arrangements for its body to be prepared by a local taxidermist, requesting him to retain all of the soft parts that he would be removing during its preparation.[23-5]

The next day, she wrote to a longstanding correspondent, Prof. J.L.B. Smith – a world-renowned ichthyological researcher at Rhodes University College in Grahamstown. She enclosed with her letter a sketch of the fish, noting its salient features, sizes of fins,

Coelacanth – discovered in 1938, this lobe-finned fish resurrected an ancient lineage of fishes hitherto believed to have died out 64 million years ago.

body, etc, and enquired whether he could offer her any opinion regarding its likely identity.[23-5]

She posted her letter later that day – but due to ill-health, Prof. Smith had left the university a few days earlier to recuperate at home over the Christmas holiday period. Consequently, coupling the time required for rerouting his post to his home with the inevitable Christmas postal delays, he did not receive her letter until 3 January.[23-5]

He opened it, read her note, looked at her sketch of the fish – and then suddenly:[24]

...a bomb seemed to burst in my brain, and beyond that sketch and the paper of the letter I was looking at a series of fishy creatures...fishes no longer here, fishes that had lived in dim past ages gone, and of which only often fragmentary remains in rock are known.

Almost reeling with incredulity, Prof. Smith had recognised the significance of the fish's combination of extraordinary features – its thick, armour-like scales, limb-like lobed fins, and tri-lobed tail. Although no previously recorded modern-day fish shared them, these features belonged to certain fishes of the distant past – a peculiar group belonging to the extinct order Crossopterygii – known as coelacanths. These fishes had flourished 200 million years ago, but were supposedly long extinct; the most recent fossils were more than 60 million years old. Yet here in his hand was a sketch of a modern-day fish, captured alive only a couple of weeks earlier, that compared precisely with these long-deceased creatures – creatures that had been contemporary with the dinosaurs. Somehow – inconceivably – a living coelacanth had been caught.[23-4]

To cut a long and intricate story short: although university commitments prevented him from examining the fish immediately, by 16 February Smith had arrived at the East London Museum and finally, allaying weeks of fear and doubt regarding the identity of Courtenay-Latimer's astounding specimen, he saw with his own eyes the coelacanth – for that is indeed what it was. In his book *Old Fourlegs* (the title referring to the coelacanth's limb-like pectoral and pelvic fins), Smith describes how, despite mental preparation beforehand, the sight of a creature lying before him that science had firmly believed to be as deceased as the dinosaurs, plesiosaurs, pterosaurs (and so many other celebrities of the prehistoric world) physically immobilised him, rendering all other thoughts and speech momentarily impossible. Not until he hesitantly touched it, to convince himself that it was real and not illusion, was the spell broken. It really was there, and it really was a coelacanth.[24-5] But what was to be done now?

First and foremost, a formal description of the new species that this specimen represented was needed – for although it was unmistakably a coelacanth, more than 60 million years of evolution (taking place after the date from which the most recent fossil forms were known) had produced a modern-day species with various prominent differences from its long-extinct ancestors. To produce such a description, it is best to have available as complete a specimen as possible – but this requirement caused considerable problems for Smith. In between Courtenay-Latimer sending her letter and Smith's receipt of it, the fish's precious soft parts (removed by the taxidermist during its preservation as a museum exhibit) had deteriorated to such an extent that they had been discarded.[24-5]

Nevertheless, the specimen was still of such tremendous value, with so many features still present that readily confirmed its identity as a 20th century coelacanth, that the publication of an official description of its species was fully warranted. On 18 March and 6 May 1939, preliminary notes introducing the coelacanth's discovery, and containing some brief notes regarding its morphology plus a photograph of it as a taxiderm specimen, were published in the British scientific journal *Nature*.[26] A longer account devoted to its morphological characteristics appeared in the Royal Society of South Africa's *Transactions*.[26-7]

The modern-day coelacanth was acknowledged throughout the world as one of the greatest zoological finds ever made. Thus, in recognition of its provenance and, especially, the person who made its discovery possible, Smith named its species *Latimeria chalumnae*. Marjorie Courtenay-Latimer was thereby granted ichthyological immortality by an anachronistic anomaly that was very nearly lost to the world beneath a pile of scuppered sharks.[26-7]

Now that one *Latimeria* specimen was on record, Smith was keen to seek more, so that the species' internal structure could finally be recorded. But how would he obtain another coelacanth? He decided to advertise for one – by printing thousands of leaflets illustrating the coelacanth, offering a reward of £100 for the first two specimens obtained, and giving firm instructions to the finders of such fishes not to clean or cut them in any way.[24]

The leaflets were distributed *en masse* throughout southeast Africa, and to ensure that language did not pose any problem every copy carried Smith's message in Portugese, English, and French. Nevertheless, as will be revealed on p. 190, it took almost 14 years for Smith's advertisement to receive a possible answer, and when it did come it was from a wholly unexpected locality with an even stranger specimen as its subject.[24]

A catfish called *Satan*

The year 1947 saw the official description of one of the world's most extraordinary catfishes, the wide-mouthed blindcat. Its story began in 1938, when biologist Dr Carl L. Hubbs was visiting the Withe Memorial Museum at San Antonio, Texas, during a zoological collecting trip to the area. At the museum, its director, Ellen S. Quillin, made available to him for study a most peculiar catfish specimen. An immature male measuring 68.7 mm (just under 3 in) long, it had been collected from an Artesian well 1250 ft deep, in the Edwards Plateau region near San Antonio, and had been donated to the museum by William Kempin.[28]

A long thin fish with a flattened head, it had no pigmentation, its ghostly white colouration relieved only by the pale pink tinge of blood vessels beneath its skin. Moreover, it was eyeless, and its nasal apertures were extremely reduced. In contrast, its mouth was notably large and wide, its body bore an extremely prominent adipose fin, and its lateral-line sensory system (for detecting water currents) was very distinct and highly developed.[28]

Hubbs and ichthyologist R.M. Bailey made a detailed study of this unique specimen, which represented a radically new species of ameiurid freshwater catfish highly specialised for life in pitch-dark underground streams. And in their paper of 28 April 1947, introducing the wide-mouthed blindcat to the scientific world, Hubbs and Bailey provided it with a distinctive scientific name to match its uncommon appearance and lifestyle. Its broad mouth earned it the specific name *eurystomus* ('wide-mouthed'), and its lifestyle as a piscean prince of darkness was the inspiration for its somewhat startling generic name – *Satan*.[28]

Smith's blind white fishes in Persia

Qanats are underground water channels that criss-cross Iran (formerly Persia), and in 1949 a zoology undergraduate at Oxford University called Anthony Smith read in a travel book that these channels supposedly contain blind white fishes that are good to eat. Smith was very intrigued by this, because at that time not a single species of blind subterranean fish had been scientifically documented anywhere in Eurasia.[29]

Eager to discover the identity of this mysterious qanat-contained curiosity, Smith organised a four-man expedition to southern Iran, setting off in June 1950 and returning home to England in October. During their visit, they saw many interesting sights – enabling Smith to write an entire book based upon their experiences. Published in 1953, it became a bestseller, and was entitled *Blind White Fish in Persia* – which was a little ironic, because despite being the principal inspiration for the expedition this unidentified species was the one important item that they did not succeed in seeing while there.[29]

Even more ironic, however, was the news that they had received not long after their return home from Iran. A newly-published paper by Danish ichthyologists Drs Anton Bruun (of *Dana* and *Galathea* fame) and E.W. Kaiser revealed that Iran's blind white fish was not unknown to science. On the contrary, it had been discovered in 1937, within the Zagros Mountains' Ab-i-Serum valley, and was actually a sightless pink species of carp, which Bruun and Kaiser formally described in their paper, naming it *Iranocypris typhlops*.[29-30]

Nevertheless, Smith's expedition was still able to make a valuable contribution, thanks to his book. Following its publication, he received a letter from an amateur pot-holer called A.G. Widdowson, working in Iraq. Widdowson had recently captured some blind white fishes in a 300-ft-deep pot-hole at Haditha, and, having read Smith's book, decided to contact him in case this information was of interest (the fishes themselves had died shortly after capture). Smith forwarded Widdowson's letter to the British Museum (Natural History), who requested Widdowson to send on any further specimens that he obtained. Not long afterwards, a number of specimens were duly delivered to the museum, and they were found to represent another new species, which was christened *Typhlogarra widdowsoni*.[29-30]

In 1976, the third episode in this long-running saga of subterranean fishes took place, when Smith visited Ab-i-Serum, the type locality of *Iranocypris*, and succeeded in procuring three specimens. One of these was donated to a helpful assistant, but Smith retained the other two, which he transported alive back to England, taking them shortly afterwards to the British Museum. There he received a great surprise. After examining them, the ichthyologist Dr P. Humphrey Greenwood informed him that whereas one was certainly an *Iranocypris*, the other was a totally different species – one that was undescribed by science. It was a cave-dwelling loach – the first such loach recorded anywhere in the world – and was officially dubbed *Noemacheilus smithi*, a much-deserved honour for the zoologist who had been so unlucky in his previous attempt to discover a new species.[29,31]

Several other species of cave fish have since been discovered in the Middle East;

and in 1978 a second species of cave loach was found, but this time in the Far East, when eight specimens were captured at Bajianjing, near Qiafang, Gejiu, in China's Yunnan Province and dubbed *N. gejiuensis*. Lacking eyes (even its eye sockets were vestigial) and body pigmentation, it was closely related to Smith's Iranian cave loach, but differed from it via its shorter body, and absence of a deep adipose ridge between its dorsal and tail fins.[32]

Galatheathauma and company – fishes that go fishing

For two very different reasons, the ceratioids or deepsea angler fishes inhabiting the ocean's inky-black abyssal depths are among the most bizarre fishes known to science.

Firstly: the female of many of these species possesses an extraordinary structure called the illicium – the highly-modified first ray of the dorsal fin, which has parted company with the remainder of the fin and is now sited on top of the fish's head (or thereabouts). A long pole-like apparatus, it resembles a human angler's fishing rod, and serves precisely the same purpose. Just as the angler attaches bait to the end of his rod, so at the end of the ceratioid's illicium is a luminous organ called the esca that the fish uses as a lure, tempting potential prey to swim within range of its cavernous jaws.[4,11]

Secondly: the male ceratioid is a radically stunted, morphologically reduced form, a veritable dwarf that actually parasitises the much larger, fully-formed female of its species, clamping itself to her body with its pincer-like jaws. In some species, moreover, it remains permanently attached to her, becoming so intimately united that its circulatory system fuses with hers, enabling it to derive all of its own nutrients directly from her bloodstream in an physiological parallel to the placenta-mediated association between a foetus and its mother. In such cases, the male's only function appears to be the fertilisation of the female's eggs; in many ways it can be looked upon as simply an organ of the female – which in turn can therefore be thought of as a functional hermaphrodite.[4,11]

The ceratioids come in a diverse range of grotesque forms, and some were first discovered long before the 20th century. Of particular interest, however, is that the most extraordinary and extreme examples (and hence the very ones that are most frequently illustrated in books) remained unknown to science until more recent times. During the 1920s, for example, the oceanographic explorations of Danish research vessel *Dana* obtained many new ceratioids. In 1925 alone, British Museum ichthyologist C. Tate Regan described 8 new genera and 24 new species, which included *Lasiognathus saccostoma* and *Linophryne arborifera* – two of the most celebrated species so far recorded.[33]

Lasiognathus saccostoma (the only member of its genus) was described from a single 3-in-long female obtained in the Caribbean, which remained its only specimen until 1962, when two more were procured, this time from Madeira (they were initially classed as a new, separate species, which was dubbed *L. ancistrophorus*). A black, dorsoventrally flattened species with bizarre facial flaps that greatly extend its upper jaws laterally, so that its upper teeth point outwards rather than downwards, *Lasiognathus* possesses the most elaborate illicium currently documented from any ceratioid. Borne upon an extremely long and mobile basal bone (four-fifths of the fish's entire length), it carries at its tip a luminous esca, which in turn bears three

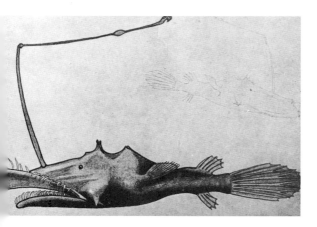

Lasiognathus saccostoma *anglerfish – its type specimen was described in 1929, and remained its only specimen until 1962.*

sophisticated ceratioid presently on record was not revealed until the early 1950s.

On 15 October 1950, the Danish oceanographic research vessel *Galathea* began a major exploration of the oceans' deepwater trenches, during which it discovered some major new species. One of these was hauled up from the sea bottom off Central America's western coast on 6 May 1952, at a depth of over 11,500 ft, and proved ·to be an 18.5-in-long female ceratioid (relatively large for this suborder of fishes), black in colour with a broad head and a huge mouth, whose upper jaw was fringed with curved, pointed teeth. It clearly represented a hitherto unknown species, but regrettably it seemed to be a damaged specimen because it lacked the ceratioids' diagnostic feature – an illicium. It was initially presumed that the delicate structure had been torn off during the fish's capture and subsequent haul to the surface. However, an examination of its mouth exposed the creature's astonishing secret.[34-6]

It was not damaged at all; it was merely different – very different. Instead of hovering in midwater, seeking to coax prey within range of its mouth via a fishing rod with a luminous lure on the end, this new species had taken the ceratioid concept one notable step further. The luminous lure, forked in shape, was actually present inside its mouth, suspended from the roof just behind its upper jaw's 'comb' of teeth. All that this fish needed to do, therefore, was to remain stationary on the sea bottom with its jaws agape, knowing that its lure would entice unsuspecting prey to swim directly into its mouth.[34-6]

In 1953, the *Galathea's* leader, Dr Anton Bruun, named this remarkable species

hooks at the end of a long line. Thus equipped with an effective fishing rod, line, float, lighted bait, and hooks, it is little wonder that *Lasiognathus* has been hailed as 'the compleat angler'.[4,11,33-4]

Black in colour with a stout, rounded body (and renamed *Linophryne brevibarbata* in 1932 by William Beebe, but this name is rarely used), *Linophryne arborifera* has a much shorter, less imposing illicium than *Lasiognathus,* which arises from its snout and is somewhat swollen in shape, with a luminous subdivided esca at its tip. Instead, what makes this species so spectacular in appearance is the intricately branched, tree-like barbel that hangs down from its chin. The purpose of this remarkable structure is currently uncertain. In some specimens it has been found to be faintly luminescent; thus it may act as an accessory lure. It may also detect water-borne movements of potential prey nearby. This species' type specimen was a 3-in-long female that was captured in the North Atlantic.[4,11,33-4]

As already noted (see p. 181), during his Bermudan bathysphere observations in the early 1930s, William Beebe sighted a still-uncaptured species of ceratioid that possesses three illicia; he named this exceptionally endowed fish *Bathyceratias trilynchus*.[16] However, the most

189

Galatheathauma axeli – commemorating its discovery by the *Galathea* expedition, and honouring the chairman of the expedition's committee, Prince Axel of Denmark.[36]

Other strange ceratioids may still await discovery – after all, *Galatheathauma* is itself known to science only from its type specimen, and we have yet to obtain any specimen of Beebe's *Bathyceratias*. At present, however, *Galatheathauma* remains the most fascinating species on record – a living fish-trap with built-in illumination, content to repose lazily upon the sea floor, emulating Lewis Carroll's famous little crocodile as it 'welcomes little fishes in with gently smiling jaws!'

'Old Fourlegs' – the incredible coelacanth (Part 2)

As documented on p. 183, the discovery off South Africa in December 1938 of *Latimeria chalumnae*, the only modern-day coelacanth species currently known to science, was not just an international sensation in zoological circles – it had also captured the imagination of the general public worldwide, so that everyone was clamouring for more news of this archaic fish that had risen like a phoenix from the ashes of the past.

No-one was more eager for news – and especially a new specimen – than the species' leading researcher, Prof. J.L.B. Smith, but the 1940s came and went, without bringing either. It seemed the inevitable doom of *Latimeria* to be known only from a single, incompletely-preserved representative.[24,37]

It was now December 1952, only two days away from the fourteenth anniversary of the first specimen's capture. Ahmed Hussein, a fisherman from Anjouan Island in the Grand Comoro archipelago northwest of Madagascar, had been fishing offshore from the southeastern Anjouan port of Comoni when he captured a very strange-looking fish of about 5 ft in length, hauled up from a relatively shallow depth of around 120 ft. At the time, he paid little attention to the fish's extremely odd appearance, and the next morning he took it to the local market to sell it, just as he did with all his catches. Destiny and good fortune evidently accompanied him, however, because, just before his fish was about to be cut up into small pieces, a fellow Anjouan pointed out that it very closely resembled the valuable fish depicted on some leaflets that had recently been distributed on the Comoro Islands.[24,37]

The leaflets were of course those of Prof. Smith, advertising his reward for the capture of a coelacanth, and as they requested anyone who caught such a fish to take it at once to someone responsible, who would know what to do with it, Hussein and a group of other men carried it some 25 miles to Smith's friend Captain Eric Hunt, who was based at the opposite end of Anjouan. Hunt had supervised the distribution of Smith's leaflets there, and he identified the fish immediately as a bona fide coelacanth. He instructed the natives to cut it only for preservation (by salting), which they did (albeit more enthusiastically than scientifically), after which he injected formalin into it, supplied by a local doctor. He then contacted Smith in South Africa with the news that his long-sought-after second coelacanth had finally surfaced, and was awaiting collection.[24,37]

Sadly, however, many obstacles prevented Smith from immediately travelling to take charge of the specimen that he so desperately needed, and he feared that the precious fish would rot in the Comoros' extremely hot climate before he could even see it, let alone study it.[24,37]

Happily, fate took a hand, in the shape of no less a personage than the prime minister of South Africa, Dr Daniel F. Malan, who recognised the extreme urgency of the situation and very generously loaned Smith a military aeroplane in which to fly directly to Anjouan. On 28 December, Smith landed on the island, Hunt lifted the shroud of cotton wool covering the specimen in its box, and revealed the armour-plated steely-blue fish with lobed fins that Smith knew only too well to be a coelacanth.[24,37]

Even though the heat of the Comoros' climate had induced from the fish a singularly powerful odour, Hunt's makeshift preservatives had functioned satisfactorily, so that the precious internal organs and tissues were available for study. As it happened, however, the specimen's external morphology was also of considerable interest – due to two features that instantly differentiated it from the first specimen.[24,37]

Whereas the first coelacanth had two dorsal fins, this second specimen only had one – the posterior, lobed version; the anterior dorsal fin, arising directly from the body of the first specimen (and possessing rays arranged in a fan-like manner) was absent. Also absent from the second coelacanth was the remarkable third lobe of the tail fin, positioned at the tip of the first specimen's backbone. As a result, Smith initially looked upon Specimen #2 as a representative of a second species of modern-day coelacanth, which he christened *Malania anjouanae*, acknowledging its provenance and the person who had been so instrumental in enabling him to reach it.[24,37]

Yet tragically, this tribute by Smith to Malan was short-lived, because his detailed examination of *Malania* convinced him that it was really nothing more than a deformed *Latimeria chalumnae*, and not a new species after all.

Nevertheless, that disappointment was more than tempered by this episode's crowning triumph – it had unveiled the coelacanth's true home, because during the next few years an impressive series of specimens was obtained off the Comoros. By contrast, no further example has ever been obtained or observed off South Africa's East London area, implying that the type specimen of *Latimeria* was a straggler, a wanderer far from its native home and, as such, an exceptionally lucky find (but see also p. 205). Also, as most of the later specimens have been captured in deep water, the relatively shallow depth at which the 'Malania' individual had been caught was again atypical for the species.[24,37]

Upon questioning the Comoro natives, Smith learnt that some of them knew the coelacanth well, referring to it as *kombessa*. No doubt with a mixture of incredulity and horror (in view of the professional awe that the coelacanth received from scientists worldwide), he also learnt that the tough scales of this species, which in the 1950s would have been priceless exhibits in any western museum, were traditionally used by the natives as sandpaper, for the humble purpose of roughening bicycle tyres when mending a puncture.[24,37]

As can be expected, a great deal has happened in relation to the coelacanth since the early 1950s, so that only the very briefest of summaries can be included here. On 12 November 1954, once more off Anjouan, the eighth coelacanth specimen known to science was captured, and proved to be the first female recorded. As the Comoros are French-owned, coelacanth research since the capture of the 'Malania' individual has been carried out predominantly by French workers, but other countries have also contributed from time to time.[24,37] In March 1972, for example, it was a joint British-American-French expedition, backed by the Royal Society, which was privileged to succeed in observing and filming for the very first time a living coelacanth. It had been captured by Comoros fisherman Madi Youssouf Kaar, who was fortunate enough to recognise what it was and bring it to the attention of the scientific team while it was still alive. It was a catch that he will never forget, because his reward was £10,000 – roughly equivalent to a century's worth of wages for a Comoros fisherman.[38]

Still to be achieved, however, was the ultimate goal of any coelacanth film-maker

Prof. J.L.B. Smith (foreground) with 'Malania' coelacanth – initially thought to represent a second species, it was merely a deformed specimen of Latimeria.*(J.L.B. Smith Institute of Ichthyology)*

– to film it underwater in its natural habitat. In January 1987, using a two-man submersible, this seemingly impossible objective was successfully accomplished by Prof. Hans Fricke, a marine biologist and documentary film-maker from Germany's Max Planck Institute for Animal Behaviour. He discovered much about coelacanth lifestyle. For example: it frequented crevices in lava rock at depths of around 650 ft; it could swim backwards as well as forwards, and sometimes drifted upside-down; contrary to expectations, it did not walk on its limb-like lobed fins across the sea bottom, although it did brace itself with them when resting on it. When swimming, its synchronisation of fin movements yielded the same gait as that of a trotting horse; and it was responsive to weak

electrical fields. Most unexpected of all was its pièce de resistance – for no apparent reason, a coelacanth would suddenly drift nose downwards with the current and stand (for up to two minutes at a time) on its head. This extraordinary behaviour may be some sort of response to the presence of electrical fields nearby, but this has not been conclusively established.[39]

The studies of the coelacanth's morphology and physiology initiated by Prof. Smith, and continued to this day by other ichthyologists, have also uncovered some major surprises – so much so that even its formal classification is nowadays a subject for controversy. There are two modern-day classes of jawed fishes. One is Osteichthyes (also called Pisces), the bony fishes – so-called because one of their principal characteristics is a skeleton composed wholly or predominantly of bone. The other class is Chondrichthyes (also called Selachii), the cartilaginous fishes – consisting of the sharks and rays, and so-called because their skeletons are composed wholly of cartilage (gristle). Fossil species of coelacanths had bony skeletons, and because many of their other features also allied them with Osteichthyes this was the class in which they had been traditionally housed.[24,37]

Studies on the modern-day coelacanth, however, have exposed various features that make the above classification of the coelacanths as a group somewhat unsatisfactory. Some of the most important of these features are as follows:[24,37]

1) Its backbone is not made of bone but of cartilage, and bears spines that are not bony and solid but are instead cartilaginous and hollow (this is the feature from which the term *coelacanth* – meaning 'hollow spine' – is derived).

2) Its gills are bony and hard, and bear teeth – very unlike the soft, cartilaginous, untoothed gills of other Osteichthyes species.

3) Its blood contains a high level of urea, similar to that of cartilaginous fishes but unlike that of bony ones.

4) Its intestine contains a spiral-shaped valve, again like that of cartilaginous fishes but unlike that of bony ones.

5) Like those of its fossil ancestors, its skull is a two-part structure with a hinge, unlike the single unit of bony fishes.

In certain ways, it even differs from its fossil relatives. For instance, it is about five times as long as most of them; and it is a marine form, whereas most fossil coelacanths were freshwater species. There are also several basic anatomical differences.[24,37]

Thus, there are several conflicting schools of thought regarding the coelacanth group's correct taxonomic position. There are those who still look upon them as bony fishes, notwithstanding *Latimeria's* varied morphological contradictions; others prefer to cite the latter's similarities to cartilaginous fishes as evidence that these and the coelacanths shared a common ancestor; and there are some who feel that the coelacanths merit a class of their own, related to the lungfishes and of equal status to the bony fishes and to the cartilaginous fishes.[24,37]

Finally: based solely upon fossil evidence, coelacanths were initially classed as the fish group most nearly allied to the land vertebrates (tetrapods); however, findings from later anatomical and biochemical studies with *Latimeria* seemed to refute that idea – until recently. From comparisons of the amino acid sequence in *Latimeria's* haemoglobin with that of various other fishes, and of some amphibians, in May 1991 a research team presented persuasive new molecular evidence for reinstating the coelacanths as the tetrapods' closest piscean relatives.[37] With ideas turning full circle, it is clear that there is still much to resolve regarding the lobe-finned lineage of 'Old Fourlegs'.

Mirapinna – a furry fish from the Azores

The year 1956 saw the description of a 2.5-in-long hump-backed fish so grotesque in appearance that it required a new family to accommodate it. Caught many years earlier (in June 1911) at the surface of the mid-Atlantic about 550 miles north of the Azores, this extraordinary fish seemed to be covered in hair. Closer examination, however, disclosed that its 'fur' was really a mass of living body outgrowths (hair, conversely, is composed of dead cells) containing secretory cells. Their function is unknown, though they may produce distasteful compounds to deter would-be predators.[11,40]

No less extraordinary than its 'hair' were its fins. The pelvic fins were large and wide, their wing-like appearance additionally enhanced by their long rays, diverging outwards from a broad base, and directed upwards rather than downwards. Equally odd was its pair of very small, reduced pectoral fins, placed much higher up on its body's flanks than those of most other fishes. Most peculiar of all, however, was its tail fin, because the rays in the lower half of its upper lobe uniquely overlapped those in the upper half of its lower lobe, and like the rays of the pelvic fins they were extremely long and spine-like. Little wonder that this

bizarre species, commonly termed the hairy fish, was given the generic name *Mirapinna* – 'wonderful fins'; its full scientific name is *Mirapinna esau*. Along with two previously described genera of much slimmer fishes (*Eutaeniophorus* and *Parataeniophorus*, collectively comprising three species known as tape-tails), the hairy fish is nowadays placed by many authorities within a distinct order, Lampridiformes, set apart from all others.[11,40]

Bathylychnops exilis – a fish with six eyes

Discovered in 1958, inhabiting depths of 300-3000 ft within the northeastern Pacific Ocean, and belonging to the spookfish (opisthoproctid) family, *Bathylychnops exilis* is a slender, 18-in-long, pike-like species with large eyes. These provide efficient prey detection in the dim light of its deep undersea world, but that is not all. Housed within the lower half of each eye is a second, smaller eye, pointing downwards and termed the secondary globe, which comes complete with its own retina and lens. This extraordinary arrangement

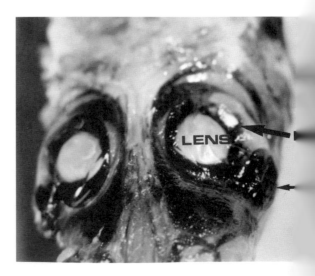

Antero-dorsal view of six-eyed spookfish's head – this bizarre deepsea species was first revealed in 1958 (SG = secondary globes, PG = primary globes). (Dr David Stein)

probably increases the species' sensitivity to light within its shadowy surroundings. Yet, as if its possession of four eyes were not sufficiently strange, behind the small ones are a pair of even tinier eye-like organs, though these do not have retinas, serving instead merely to direct incoming light into the fish's large, principal eyes. Intriguingly, its pair of secondary globes were once thought to be light-producing organs – hence its name, *Bathylychnops* ('deep lamp-eye').[41] In popular parlance, it is called the six-eyed spookfish.

Denticle herring – Nigerian anomaly with teeth on its head

In 1959, a little silver-coloured fish was discovered that proved so peculiar that the creation of a new suborder (within Clupeiformes, the herring order) was needed, in order to define adequately its emphatic taxonomic independence from even its closest relatives.[42]

Recorded only from the medium-sized alkaline streams of certain southwest Nigerian rivers, this 2-in-long, shoal-forming species was named *Denticeps clupeoides* ('herring-like tooth-head'), and is commonly called the denticle herring. Both names not only allude to its herring-like form, but also stress its most bizarre characteristic. Its head and its body's most anterior region are covered in small teeth. Known as denticles, they are so densely packed on the underside of its head that they make it appear almost furry on first sight.[11,42]

Coincidentally, at about the same time that this modern-day species was discovered, a very similar fossil form was also reported, its remains having been found in Tanzanian rocks dating back to the Miocene or Oligocene epochs (15-45 million

years ago). As a token of its comparability to the denticle herring, it was dubbed *Palaeodenticeps tanganyikae*.[42]

Lepidogalaxias and *Grasseichthys* – a pair of very puzzling pisceans

The pikes are a northern-based family of fishes related to another northern-based family, the salmon. The counterparts of salmon in the southern hemisphere comprise a family known as the galaxiids, but the pikes did not seem to have any southern equivalent – and then along swam *Lepidogalaxias salamandroides*.

An inhabitant of acidic pools all over southern Australia, this small, slender species was described as recently as 1961. It bears a distinctive black band on each side of its body, running from its gills along the entire length of its flank to the base of its tail. It looks like a galaxiid on first sight, but its dorsal and anal fins are much closer to the front of its body than are those of true galaxiids, and the structure of the adult male's anal fin is very specialised. Most distinctive of all, and setting it completely apart from galaxiids, is its well-scaled body (hence *Lepidogalaxias* – 'scaled galaxiid'); galaxiids are scaleless. Based upon detailed anatomical studies, ichthyologists now suspect that this strange fish is more closely related to the pikes than to the galaxiids, but its precise taxonomy remains controversial.[43]

On 29 October 1964, an equally strange fish was obtained from the Ivindo Basin in Gabon, West Africa. In honour of eminent French zoologist Prof. Pierre Grassé, its species was christened *Grasseichthys gabonensis*. Although only 1 in long, it is very distinctive, as it lacks scales, teeth, and a lateral-line sensory system; even its gill slits are restricted. Although its overall anatomy reveals that it is an offshoot of the salmon lineage of fishes, there has been much dispute concerning its precise classification within this taxonomic order, and Dr Jacques Géry, who described it in 1964, placed it in a family of its own.[4,44]

Siphonophore fish – appearances can deceive

In 1965, an astonishing fish called *Kasidoron edom* was described.[45] Sole member of a totally new family (until a second, similar species, *K. latifrons*, was recorded in 1969[46]), it became known as the siphonophore fish – due to its wonderful pelvic fins. These were greatly modified, having transformed into a long, multi-branched tree-like organ hanging underneath its body, and closely resembling the tentacular appendages of those jellyfish-like composite creatures the siphonophores (exemplified by the famous Portugese man o'war *Physalia*).[45]

Known only from waters of around 6-165 ft depth, about 150 miles east of Florida's Cape Canaveral and northeast of Bermuda, this 1.25-in-long velvet-black fish attracted appreciable interest, on account of its conjoined pelvic fins' unique structure. This was assumed to be a device for warding off predators, which would be likely to mistake its harmless form for the deadly stinging tentacles of genuine siphonophores.[45]

After a time, however, the remainder of this fish's anatomy began to receive attention too, and researches ultimately disclosed that in spite of its distinctive appearance, the siphonophore fish was not a new species at all.[47] On the contrary, it was unmasked as the hitherto-unknown juvenile form of an odd little species called the gibber fish *Gibberichthyes pumilus*, described in 1933.[48] Previously known only from four specimens, this deepwater

denizen attains a total length of 4.5 in, and inhabits the western North Atlantic, as well as the South Pacific waters close to the Samoan Islands. With a very large head, a deep, laterally flattened body, and perfectly normal fins lacking any vestige of its juvenile's tentacle-impersonating structure, the gibber fish is placed within a family of its own, most akin to the squirrelfishes and slimeheads (p. 176).[48]

The curious case of the bottled sea serpent

The 1970s began with the conclusion of one of ichthyology's most enigmatic episodes – the curious (and confusing) case of the bottled sea serpent. This had attracted particular attention in 1965, when sea monsters enjoyed a renaissance in scientific respectability – thanks to the publication that year of a now-classic tome by cryptozoologist Dr Bernard Heuvelmans, entitled *Le Grand Serpent-de-Mer* (a somewhat different English version, *In the Wake of the Sea-Serpents*, appeared in 1968, also incorporating a greatly condensed version of another of his books). Within his book, Heuvelmans provided convincing evidence for believing that 'the great sea serpent', one of cryptozoology's most celebrated creatures, was actually a non-existent composite – i.e. it had been 'created' via the erroneous lumping together (by previous investigators) of eyewitness reports that in reality feature a number of totally different types of animal. In short, there was no single, morphologically heterogeneous species responsible for all sea serpent reports on record; instead, there were several well-defined, separate species collectively responsible for those reports.[49]

Some of these, according to Heuvelmans, were species still unknown to science, and included various unusual seals and whales, a giant turtle, a marine reptile, and a giant-sized 'super eel'. If his hypothesis was correct, this would have profound ichthyological implications; for as a result of a chance discovery made more than 30 years earlier, it meant that at least one bona fide sea serpent had already been captured – a sea serpent whose remains, moreover, were preserved, bottled, and freely available for scientific scrutiny.[49]

On 31 January 1930, the Danish research vessel *Dana* captured an exceptionally long eel larva (leptocephalus) at a depth of about 900 ft, west of the Agulhas Bank and south of the Cape of Good Hope. Whereas leptocephali of the common eel *Anguilla anguilla* measure a mere 3 in long at most, and even those of the formidable conger eel *Conger conger* only reach 4 in, the *Dana's* remarkable specimen was a colossal 6 ft 1.5 in in length. This in itself was quite staggering, but its implications were even more astounding.[50]

During their metamorphosis from leptocephalus to adult, true eels (anguillids) greatly increase their total length – the precise index of growth varying between species. In the common eel, the increase is generally eighteen-fold, producing adults measuring around 4.5 ft; in the conger, it can be as much as thirty-fold, yielding adults of up to 10 ft. Consequently, as conceded by *Dana* ichthyologist Dr Anton Bruun, in the case of the *Dana* leptocephalus, which was already 6 ft long, there existed the incredible possibility that this could have metamorphosed into a monstrous adult measuring anything between 108-180 ft, with a length of 50 ft seemingly the very minimum (less than a nine-fold increase) that even the most prudent estimator might expect of such a larva. Needless to say, any species of eel attaining such stupendous lengths as these would make an excellent candidate for those sea serpents grouped within Heuvelmans's 'super eel' category.[49]

After its capture, the *Dana* leptocephalus was preserved in alcohol and has since resided in a specimen bottle within the collections of Copenhagen University's Zoological Museum. Periodically, it has been taken out of its bottle to be examined, and as a result it has gradually shrunk, but it remained a notable riddle in need of an answer – especially when, as the years progressed, a few other inordinately long leptocephali were obtained.[50]

In 1959, an anatomically similar but somewhat shorter specimen, just under 3 ft long and procured in New Zealand waters, was described as a new species – *Leptocephalus giganteus* – to which the *Dana* specimen was later assigned. Interestingly,

Dana *giant leptocephalus – for many years this was mistakenly believed to be the larva of an unknown species of gigantic eel, up to 180 ft long. (Prof. Jørgen Nielsen, courtesy of Lars Thomas)*

the Danish research vessel *Galathea* supposedly obtained a 6 ft leptocephalus during its voyages in the early 1950s, but no formal record of this (let alone the specimen itself) appears to exist.[50]

Even so, two specimens of *L. giganteus* certainly did exist, and the reality of the elusive sea serpent, or at least one of its constituent members, seemed at last to have been fully endorsed. Inevitably, however, the truth proved very different. In 1966, two much smaller specimens of *L. giganteus* were documented; measuring just under 4 in and 11 in respectively, they had been sifted from the stomach contents of an *Alepisaurus* lancet fish captured in the western Atlantic. Except for their modest lengths, they corresponded very closely to the New Zealand example, and were carefully studied by Miami University ichthyologist Dr David G. Smith, in a bid to pinpoint conclusively the taxonomic affinities of *L. giganteus* in relation to the many other species of eel known to science.[52]

In March 1970, he exploded the sea serpent scenario for *L. giganteus* – by revealing that its two smaller specimens were the larvae of a notacanthid (spiny eel), not of an anguillid (true eel). This spelled doom for their species' claim to fame as (in its adult phase) a genuine sea serpent – because in stark contrast to the leptocephali of true eels, those of notacanthids do not greatly increase their length during metamorphosis from larva to adult. In other words, predictions that mature specimens of *L. giganteus* would measure over 100 ft were totally unfounded. Instead, when (if ever) the still-unknown phase of this species is finally collected, it will be very little longer than the leptocephalus, i.e. a mere 6 ft or so.[52]

Of course, there may indeed be eels of gigantic length still eluding scientific detection in the vastness of the oceans – giant anguillids, for example, that are compatible with Heuvelmans's concept of the 'super eel' category of sea serpent – but unlike *L. giganteus*, these have yet to be captured, preserved, and bottled.

Megamouth shark – the 'big one' that didn't get away

Most fishermen have a cherished tale or two about 'the big one that got away', but none can surely compete with the following version – in which, just for a change, the whopper in question did not get away, much to the delight of marine biologists throughout the world.

On 15 November 1976, a team of researchers from the Hawaii Laboratory of the Naval Undersea Center (now known as the Naval Ocean Systems Center) was aboard the research vessel *AFB-14*, sited about 26 miles northeast of Kahuku Point, Oahu, in the Hawaiian Islands. During the course of their work, two large parachutes employed as sea anchors were dropped overboard, and lowered to a depth of 500 ft. Later that day, when the boat was ready to leave for home, the researchers hauled the parachutes back up – and found that one of them had drawn up the greatest ichthyological discovery since the coelacanth. Entangled in the parachute was a gigantic shark, measuring 14.5 ft in total length, weighing 1653 lb, and differing radically in appearance from all other sharks on record.[53-5]

Recognising its worth, the team hauled its mighty body aboard on rollers, and sent it at once to the Naval Undersea Center's Kaneohe Laboratory, where biologist Lieut. Linda Hubbell lost no time in contacting the University of Hawaii. The very next morning, it was examined by Dr Leighton R.

The aptly-named megamouth shark – unknown to science until November 1976. (Charles Okamura/Honolulu Advertiser)

Paul Struhsaker of the Fisheries Service, and shark specialist Dr Leonard Compagno from San Francisco State University. Preserved, the specimen is now held at Honolulu's Bernice P. Bishop Museum.[53-5]

The head of this strange shark was very large, long, and broad, but not pointed like that of more typical sharks, whereas its lengthy, cylindrical body tapered markedly from the broad neck to the slender heterocercal tail (i.e. the tail's upper lobe was much longer than its lower lobe). Its pectoral fins were also long and slender, but its pelvic fins

Taylor, director of the university's Waikiki Aquarium, after which its body was quick-frozen at a firm of tuna packers, and retained there until, on 29 November, it was transported (still frozen) to a specially-constructed preservation tank at the National Maritime Fisheries Service's Kewalo dock site. It was then thawed and injected with formalin, procedures that marked the commencement of what was to be an intensive period of study of this specimen – swiftly recognised to represent a new species never before brought to the attention of science. The study lasted almost seven years, and was undertaken jointly by Dr Taylor, Dr

and anal fin were very small – smaller than the first of its two dorsal fins. Identifying it straight away as a male, its pelvic fins bore a pair of elongate claspers (a male shark's copulatory organs).[54-5]

The specimen's huge size made its species, on average, the sixth largest species of modern-day shark known to science, but even more striking than its overall bulk was its mouth. Relative to the rest of its body, its mouth was exceedingly large and wide – a feature that soon earned it in newspaper reports a very fitting soubriquet – 'megamouth'. This became accepted by science as this species' official English name.

In addition to its size, the megamouth's mighty orifice was distinguished by thick lips, more than 400 tiny teeth arranged in 236 rows, a very unusual anatomy which meant that its jaws did not lower at the bottom like those of most sharks but flapped open at the top instead, and – most startling of all – a silvery mouth-lining that glowed in the dark.[54-5]

Despite initial speculation that this unexpected last-mentioned feature was due to light-emitting structures comparable to the bioluminescent organs of many deepsea fishes and other benthic life, insufficient evidence was obtained from the study to verify this. Nonetheless, when taken together with the megamouth's immense size but only tiny, relatively useless teeth, various other anatomical attributes, plus the great depth at which it was captured, its glowing jaws indicated that this mysterious marine form was itself a deepsea denizen, whose lifestyle probably consisted of slow cruises through the inky darkness of the sea's depths with its huge, glowing jaws held open, to entice inside great numbers of tiny marine organisms. Thus, the megamouth was a harmless plankton feeder, a gentle giant.[54-5]

All of this and much more was recorded in the paper prepared by Taylor, Struhsaker and Compagno, comprising the megamouth's formal scientific description and published on 6 July 1983.[55] Their study had revealed this mighty creature to be so unlike all other sharks that they had not merely classed it as a new species, they had also placed it in an entire genus and family all to itself. Approving of 'megamouth' as its common name, Taylor and colleagues made it the basis of this species' scientific name too, christening it *Megachasma pelagios* ('great yawning mouth of the open sea') – sole member of the family Megachasmidae,

but most closely allied to the basking shark *Cetorhinus maximus,* another plankton feeder.[55]

Attempts to catch a second megamouth for comparison purposes proved unsuccessful until November 1983, when a second megamouth was caught, once again completely by accident. This time, a commercial fishing vessel named *Helga* took the honours, snaring it unknowingly within a gill net at a depth of only 125 ft, while based close to California's Santa Catalina Island, near Los Angeles. Needless to say, this priceless specimen was carefully brought ashore, and was sent at once to the Los Angeles County Museum of Natural History. Tissue samples were taken and stomach contents removed, after which its 14-ft-long body was stored in a frozen state within a temporary case until work upon a specially-prepared fibreglass display unit was completed, whereupon the new megamouth was preserved and retained thereafter within its 500 gallons of 70% ethanol.[56]

The megamouth's known distribution range expanded dramatically with the third specimen's discovery. On 18 August 1988, an adult male almost 17 ft long (hence the largest megamouth currently on record) was found washed up on a beach near Mandurah, a holiday resort south of Perth, Western Australia. When news of its appearance reached the Western Australian Museum, ichthyologist Dr Tim Berra (visiting from Ohio State University) and a team of fish researchers swiftly travelled to the beach to salvage the shark's body. This was just as well, because some of the resort's residents, not realising its immense scientific significance, had been attempting (albeit unsuccessfully) to push it back into the sea.[57-8]

The scientists were delighted to find that this latest megamouth was still in good condition, and it was ultimately preserved and housed in a fibreglass display tank like that of the Los Angeles specimen. During the tank's construction, it was retained in a frozen state, enabling the museum's taxidermist to prepare a plaster cast of its body for exhibition.[57-8]

On 23 January 1989, a fourth megamouth appeared, stranded dead on the sandy beach of Hamamatsu City in Japan's Shizuoka Prefecture, yielding the first record of this species from the western Pacific. An adult male, estimated at over 13 ft in total length, it attracted the notice of a photographer who took some good pictures of it that demonstrated beyond any doubt that it really was a megamouth – all of which was very fortunate, because shortly afterwards, the specimen was washed back out to sea and lost. The photos, however, were sent to Dr Kazuhiro Nakaya, who published them in a short *Japanese Journal of Ichthyology* report.[59] Less than six months after this specimen's brief appearance, a second Japanese megamouth made the headlines, when on 12 June a living specimen was caught in a net in Suruga Bay. Photographs confirming its identity as a megamouth were taken, after which it was released unharmed.[57]

The most recent megamouth episode, however, was truly spectacular. On 21 October 1990, a sixth specimen (measuring 16 ft 3 in) turned up, snared in a drift net off Dana Point, in California. It was towed to shore by the net's vessel, and was found to be still alive. Marine biologist Dr Dennis Kelly, from the Orange Coast College, gently examined the huge fish, and decided that although it would not survive in captivity, it would probably live if released back into the sea. And so, very carefully, it was set free, and was filmed underwater as it swam slowly down into the depths from

which it had earlier arisen. Moreover, capitalising upon this unique opportunity to discover a little more about its species' lifestyle, a radio transmitter was attached to its body. This enabled researchers to track it in the sea for the next three days (after which time the transmitter's batteries ran out), and revealed that it exhibited vertical migration – moving to the ocean surface only at night, and descending back into the depths at dawn – which explains how this extremely large and striking species had escaped scientific detection for so long.[57]

An intriguing footnote to the megamouth history is that this species' own discovery set the scene for a remarkable parasitological parallel. During the study of the very first megamouth, an extremely strange form of tapeworm was found inside its intestine. When closely examined, this peculiar parasite proved to be not just a new species (later named *Mixodigma leptaleum*), but one so different from all others that it required a completely new genus and family – exactly like its megamouth host.[60]

Hexatrygon – world's only known species of deepwater stingray?

On 5 July 1980, a 41-in-long fish found washed ashore on a beach at Port Elizabeth, South Africa, proved to be a species so drastically different from all others that a completely new suborder was created to receive it. On first sight, it resembled an ordinary stingray, but closer inspection exposed some very fundamental differences. First and foremost, it had six pairs of gill openings – in stark contrast to every other modern-day ray or skate, which only have five pairs. This is the diagnostic feature of the new fish that inspired its scientific name – when it was officially described by Drs P.C. Heemstra and M.M. Smith from the

J.L.B. Smith Institute of Ichthyology, they named it *Hexatrygon bickelli*.[61]

Like other rays and skates, just behind its eyes was a pair of reduced gill openings called spiracles, but *Hexatrygon* was uniquely able to open and close them, thanks to a pair of large, mobile flaps of skin. Equally distinctive was its very long, thin, flaccid snout, which contained a transparent, jelly-like substance that rendered it translucent. The underside of this snout, moreover, was well supplied with remarkable little organs known as Lorenzini's ampullae, which can actually detect the weak electrical currents running through the nervous systems of organisms lying in the thick sludge at the sea bottom.[61]

The possession of such organs by *Hexatrygon* suggests that it is a deepwater species, using them to detect potential prey buried in this ooze. Other aspects of its anatomy and morphology indicating this mode of existence are its tiny eyes, unusually small brain, and thin black dorsal skin – all features typical of deepwater fishes – so that ichthyologists believe that in life it dwells at depths of around 1300-3300 ft. If correct, this adds a further distinction to this already radically distinct creature, because it would then constitute the world's only known deepwater stingray – all other species inhabit fairly shallow zones.[61]

A veritable fish out of water

An ostentatiously out-of-place creature was the extraordinary 1-in-long entity that ichthyologist Dr Peter Henderson spotted wriggling amongst the leaf-litter on a bank at least 2 ft above an Amazonian blackwater stream called the Taruma-Mirim, near Manaus, Brazil, in 1984. Bright red, eyeless, worm-like, with scaleless skin and whisker-like projections around its face, it presented a formidable challenge to anyone merely wishing to assign it to any known *phylum* of animals, let alone any known species. Closer observation, however, exposed its true nature – it was, of all things, a fish.[62]

Later researches uncovered that it was a new species of trichomycterid (also termed pygidiid) catfish – freshwater species that are normally parasitic – highly-modified for survival on land. Indeed, this bizarre little catfish (for which Dr Henderson has proposed the name 'Phreatobius walkeri') seems actively to prefer a terrestrial existence to an aquatic one. When some captive specimens were taken from their leaf-litter and placed into water, they promptly climbed back out. Moreover, as its gills are greatly reduced structurally, it appears to obtain oxygen by absorbing it directly through its skin – which is extremely vascularised (explaining its intensely red colouration). Its food apparently consists of small insects and other organisms sharing its leaf litter habitat.[62]

The monster fishes of China's Lake Hanas

Officially, the largest specimen of freshwater fish on record is a 15 ft European catfish *Silurus glanis*, caught in Russia's Dniepper River sometime prior to the mid-1800s (though this species as a whole is generally shorter than the pa beuk, officially deemed to be the world's largest freshwater fish – see p. 179). As a consequence, the lake-dwelling fishes reported in July 1985 by no less an authority than China's eminent biologist Prof. Xiang Lihao, from Xinjiang University, attracted appreciable scientific interest.[63]

In July, the professor and a party of students arrived at a large but remote body of water called Lake Hanas, situated in northwestern China's Xinjiang Autonomous Region, in order to examine its potential as the site of a future nature reserve. On 24 July, one of the students observing the lake from a watchtower built two years earlier noticed several huge reddish-coloured objects moving at the water's surface. When the professor and students scrutinised them closely through binoculars, they discovered to their astonishment that they were enormous salmon-like fishes, whose heads, tails, and spiny dorsal rays could all be clearly discerned. Just how enormous they were, however, was not revealed until the next day.[63]

That morning, while again being observed through binoculars by Xiang Lihao, one of the fishes very obligingly aligned itself in parallel with a stretch of the bank extending between two trees. Armed not only with binoculars this time but also with a camera, the professor took some photos, then measured the distance between the trees. Using this measurement, he was able to calculate from the photos that the fish was at least 33 ft long.[63]

A large salmon known as the taimen *Hucho taimen* is indeed known from several rivers in northern China, but this species' maximum recorded length is a mere 6.5 ft – far short of the Lake Hanas monsters. Worth noting is that giant red fishes in this lake have been reported for decades by local villagers, but as the lake had not previously attracted scientific attention such reports had not been widely circulated. Now, with an eyewitness of Prof. Xiang Lihao's scientific standing, there can be no question concerning their existence or authenticity as giant fishes. So unless they are abnormally huge taimen, the Lake Hanas fishes must surely comprise a new species requiring formal description and study.[63]

A whip-tailed whopper from Thailand

In 1983, a series of reports appeared in various Thailand newspapers revealing the existence of an enormous form of freshwater stingray (reputedly weighing at least 660 lb) in the Chao Phraya and Mekong Rivers, and the capture of two such fishes, one from each river. Unfortunately, they were not preserved for scientific examination, but from the description and photos in the reports it seemed clear that they represented a species undescribed by science, so ichthyologists eagerly awaited news of further captures.[64]

On 9 November 1987, their period of waiting came to an end, with the procurement of a male Chao Phraya specimen at Pichit, roughly 286 miles upriver from the Gulf of Thailand. With a total length of almost 11 ft and a body disc measuring 3.5 ft in width, it proved to be a hitherto unknown species of whip-tailed stingray – with a projecting snout, small eyes, a very narrow tail base, and a broad but thin, oval body disc, brownish-grey on top, white underneath, and black around its underside's margins. On 14 June 1988, an even larger specimen was captured, again in the Chao Phraya but this time at Chumsang (about 37 miles upriver of the Gulf of Thailand). A female, it measured just under 15.5 ft in total length, with a body disc width of almost 6.5 ft. A third Chao Phraya specimen, a female just over 7 ft long with a body disc 2 ft 7 in wide, was caught on 31 May 1989 at Ayutthaya (about 62 miles upriver from the Chao Phraya's mouth), and was designated the type specimen of this impressive new species – which in 1990 was named *Himantura chaophraya*.[64]

According to fishermen along the Chao Phraya and Mekong rivers, the largest specimens that they have captured so far have weighed as much as 1100-1320 lb; if true, *H. chaophraya* is one of the largest new species of fish revealed in recent years.[64]

Opal allotoca – when home is a polluted cattle trough

Even the least glamorous of tasks can occasionally prove rewarding, as ichthyologist Michael L. Smith from the American Museum of Natural History found out in 1990. In a remote valley tucked away amid the mountains of west-central Mexico, he and three colleagues had been undertaking the distinctly unpleasant task of wading neck-deep in a scum-covered, sulphur-polluted artificial pond used for watering cattle and covering about three acres – when, after spending several hours scooping up water from its murky, stench-exuding depths, their long-handled nets drew up a mass of small, iridescent fishes that instantly made all their discomfiture well worthwhile.[65]

The survival of anything in such a seemingly hostile environment was in itself quite remarkable, but far more so was the identity of these fishes. They were opal allotocas *Allotoca maculata* – a species hitherto believed extinct for 20 years. Relatively nondescript in shape, and only 2 in long, its unassuming form is compensated for by the shimmering scales on its flanks, which glisten like the precious stone after which it is named. Closely related to those popular aquarium species the killifishes, the opal allotoca belongs to the goodeid family, which has many species in this region of Mexico.[65]

Following their unexpected discovery of this 'extinct' fish, Smith and his colleagues brought back ten living specimens, and successfully established a breeding population of opal allotocas within the luxury of the New York Aquarium – a far cry indeed from the sulphur and scum offered by their previous accommodation.[65]

Red-finned blue-eye – a prize in a puddle

No less surprising than the opal allotoca's reappearance was the discovery of the red-finned blue-eye *Scaturiginichthys vermillipinnis*. Sole member of a new genus and subfamily, this small but brilliantly-coloured species made its scientific debut in a tiny 3-in-deep puddle, for this is where Peter Unmac of the Australia-Papua New Guinea Fishes Association found its type specimen in December 1990. It was subsequently found in four others too, all situated on a grazing property called Edgbaston Station, near Longreach, in Queensland.[66]

'Old Fourlegs' – the incredible coelacanth (Part 3?)

Is *Latimeria chalumnae* the only species of living coelacanth? Bringing this ichthyological section to a close is a selection of intriguing evidence suggesting that the thrilling discovery of 'Old Fourlegs' in 1938 may some day have one or more equally momentous sequels.

In 1949, Dr Isaac Ginsburg of the U.S. National Museum received a fish scale sent by a souvenir seller from Tampa, Florida, who had bought an entire gallon-sized can of them from a local fisherman to use for decorating her souvenirs. The closest match that Ginsburg could make with the scale was with those of the coleacanth *L. chalumnae*. Sadly, the scale's current whereabouts are unknown, but the startling possibility raised by its onetime existence remains. Could there be a species of coelacanth living off one of America's coastlines?[67]

Equally thought-provoking is an exquisite 19th century silver statuette of a fish, brought to zoological notice by Argentinian chemist Dr Ladislao Reti, who saw it hanging in a village church near Bilbao, Spain, in summer 1964. Reti bought it from the church's priest, because he recognised that the fish it represented was unquestionably a species of coelacanth. Every feature was correct – the two separate dorsal fins of which the first was fan-like and the second lobed; the leg-like pectoral fins, pelvic fins, and anal fin; and the unmistakable three-lobed tail fin. Yet this artifact had been made at least 70 years before the discovery of *Latimeria*. True, one might argue that it had been based upon fossil coelacanths, but its three-dimensional shape compared so well with *Latimeria's* that it seems almost inconceivable that a sculptor could have achieved such accuracy when equipped only with flat fossils as models. Coelacanth researcher Prof. Hans Fricke thus believes that it was inspired by a modern-day specimen – perhaps even one from an undiscovered population in Mexican waters, as, according to recent investigations, the silver statuette appears to be of Mexican origin. In 1965, a second antique coelacanth-like statuette in silver came to light – bought in a Toledo antique shop by Belgian student Maurice Steinert (now a molecular biologist).[68]

In the late 1980s, moreover, a South American chemist visiting the Mediterranean island of Mallorca was convinced that the large, strange-looking fish seen on sale at a fish market in Palma was a genuine coelacanth.[68]

Also worthy of note is the unidentified coelacanth-like fish with leg-like fins, known as *patuki*, that features in the legends and depictions from Easter Island.[68]

Finally: it has traditionally been assumed that *Latimeria's* type specimen, the only example ever captured in South African waters, was a unique lone straggler that had wandered far from its species' typical Comoros provenance. However, there may have been at least one precedent. When, on 18 March 1939, Prof. J.L.B. Smith documented the above specimen's existence, he noted that a responsible citizen-angler of East London claimed that about five years earlier he had seen just such a fish himself, washed ashore on a lonely part of the East London coastline. He had left it there in order to fetch some assistance in transporting it (as it was apparently somewhat larger than *Latimeria's* type specimen), but by the time that he and his helpers had returned, the tide had carried the carcase back out to sea. Moreover, in August 1991 a female was captured off Quelimane, Mozambique. However, results from Fricke's recent DNA fingerprinting studies with the Mozambique example and five Grand Comoro specimens revealed no significant differences between them, thus implying that the Mozambique and South African coelacanths were not derived from some undiscovered coastal African population, but were, after all, merely wanderers originating from the Comoros.[69]

Lasionectes entrichoma (remipede) (Dennis Williams, courtesy of Dr Jill Yager)

INVERTEBRATES

Cooloola Monsters and Wonders
of the Vent World

Shortly after arriving at my new post as Curator of Orthoptera, CSIRO, Canberra in 1977 I was presented with a small parcel from Mr E.C. Dahms, Curator of Insects, Queensland Museum, Brisbane with a note 'Here's something to introduce you to the Australian fauna'. After some amusement at the technical excellence of the apparently manufactured monster, it was determined that it was a genuine complete cricket-like insect.

DR DAVID C.F. RENTZ (DESCRIBING THE COOLOOLA MONSTER'S DISCOVERY)
MEMOIRS OF THE QUEENSLAND MUSEUM (1980).

Writers and adventurers have often speculated about a "lost world," where supposedly extinct or unknown animals thrive in their own isolated environment, unknown to humans and unaffected by human activities. Not only has such a "lost world" been found, but even more astonishing, it does not depend on the sun for energy, a situation believed almost unique in the Earth's natural history. The "lost world" in question is located at a depth of 8,500 feet in the Pacific Ocean, about 150 miles south of Baja California, where scientists aboard the U.S. Navy's three-person submarine Alvin have been studying it. The focus of interest is a number of volcanic vents with slowly seeping lava which support enormous worms, snails, crabs, clams, jellyfish, and other invertebrates, all of which are new to marine science.

J. RICHARD GREENWELL – 'MINI-"LOST WORLD" AT 8500 FEET' (*ISC NEWSLETTER*, WINTER 1982).

Although they may not incite as much public interest as do the more showy and familiar mammals, birds, reptiles, amphibians and fishes, in terms of scientific significance the invertebrates (animals without a backbone) include among their multifarious assemblage an appreciable number of this century's most important new and rediscovered animals. Indeed, as will be seen in this section, three such species have each been responsible for the creation of an entirely new animal phylum (the highest echelon within the hierarchy of taxonomic categories employed in animal classification). Others of distinguished scientific standing documented here include: a giant bee and a super flea; sea daisies and spaghetti worms; an ostensibly innocuous insect unmasked as a bona fide vampire moth, and a sea creature capable of inflicting the most excruciating pain known to mankind; an assortment of marine curiosities collectively representing four totally new subclasses of crustacean, plus a forgotten little crustacean belonging to a group previously believed extinct for at least 50 million years; a monstrous grasshopper, and a monster-sized earwig; as well as an uncommonly long-tongued hawk moth whose existence was predicted by Charles Darwin several decades before it was actually discovered. Most spectacular of all: while man was seeking new life forms in outer space, an entire new world was awaiting discovery back on Earth – a world teeming with extraordinary animals never before seen.

Jewelled squid – living rainbow from the sea

Despite its close affinity to the often less-than- handsome squids and octopuses, *Lycoteuthis diadema* is unquestionably one of the world's most exquisite sea creatures, and is popularly called the jewelled squid – for very good reason. Its body is transparent, thereby enabling observers to discern clearly its internal organs – of which no fewer than 22 are special light-emitting (bioluminescent) structures, whose combined visual effect is a surrealistic, psychedelic panorama of glistening rainbow colours. Two of these remarkable organs are present on each member of the squid's pair of extra-long prey-capturing tentacles, a further five along each eye's lower rim, and the remaining eight on its body's undersurface.[1]

In 1899, the first two specimens of this species to attract scientific attention were examined while still alive by German marine biologist Dr Carl Chun. He formally described their species in 1900; and in 1903, documenting its light-emitters, wrote:[1]

Among all the marvels of colouration which the animals of the deep sea exhibited to us nothing can be even distantly compared with the hues of these organs. One would think that the body was adorned with a diadem of brilliant gems. The middle organs of the eyes shone with ultramarine blue, the lateral ones with a pearly sheen. Those towards the front of the lower surface of the body gave out a ruby-red light, while those behind were snow-white or pearly, except the median one, which was sky-blue. It was indeed a glorious spectacle.

Inhabiting the Atlantic's open waters, the jewelled squid is relatively small, no more than 5 in long, but its unparalleled display of multicoloured, glittering bioluminescence certainly compensates for any deficiencies in dimensions.[1]

A hawk moth foretold

Charles Darwin and Alfred Russell Wallace are immortalised in the annals of science as the originators of the Theory of Evolution. Less well known is that they predicted the existence of a very unusual moth – more than 40 years before it was actually discovered.

One of Madagascar's native orchids is *Angraecum sesquipedale*, whose nectar-producing organs (nectaries) are almost 12 in deep (much deeper than those of other orchids), although only the lowermost 1.5 in contains nectar. In 1862, Darwin recognised that for this species to be insect-pollinated like other orchids, Madagascar must house a butterfly or moth with an extraordinarily long proboscis (tongue), measuring at least 10-11 in, in order to be able to reach the nectaries. (In so doing, the insect would inevitably brush against the orchid's pollen-producing organs, causing pollen grains to stick to its body and thus be passed to the next *A. sesquipedale* orchid that the insect visited, thereby effecting pollination.)[2]

Yet no such insect was known from Madagascar, hence Darwin's prediction was scorned by many scientists; but the existence of *A. sesquipedale* was sufficient for him to remain convinced that one would certainly be discovered there eventually. In 1870, Wallace suggested that such a species might be closely related to the tropical African hawk moth *Xanthopan (Macrosilia) morgani*, which is equipped with an 8-in-long proboscis. And in 1903, their prediction was confirmed by the documentation of a new, Madagascan subspecies of *X. morgani* – with an 11-in-long proboscis. It was aptly christened *X. m. praedicta*.[2-3]

In 1992, Ohio entomologist Dr Gene Kritsky pointed out that another Madagascan orchid, *A. longicalcar*, could be pollinated only by a hawk moth with a 15-in-long proboscis. Therefore, he has predicted that such a moth, as yet unknown to science, must await discovery in Madagascar.[4]

Enormous butterflies and giant sea urchins

With a wingspan of up to 11 in recorded from some female specimens, Queen Alexandra's birdwing – a rainforest species mostly restricted nowadays to New Guinea's Popondetta Plain – is undoubtedly the world's biggest butterfly. This makes all the more surprising, at least upon first consideration, the fact that it eluded scientific documentation until 1907. Like many other birdwings, however, it flies only at heights well beyond the reach of even the most ardent collector, generally remaining 50-100 ft above the ground. Consequently, the first specimen to come to scientific attention, in 1906, was not obtained by traditional means (i.e. via a capacious net), but instead with the aid of a somewhat less orthodox piece of butterfly-acquiring apparatus – a shot gun.[5-6]

That specimen, a large female with handsome chocolate-brown wings edged with cream scalloping, became the type specimen of this previously undescribed species, which Lord Walter Rothschild officially documented a year later, naming it *Ornithoptera alexandrae*. Male specimens were later obtained, and these, although smaller in size, proved to be much more showy than the females, displaying delicate shades of shimmering green and blue upon a jet-black background. In both sexes, the head and thorax are black, the abdomen yellow.[5-6]

Another invertebrate record-breaker first described in 1907 was *Sperosoma giganteum*, the world's largest sea urchin. A Japanese species, found off Omai Saki Light in 1906 by the U.S. Fish Commission Steamer *Albatross*, it attains a diameter of just over 1 ft.[7]

Proturans – world's most primitive insects

An entirely new insect order, Protura, was created in 1907 by Italian entomologist Dr Filippo Silvestri, to house some minute creatures recently discovered at Genoa that were totally unlike any previously known to science, and which are nowadays usually considered to be the world's most primitive insects. They measure no more than 3 mm (just over one-tenth of an inch) long, with slender bodies tapering to a pointed tip at the rear, no eyes nor wings, and with peculiar mouthparts that look like a collection of tiny needles. Indeed, the soil-dwelling proturans (also called myrientomatans) have so strange a general appearance that they seem to constitute a major exception to several fundamental zoological rules hitherto used in defining just what makes an insect an insect.[8]

For example: whereas all other insects possess 11 abdominal segments when adult, proturans have 12; and while all other insects hatch from the egg with all 11 of these segments already present, proturans hatch with only nine, adding the remainder by successive subdivision of the original segments when moulting. This process of segment multiplication after hatching is termed anamorphosis, and is unique to proturans among insects but prevalent among various other jointed-limbed animals, notably millipedes.[8]

Equally important is that whereas all other insects bear a pair of antennae or feelers on their head, the proturans have none. Instead, they hold up their first pair of legs and use these as antennae. Indeed, this behaviour is deemed by some to be an indication of how true antennae evolved in higher insects – by specialisation of a front pair of legs. Moreover, although most insects bear legs only upon the segments of their thorax, the proturans have leg-like appendages upon their abdominal segments too. (This is also true of the springtails – but these latter creatures are in any case so peculiar that many entomologists nowadays remove them from the insect class altogether and treat them as a class all to themselves, Collembola.) Also of note is that the proturans have all manner of mysterious structures, projections, and pits of unknown function on their body surface (cuticle); these may serve as types of sense organ, but are not present on any other form of insect.[8]

As for their lack of wings, this is due to the fact that proturans have descended from an early line of insects that lived before wing evolution took place. Thus, unlike fleas and lice (whose present-day winglessness is due to their ancestors' gradual loss of wings during successive generations of adaptation for an efficient parasitic existence), proturans have no wings simply because their ancestors never had any either.[8] The first modern-day proturan to be formally recognised was *Acerentomon doderoi*, from Genoa. Since

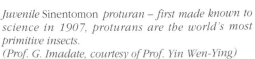

Juvenile Sinentomon *proturan – first made known to science in 1907, proturans are the world's most primitive insects.*
(Prof. G. Imadate, courtesy of Prof. Yin Wen-Ying)

then, over 200 species have been described, from all over the world, but unfortunately their lifestyle and biology remain almost as obscure today as they were at the time of Silvestri in 1907.[8]

Another extraordinary insect, the Indian stick insect *Carausius morosus* is today one of the world's most familiar captivity-maintained invertebrates – with millions in laboratories and schools as study specimens, and in countless homes as unusual children's pets. Remarkably, however, it remained undescribed by science until 1908.[9]

Titanus giganteus – extraordinary reappearance of an insect giant

The largest species of beetle in the world and also one of the most legendary is the fittingly-named *Titanus giganteus*, a shiny black colossus of a coleopteran that can attain a total length of 8 in (in the male). A member of the cerambycid or longhorn family, it is indisputably the premier prize of any beetle collector, but few can boast a specimen – on account of its unaccountable rarity. Even its scientific debut was shrouded in mystery.[4]

It was formally named in 1778, by Linnaeus, but there was no type specimen. Instead, Linnaeus based his description of the species upon a coloured plate, contained in a work published 13 years earlier by French zoologist Louis J.M. Daubenton. During the next century, collectors scoured Amazonia for this impressive insect, but mostly in vain. Those that were obtained consisted of dead specimens found floating in the Rio Negro, near to Manaos, Brazil. As *T. giganteus* is not an aquatic species, they must have fallen (or have been blown) into the river during long, exhausting flights from southern Guyana's relatively unexplored mountainlands.[4]

By 1900, only a handful of specimens were on record, and the species was in such demand among the wealthier collectors that during this same year one specimen was sold at a London auction for what was then the very princely sum of £150. Ten years later, however, a strange event occurred that revealed a regular, if unexpected, means of procuring further specimens of this elusive insect. One evening in 1910, while setting up his tent near to Brazil's Rio Branco, German orchid collector Jacob Wörner watched one of the local Indians spear a big fish, open it up, and take something large out of its gut. The Indian was just about to throw the object into the river when Wörner intervened, taking it from him and examining it closely. It proved to be a complete specimen of *T. giganteus*. This remarkable incident came to the attention of a German entomologist called Dr Bossmann, who thereafter paid the Indians to fish for more specimens in the river, which he then sold to European collectors. Consequently, the presence of *T. giganteus* in collections gradually increased.[4]

Moreover, in late 1957 a number of living specimens were finally discovered – captured during the rainy season (when they fly), after the *National Geographic Magazine's* consultant zoologist, Dr Paul Zahl, had placed 'reward' posters throughout a mining camp in Brazil's Territory of Amapa. Since then, others have made their presence known in a memorable way – attracted by the bright illumination, they have been spied crawling like diminutive tanks beneath various towns' street lamps.[4]

Sclerosponges – in a class of their own

The year 1911 saw the official description of *Ceratoporella nicholsoni* – a perplexing sea creature that has baffled zoologists for over a century. It first came to scientific attention in the 1870s, when it was dredged up off the coast of Cuba at a depth of just over 65 ft by the U.S. Coast Survey Steamer *Blake*, and in 1878 biologist Prof. Louis Agassiz classed it as a living representative of a hitherto extinct genus of tabulate coral. Ten years later, however, he changed his mind, reassigning it to a completely different phylum – by labelling it as a bryozoan (moss animal). In 1911, its identity changed again, when S.J. Hickman reclassified it as a coral – but this time as a species of hard coral (octocoral).[11-12] And thus it remained for several decades, until its correct identification was at last achieved – whereupon it proved to be neither coral nor bryozoan. Instead, it was a sponge, but of a type most comparable to the extinct stromatoporoids, and hence markedly distinct from all three previously-recorded classes of modern-day sponge. Its skeleton contained three different constituents – organic fibres, spicules of silicon, and crystalline aragonite (calcium carbonate).[12] In contrast, that of the calcareous sponges (class Calcarea) is composed solely of calcium carbonate spicules; the skeleton of the glass sponges (Hexactinellida) consists solely of siliceous spicules; and that of the demosponges (Demospongiae) comprises siliceous spicules and/or fibres of spongin (a collagen-like protein).

During the taxonomic transference of *Ceratoporella* from one group of animals to another, some new species were being discovered that were more readily recognisable as sponges but which nonetheless shared its characteristic tripartite skeleton. In 1900, for example, *Astrosclera willeyana* was described, hailing from the Pacific islands of Funafuti and Lifu. Interestingly, scientists initially believed that its siliceous spicules were not a genuine part of its skeleton but had instead been incorporated artificially by some means.[13] In 1910, however, R. Kirkpatrick of the British Museum (Natural History) revealed that they were a genuine constituent, secreted by the sponge itself. Just a year earlier, Kirkpatrick had described a related species, *Merlia normani*, from Madeira's Porto Santo Island.[14]

In 1970, these various intriguing species finally received the taxonomic recognition that they clearly deserved, when marine biologists Drs W.D. Hartman and T.F. Goreau grouped them all together within their very own class, Sclerospongiae, and to which they added five new species that they had discovered in the Jamaican fore-reef slope environment. One of these was a new *Merlia* species; the other four collectively yielded three new genera, and comprised *Stromatospongia vermicola*, *S. norae*, *Hispidopetra miniana*, and *Goreauiella auriculata*.[12] Additionally, in 1975 a totally new order of sclerosponges was created by Hartman and Goreau, to house another newly-found species, *Acanthochaetetes wellsi*.[15] On account of their coral-like appearance (exemplified by *Ceratoporella*), the sclerosponges are often referred to as the coralline sponges.

Zorapterans – to be winged, or not to be winged?

Zorapterans comprise an order of insects entirely unknown to science until 1913, when Dr Filippo Silvestri (discoverer of the first proturan in 1907 – see p. 210) described the first species;[16] there are now more than 20 on record, all belonging to the single genus *Zorotypus*. They are tiny creatures, none exceeding 0.1 in long, which live in colonies concealed under moss, leaves, or

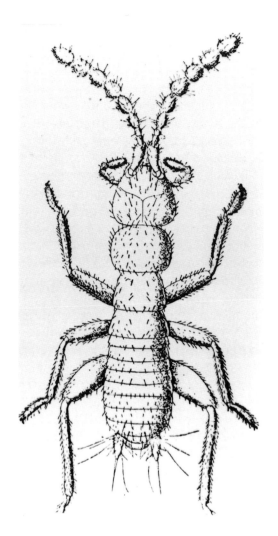

Zorapteran – these tiny colonial insects were not discovered until 1913.

With regard to certain other features, zorapterans fall into two well-delineated types, both of which can occur within a single species. Winged individuals have two pairs of slender, sparsely-veined wings of which the front pair is largest; compound eyes and simple light-sensitive cell clusters termed ocelli; and a tough, shield-like structure covering the thorax. Wingless individuals lack all of those features, and their unprotected thorax has only a thin, delicate cuticle. Some species do not produce winged individuals at all, whereas in certain others the latter lose their wings after attaining maturity, like termites.[17-18]

Zorapterans have a widespread distribution, occurring in the U.S.A., South America, the West Indies, the Hawaiian Islands, southeast Asia, and western Africa, and appear to be most closely related to an order of equally inconspicuous insects known as psocids or booklice, although they also exhibit certain affinities with termites and cockroaches.[17-18]

Grylloblattids – insects of ice and fire

Scarcely before the ink had dried on Silvestri's description of the first zorapteran species, news emerged of another minuscule insect of great significance which differed so radically from all others that a second new order was required. Engendering this latest entomological revolution was a tiny wingless form found under some stones in the Rocky Mountains of Alberta, Canada, by entomologist Dr E.M. Walker, who described it in 1914.[19]

Morphologically, it seemed to comprise an amalgam of at least three completely different orders of insects. Its ovipositor

tree bark, or in soil, decaying wood, and sometimes even in termites' nests; but they are not social in the sense that many termites, ants, bees, and wasps are. Their most notable external characteristics include their distinctive nine-segmented antennae (each resembling a series of beads strung together), and the unusual construction of their thorax – its three segments are quite separate from one another (in other insects, at least two – if not all three – of these segments are fused together).[17-18]

Orthoptera – the cricket and grasshopper order. And so a brand new order came into being – Grylloblattoidea (occasionally referred to as Notoptera), which is considered by some entomologists to represent a primitive level of evolutionary development comparable to that attained by the ancestors of orthopterans.[17-18]

Since 1914, a few other grylloblattid species have been found – in the U.S.A., Japan, and the former U.S.S.R. Measuring 0.5-1.5 in long, with soft, pale brown or yellow bodies, they have unusually long lifespans (relative to those of most insects); their entire development from egg, through various larval stages, to adulthood and eventual death can take up to eight years. And as a further claim to fame, the Canadian *G. campodeiformis* is renowned for thriving at temperatures near 0°C in the icy portions of its Rocky Mountain haunts.[17-18]

Finally, there is at least one species with the unhappy status of an endangered species. This is the Mount St. Helens grylloblattid *G. chirurgica*, described in 1961.[20] Confined exclusively to a single lava flow on Washington's notorious volcano, Mount St. Helens, its continuing survival is threatened not only by its home's irascible, unpredictable tendency for violent eruption but also by human interference.[6]

A very odd octopus

The large, prominent eyes of cephalopods (octopuses, squids, cuttlefishes, nautiluses) are noted for their remarkably complex, highly-evolved structure. Consequently, *Cirrothauma murrayi* – discovered during the *Michael Sars* North Atlantic Deep-Sea

(egg-laying tube) was made up of six components, joined together in a manner that invited comparison with the ovipositors of certain crickets (of the genus *Gryllus*); whereas its five-segmented legs and pair of long segmented filaments (cerci) at the posterior tip of its abdomen were features shared by some cockroaches (genus *Blattus*). Yet its delicate body cuticle, blindness, and absence of wings superficially allied it with *Campodea*, a primitive insect known as a dipluran. In recognition of its composite construction, Walker named his minute discovery *Grylloblatta campodeiformis*.[19]

In truth, however, its resemblance to *Campodea* was due merely to convergent evolution (unrelated animals evolving in a similar manner due to their existence in the same type of habitat) rather than to any close taxonomic kinship. Equally, its correspondences with cockroaches were present simply because they were basic insect features retained by all primitive insect groups. Nor did its cricket-like ovipositor provide sufficient reason on its own to include the new insect within

Expedition of 1910, first described in 1914 by Dr Carl Chun, and not recorded again until 1967 – is little short of heretical, because this highly aberrant species of deepsea cirrate octopus is blind.[21]

Even though this condition is quite common among deepsea creatures, all of the squids existing in such habitats have well-formed eyes, so why should their octopod counterpart be sightless? In fact, it does possess eyes, but as they have neither retina nor lens, and are embedded beneath the surface of its gelatinous tissues, they are non-functional.[18,21]

The rest of its morphology is equally strange. Whereas the body of more familiar octopuses is globular and bulky, that of *C. murrayi* is gelatinous and fragile, like a jellyfish's. This is an adaptation for living at depths of 6650-10,000 ft, where the surrounding water pressure is immense (around 1 ton per square inch). Similarly, whereas the tentacles of more familiar octopuses are separate from one another, those of *C. murrayi* (and other cirrate octopuses) are interconnected by a membranous web that reaches almost to their tips, giving the animal itself the appearance of a semi-transparent, eight-spoked umbrella.[18,21]

And whereas most cephalopods move by ejecting water in best jet-propulsion style through a tube termed the funnel, in *C. murrayi* this latter structure is greatly reduced. Its locomotory function has been superseded by the tentacles' interconnecting web – for *C. murrayi* moves by slowly opening and closing this web, once more in faithful

imitation of an animated parasol. Like other cirrate ('hairy') octopuses, in addition to suckers, each of its tentacles has two rows of delicate hair-like filaments (cirri), which are probably used for trapping minute particles of food. Its only other noticeable external feature is a single pair of paddle-like fins, possibly of auxiliary assistance in locomotion.[18,21]

'Super Flea'

In 1921, publication of *Hystrichopsylla schefferi's* formal description introduced zoologists to the world's largest species of flea. When its original name, *H. mammoth*, was disallowed on a nomenclatural technicality, it was renamed *H. schefferi*, after its discoverer, agricultural researcher Theophilus Scheffer, from the U.S.A.'s Bureau of Biological Survey. He had collected the type specimen while in Washington State, finding it inside a nest belonging to the world's most primitive species of rodent – *Aplodontia rufa*, generally known somewhat inappropriately as the mountain beaver (it is neither a mountain-dweller nor a beaver). Other specimens have been collected since, some of which are more than 9 mm (0.36 in) long.[22]

Subsequently nicknamed ' Super Flea', *H. schefferi* appears to be a specific parasite of the mountain beaver; most specimens have

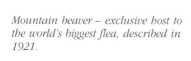

Mountain beaver – exclusive host to the world's biggest flea, described in 1921.

215

been obtained from individuals of this rodent, or from their nests. A few have also been taken from the fur of mink and spotted skunks, but as these are carnivores that are known to prey upon mountain beavers it is likely that they received their over-sized parasites directly from their prey or, once again, from its nests. Little is known about the natural history of 'Super Flea' or about that of its host, so the mystery of why the world's most primitive rodent should be exclusively parasitised by the world's largest flea has yet to be solved.[22]

Ophiocanops – world's most primitive brittle star

Brittle stars look like starfishes with unusually long and slender, mobile arms that are sufficiently serpentine in appearance and movement for brittle stars to be known scientifically as ophiuroids – 'snake tails'. Unlike starfishes, which rely upon the tiny suckered tube-feet underneath their arms for locomotion, brittle stars move by direct motion of the arms themselves. They also differ from starfishes via certain anatomical traits.

Despite these differences, however, starfishes and brittle stars are quite closely related, and are believed to have diverged from a common ancestor many millions of years ago. An inkling of what this common ancestor may have been like was obtained in 1922, when the world's most primitive living species of brittle star was discovered. Obtained off Indonesia, and named *Ophiocanops fugiens*, it bridges the gap between brittle stars and starfishes; because, although it is evidently a brittle star, it possesses certain features normally characterising starfishes. Most notable of these is the presence within each of its arms of extensions from the gut, coelom (body cavity), and reproductive organs (other

brittle stars lack these extensions). Also, whereas the longitudinal (ambulacral) groove underneath each arm in other brittle stars is covered by calcareous plates called ossicles, in *Ophiocanops* each such groove is covered with nothing more than a very thin layer of skin – thereby corresponding more closely with the uncovered grooves of starfishes.[23] Underlining the singular nature of its anatomy, *Ophiocanops* is set apart from all other brittle stars in its own taxonomic order – Oegophiurida.

Thermosbaenaceans – some like it hot

In 1923, L-G. Seurat collected some small but very peculiar crustaceans inhabiting the shallow hot spring of Hel Hamma, close to the ruins of an ancient Roman bath near Tunis. Little more than an eighth of an inch long, lacking any vestige of eye-stalks or eyes, and with a short body composed of a series of near-identical segments bearing unspecialised limbs, these tiny, cylindrical organisms were at first thought to be the larval stage of some currently unknown crustacean, but careful examination of the specimens finally convinced scientists that in reality they were adults, but nonetheless of a wholly new species.[24-5]

The following year, French zoologist Dr Theodore Monod described this species, naming it *Thermosbaena mirabilis* – emphasising its hot spring home and novel form. It seemed most closely related to the peracaridan crustaceans (woodlice, sandhoppers, and many shrimp-like species – all characterised by the possession of a brood pouch formed from special plates on the limbs of their thorax). Yet in conspicuous contrast to these, whose brood pouch is situated on their body's underside, *Thermosbaena's* was located on its back.

Together with a number of other unique features, its overall morphology was distinct enough to convince Monod that *Thermosbaena* required special taxonomic treatment, so he created an entirely new peracarid order especially for it, which he named Thermosbaenacea.[24]

Resulting from the interest aroused in zoological circles by the discovery of *Thermosbaena*, other bodies and sources of water were examined for the presence of any related species, and several were eventually found. Between 1949 and 1953, three close relatives were obtained – one from a freshwater Tuscan cave, the others from the slightly brackish waters within an Italian Adriatic cave and a Croatian cave at Dubrovnik. These species were all assigned to a new genus, *Monodella*, but shared the diagnostic dorsal pouch of *Thermosbaena*. In 1976, two more new genera were described – *Limnosbaena* and *Halosbaena*, from Yugoslavia and the West Indies respectively. A single North American species is also known – Texas's *Monodella texana*. *Thermosbaena*, however, remains the only hot spring dweller, capable of surviving in water temperatures of 36.5-47.5°C; all of the others are cool-water species, at temperatures of 12.5-15.5°C.[25]

Exposure of a vampire moth

In 1926, entomologist G. F. Hampson described a small species of Malaysian moth with brown forewings and black-edged orange hindwings, related to Britain's familiar red, yellow, and orange underwing moths (noctuids). Now known as *Calyptra eustrigata*, it attracted little attention – until its extraordinary, sinister secret was uncovered in April 1967 by Swiss entomologist Dr Hans Bänziger, while working in Kuala Lumpur's zoological gardens.[26-7]

There are a number of moth species that idly lap up animal fluids – tears, sweat, urine, blood seeping from an already-open wound – but following his observations of a *C. eustrigata* specimen discovered on the flank of one of the zoo's tapirs, Bänziger suspected that this particular species had taken that process one crucial step further, involving behaviour hitherto unknown among moths. There was only one way to obtain a conclusive answer – so he caught a specimen of *C. eustrigata*, made a small incision in the back of one of his own fingers, allowed the blood to ooze gently from the wound, and then offered his finger to the moth, to observe its reactions. Would it be content merely to lap up the blood flowing from the wound, or would it proceed beyond this?[27]

Losing no time in answering Bänziger's question, the moth totally ignored the blood. Instead, it immediately stabbed its unusually short, sturdy, non-tapering proboscis directly through the skin exposed by the wound, and began actively sucking up the blood from beneath the skin's surface. Bänziger's suspicions were confirmed. This was no innocent lapper of wound-leaking blood; on the contrary, preferring to make its own wound and purposefully suck the blood from it, *C. eustrigata* was, quite literally, a vampire moth.[27]

This unique, blood-sucking species probably descended from fruit-piercing forms (which have similar types of proboscis), subsequently transferring its attention from fruit juices to animal blood. Ironically, like so many notable zoological discoveries, the sanguinivorous secret of *C. eustrigata* might have been exposed much earlier if science had heeded the words of local people. Malaysia's Jakun natives, who inhabit part of this species' wide distribution range, have long known that certain moths are capable of 'biting'.[27-8]

Planctosphaera pelagica – after 61 years its adult form is still unknown

In 1932, the *Michael Sars* Deep-Sea Expedition collected two specimens of a very strange organism from the plankton of the North Atlantic's Bay of Biscay, at a depth of 830 ft. Each resembled a transparent, gooseberry-sized sphere, containing a glassy jelly through which its almost U-shaped gut and other internal organs could be clearly perceived. On its external surface it bore a highly-branched tract of hair-like structures called cilia.[29]

Later in 1932, this peculiar organism was formally named *Planctosphaera pelagica*, and not long afterwards it was classed as the larval form of some member of the phylum Hemichordata, but sufficiently distinct from any species within it to warrant the creation of a new hemichordate class – Planctosphaeroidea. In time, however, detailed studies of the fine structure of *Planctosphaera* convinced researchers that it was most similar to the larval type (known as a tornaria) produced by the acorn worms or enteropneusts – the most well-known class of hemichordate. Even so, it was much larger than the tornaria of any known acorn worm, and its ciliary tract was much more complex in form. Researchers thus assumed that it was the larva of some still-undescribed acorn worm, probably an abyssal species.[29]

Since its initial discovery, only a handful of *Planctosphaera* larvae have been obtained. Moreover, until the 1970s it was still known only from the North Atlantic, but in May 1974 and again in September 1977 and 1982 four specimens (including the largest so far recorded) were trawled up from the North Pacific, at depths of 250-1660 ft, thereby expanding this larva's known range by roughly 5000 miles.[29-30] Nevertheless, science is still no nearer to solving the fundamental mystery concerning *Planctosphaera* – what does its adult form look like? For no adult specimen of this species has ever been knowingly obtained, and its likely shape and size cannot even be predicted, because metamorphosis from the tornaria to the adult in acorn worms is a very drastic process – the spherical tornaria bears no resemblance to the slender, vermiform adult.[30]

One intriguing suggestion, by Hawaiian researchers Drs M.G. Hadfield and Richard E. Young, is that *Planctosphaera* larvae do not belong to any distinct species at all; instead, they are merely abnormally-enlarged tornariae of some already-known species, their enlargement an outcome of failure to find suitable substrata for settlement and thence metamorphosis into the adult, so that they continue to drift through the sea, growing larger and larger. According to Hadfield and Young, their specific morphology implies that they may be swollen tornariae of some species from a group of acorn worms termed ptychoderids.[30]

Ultimately, however, there would seem to be only one conclusive way of determining the identity of the *Planctosphaera* larvae, and that is to maintain them in aquaria, in order to observe their metamorphosis and thus reveal the precise nature of the resulting adults. Yet sadly, as these larvae are so very rarely encountered, it is likely to be a long time before this vital and quite fascinating experiment can be accomplished.

Sea spiders – 'all legs'

Without a doubt, sea spiders are among the strangest of all animals known to man. Referred to scientifically as pycnogonids, on first glance they appear to be composed entirely of legs, hence they are also known as pantopods – 'all legs'. Only on closer observation can they be seen to possess a small head and body too. Despite their common name, sea spiders are only distantly related to true spiders. Indeed, these bewildering, exclusively marine creatures, whose species range in size from well below an inch to a little over 2 ft across, do not seem to be very closely allied to any other group of animals.

Most species of sea spider have four pairs of legs, but a few have five. In 1933, a new precedent was set when Dr W.T. Calman, Keeper of Zoology at the British Museum (Natural History), announced that during the recent British, Australian, and New Zealand Expedition, Sir Douglas Mawson had captured a sea spider in the Antarctic Ocean that possessed six pairs of legs. This species was duly dubbed *Dodecolopoda mawsoni* ('Mawson's twelve-legs'). At first, various authorities suspected it to be simply a freak, extra-limbed individual of some already-known species, but later finds of other *D. mawsoni* specimens (as well as specimens of some new 12-legged species) refuted this theory.[31]

Ricinuleids – world's most elusive order of animals?

Moving from one group of strange spider-like creatures to another, ricinuleids (also called podogonids) are notoriously mysterious creatures, inhabiting damp caves and lurking beneath leaf mould in various regions of West Africa and tropical South America. Superficially they resemble tiny eyeless spiders, but closer examination has revealed them to be sufficiently different to require a taxonomic order of their own.

Notable among their many curious features is a peculiar hood-like structure (cucullus) capable of being lowered over their

mouthparts, plus an abdomen divided dorsally into 12 separate regions. Equally odd is their extraordinarily thick body cuticle, which is resistant to even the sharpest of scalpels and other cutting tools used by researchers when attempting to investigate these strange animals' internal design.

Originally known only from ancient fossils, the first recorded specimen of modern-day ricinuleid – a round-bodied individual measuring all of 8 mm in total length – was collected in 1838 near the coast of Guinea by Swedish naturalist C. Westermann, and was named *Cryptostemma* [now *Ricinoides*] *westermanni* after him by Guérin-Méneville. Although it was subsequently lost, other specimens, belonging to several additional species, were later obtained – but only infrequently, and in very small numbers. By 1900, only 19 specimens were known (ultimately shown to represent eight different species), and zoologists began to despair of ever obtaining

Ricinuleid – an infamously reclusive relative of the spiders and scorpions.
(Prof. John Cloudsley-Thompson)

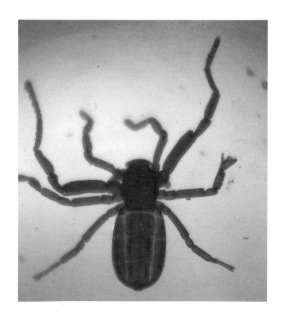

enough examples to discover anything substantial about these obscure arachnids.[32] And then along came Ivan T. Sanderson.

Meant only as a light-hearted joke (being only too aware of their famous rarity), in 1933 zoologists from the British Museum (Natural History) playfully beseeched Sanderson – a noted zoologist and leader of the forthcoming Percy Sladen Trust Expedition to Nigeria and Cameroon – to be sure to come back with plenty of ricinuleids. To their amazement, they learnt that Sanderson had taken them at their word – for he succeeded in bringing back from Cameroon no less than 317 ricinuleids. The number of ricinuleids on record instantaneously soared upwards to yield a very respectable three-figure total.[32-3]

Sanderson's collection all belonged to the species C. [now R.] sjostedti, and about 20 of them actually lived for a year in an incubator at the British Museum, giving scientists a unique opportunity to observe their activity – though as they refused to eat anything, their feeding behaviour and preferences remained a mystery.[32-3]

Although further specimens and species have since been uncovered, and a little more is known of their biology, it would be difficult to match the outstanding record for ricinuleid revelation set by the resourceful Mr Sanderson.

Nothomyrmecia – an archaic ant from Australia

Australia is home to *Nothomyrmecia macrops* – the world's most primitive species of ant. Officially described in 1934, from two worker specimens housed in the zoological collections of Victoria's National Museum, and first collected on a track near Western Australia's Mount Ragged, *N. macrops* is distinguished by its large eyes, unusually short wings (which in queens are incapable of sustaining flight), the location of its stridulatory organ (which produces chirping sounds) underneath its abdomen rather than on top of it, and by the close morphological similarity of its queens to its ordinary workers.[34]

After the 1930s, *N. macrops* was not reported again for many years; but in 1977 it was formally rediscovered, near Ceduna in South Australia's Eyre Peninsula – when on 22 October a CSIRO field party collected some workers and dealate queens (i.e. queens whose wings had been shed, following fertilisation).[34]

The mysterious mystacocarids – cryptic crustaceans from Cape Cod

Measuring no more than 0.5 mm (0.02 in) in total length, the 60 or so specimens of an unusual but tiny, colourless crustacean collected from intertidal sand at Cape Cod, Massachusetts, by ecology researchers Drs Robert W. Pennak and Donald J. Zinn in 1942 could have been easily overlooked. Thankfully, as Pennak and Zinn specialised in studying the microfauna of these habitats, those odd creatures attracted their fair share of attention – which was just as well. At first, they seemed to be nothing more than copepods – a well-known subclass of crustaceans with the ubiquitous freshwater *Cyclops* and the planktonic *Calanus* among its most familiar members. Closer examination, however, exposed significant differences.[25,35]

In contrast to previously known copepods, for example, the tiny Cape Cod crustacean had a distinct carapace ('shell'), its thoracic limbs were much simpler in structure, both pairs of antennae were relatively long and well-developed (in copepods, the second pair is extremely

A pogonophoran, Oligobrachia ivanovi – *nowadays of great zoological worth, such creatures were once mistaken for fibrous marine detritus and were duly discarded.*
(Prof. Alan and Dr Eve Southward)

short), the front portion of its head was divided from the remainder by a distinct transverse groove, and its genital opening was located on the first thoracic body segment (most crustaceans bear it close to the body's rear end). As a result, this aberrant species, named *Derocheilocaris typicus* by Pennak and Zinn in 1943,[35] became sole member of a new crustacean subclass, Mystacocarida, the first of four erected so far this century.[25]

Since then, however, other species have been found – from as far afield as New England, South Africa, the French, Italian and Spanish Rivieras, and the coasts of South America; just under a dozen are currently known. Mystacocarids feed on minute particles of detritus; and on account of being so very small themselves, they do not possess a blood-circulatory system – oxygen simply diffuses directly into their body across its external surface.[25]

Pogonophorans – bizarre beard-bearers constituting an entirely new animal phylum

Scientific sensations come in all shapes and sizes. In this particular instance, it took the form of a long, bedraggled worm- like creature – represented by specimens dredged up from the sea bottom's sludge off the coast of Indonesia in 1900 by the Dutch research vessel *Siboga*. More closely resembling slender lengths of mangled string than any type of animal, these strange entities seemed totally unclassifiable, and so after being bottled they were duly ignored for the next decade.[36] In 1914, however, their pickled remains attracted the attention of French zoologist Dr Maurice Caullery, who became so amazed and fascinated by them that he spent the next 30 years painstakingly studying every minute aspect of their morphology and anatomical structure, in a determined bid to extract the secret of their identity. He named their representative species *Siboglinum weberi* (after the *Siboga* expedition and its leader, M. Weber), and could see that it was a novel creature, unallied to any other animal group. Very tentatively, he placed it within the phylum Hemichordata – housing the acorn worms (see p. 218).[37]

Meanwhile, in 1932 Soviet scientist P.V. Uschakow had discovered an odd-looking creature in the Sea of Okhotsk. The following year, he named it *Lamellisabella zachsi*, and classed it as an aberrant species of sabellid fanworm, belonging to the polychaete class of segmented (annelid) worms.[38] This classification of *Lamellisabella*, however, did not satisfy Swedish researcher Dr K.E. Johansson. His studies, undertaken during the late 1930s, assured him that it was not a polychaete at all, and that it deserved a class completely to itself, which he named Pogonophora ('beard bearer')[39] – but in which phylum should it be placed? It did not seem to have any affinity either with Annelida or with any of the others.

In 1944, zoologist Dr V.N. Beklemishev proposed that there was only one satisfactory solution for the problematical *Lamellisabella* – to elevate Pogonophora from a class to a phylum.[40] The scientific world agreed with this new status for Pogonophora, and so it became the first new animal phylum to be created and fully accepted during this century.

So far, no-one had suggested that *Lamellisabella* might be related to the equally odd *Siboglinum* – both were perplexing, but that was all. By careful comparison, however, a third Soviet scientist, Dr A.V. Ivanov, demonstrated beyond any doubt that the two were indeed closely allied to one another. Accordingly, in 1951 *Siboglinum* was formally removed from Hemichordata and reassigned to Beklemishev's new phylum, containing *Lamellisabella*.[36,41]

Since then, many new species have been discovered and described – more than 200 are currently recognised and have been collected from a variety of different geographical locations in the Pacific, Indian, Atlantic, and Antarctic Oceans, and not just from marine, deepwater localities. Some specimens, for example, have been obtained from the Norwegian fjords in relatively shallow water.[42] Most ironic of all, it is now known that innumerable specimens had been scooped up from the Pacific long before their scientific significance had been recognised, but as they had simply looked like fibrous rubbish they had been unceremoniously tipped back into the sea again.[43]

Moreover, Dr Eve Southward's re-examination of the *Siboglinum weberi* specimens studied by Caullery revealed in 1961 that this 'single species' actually consisted of at least 16 different species. Caullery's failure to detect this had been due to the specimens' poor state of preservation, and the lack of other pogonophorans for comparison at that time.

And so, these once-discarded denizens of the deep (and fjords) are now unequivocally recognised to be one of this century's most important zoological discoveries – but what makes a pogonophoran a pogonophoran, and what makes them so very special? Ranging in length from 2-12 in (depending upon the species concerned), and inhabiting somewhat longer tubes, they exhibit a unique combination of morphological features.

When removed from its tube, the body of a pogonophoran is seen to consist of three sections. The short, front section or forepart houses the brain, and bears a crown of long tentacles (the 'beard'), which may number up to 250 (and even exceed 2000 in one rather special species, discussed later). Behind the forepart is the long, slender, worm-like trunk. This is the principal body section, yet so extraordinarily slender that its width can measure less than 1/500th of the animal's length. Nevertheless, within this fragile, gossamer-like body beats a well-formed heart supplied by a complex system of blood vessels. It also houses a pair of reproductive organs (the sexes are separate in pogonophorans), and a sturdy nerve cord running down its middle from the brain into the third, rearmost body section – a very short segmented portion called the opisthosoma, so delicate that it is easily detached and lost during the collection of specimens. Indeed, its very existence was unknown until 1970, because it had always broken off from specimens obtained prior to then.[18,36]

So far, a pogonophoran would seem to have (in some form or another) most of the major body constituents present in animals of all types – but there is one fundamental omission. Pogonophorans lack any form of digestive system – they have neither a mouth nor a gut. Instead, it is believed that they feed by absorbing nutrient micro-particles from the all-embracing seabottom ooze directly through their body surface – analogous to the way in which the endoparasitic tapeworms obtain their food (absorbing it from the surrounding supply ingested by their unfortunate host). As for breathing, it seems likely that pogonophorans respire by exchanging gases across the surface of their tentacles.[18,36]

All in all, a remarkable combination of characteristics that seemed unlikely ever to be duplicated – an assumption which, as it happened, proved to be somewhat premature. In 1966, some very odd worm-like creatures were collected at a depth of 3750 ft off the coast of California, near San Diego. Their species was described three years later by Dr Michael Webb, from South Africa's Stellenbosch University, who named it *Lamellibrachia barhami*.[44] A little over 3 ft long but less than 0.5 in thick, and with more than 2000 tentacles, it proved to be a pogonophoran, but one so essentially different from all others that Webb placed it in a brand new pogonophoran class – Afrenulata. Notable among the distinguishing features of *L. barhami* was the vestimentum – a special body section present between its crown of tentacles and its trunk. *L. barhami* thus became known as a vestimentiferan. In 1970, a second species of vestimentiferan was found at a depth of 1665 ft, from Guyana's continental slope, and christened *L. luymesi*.[44]

Yet despite their distinction from other pogonophorans, the two *Lamellibrachia* species paled into insignificance when compared to the vestimentiferans found in 1977 – because these latter proved so exceptional that they are recognised today as being among the most bizarre and visually spectacular creatures ever witnessed by man, as revealed on p. 240.

Vampire squid – unmasking a nightmare from the deep

In 1946, the published exposée of a certain grotesque marine creature's true identity sent shock waves through zoological circles worldwide.

First collected during the *Valdivia* deepsea expedition of 1903, and introduced that same year to the scientific world by noted marine biologist Dr Carl Chun,[45] it was immediately a source of wonder and puzzlement, for whereas the most famous attribute of any octopus species hitherto described had been its possession of eight arms, this new, superficially octopus-like creature had ten, like squids. The rest of its external morphology was equally strange. Its eyes were distinctly sinister – huge, deep-red orbs that glittered eerily. Even more macabre, however, was the purplish-black web between its eight longest arms, connecting each to the next like a dark, membranous bat wing. The resulting combination of glittering crimson eyes, nightmarish web, and squid-like complement of ten arms inspired Chun when officially describing this new creature to name it *Vampyroteuthis infernalis* – 'hellish vampire squid'.[45]

Yet despite its ten arms and corresponding squid appellation, in overall external form *Vampyroteuthis* seemed similar enough to octopuses to be classed with them. As for its arms: eight were long, and on the underside of each of these was a central row of suckers, running down its length and bordered on each side by a row of pointed, protruding structures called papillae or cirri. The remaining pair of arms was much shorter, each of its two members resembling a coiled, reduced version of the longer arms, and capable of being withdrawn into a pouch. Unlike the eight main arms, these two smaller ones were not linked to the membranous web, and appeared to act as tactile organs or feelers.[18,45-6]

The vampire squid's body was fat and bulbous, as with typical octopuses, but its ink sac was very degenerate, unlike the prominent structures of the octopuses. Its body bore a short pair of paddle-like dorsal fins, resembling those of squids, and certain internal features also suggested a squid affinity. Clearly, its classification as an aberrant octopus was unsatisfactory, but it remained as such for the next four decades.[18,45-6]

Yet for much of that time it was not a solitary species, because between its discovery in 1903 and its identity's denouement in the mid-1940s no less than eleven fresh species of vampire squid (assigned to eight different genera) were brought to scientific attention, and were distinguished from one another by reference to certain external idiosyncrasies.[18,46]

During the early 1940s, *Vampyroteuthis infernalis* had been meticulously studied by American biologist Dr Grace Pickford – who revealed two remarkable findings when she published her researches in 1946. Firstly, the other species of vampire squid were based upon nothing more than poorly-preserved specimens of *V. infernalis*; the chemicals used in preserving them had distorted their appearance to give the impression that they were quite different from the single original species. Secondly, the vampire squid was neither an octopus nor a squid. Instead, it was a last survivor of an ancient group related to (but separate from) both of these

taxonomic orders; in particular, its horny skeletal shield (gladius) resembled those of long-extinct species called loligosepiids.[46]

As a result, the vampire squid required the creation of a modern-day order all to itself, and once again its appearance inspired the choice of name – the newly-established order was duly named Vampyromorpha ('vampire-shaped'). A totally new order of molluscs had been added to the catalogue of present-day animals.[46]

Although the last member of an ancient lineage, as a species the vampire squid is by no means uncommon. Since its discovery, well over a hundred specimens have been obtained, the larger ones almost 1 ft long, with a worldwide distribution in subtropical and tropical oceans, inhabiting the cold, lightless, abyssal zone present at depths of about 5000-8350 ft. In a world without sunlight, its huge eyes might seem somewhat incongruous and superfluous, but they probably serve to detect the many types of bioluminescent life forms that occur at these depths, and upon which it presumably preys. Indeed, the vampire squid itself has quite an array of bioluminescent structures, their lights flickering like coloured stars amongst the dark folds of its 'wing'.[18]

Neopilina – ending 350 million years of extinction

Probably the most spectacular zoological comeback of all time occurred in 1952, restoring to life an archaic lineage previously believed to have vanished over 350 million years ago.

On 6 May, trawling off Mexico's western coast at a depth of almost 12,000 ft in dark, muddy clay, the Danish research ship *Galathea* hauled up ten complete specimens and three empty shells of a small, seemingly unremarkable mollusc superficially resembling a limpet.[47]

Closer observation, however, disclosed that they were not limpets but a hitherto undescribed species distinct from all other living molluscs known to science. Yet they were not wholly unknown. The zoological world was astounded to learn that they were unquestionably akin to a class of molluscs known previously only from fossil forms – forms whose most recent representatives died out more than 350 million years ago, during the Carboniferous Period, when the dominant creatures were ammonites and giant fishes. For these newly-discovered limpet-resembling animals were monoplacophorans, and as such were now the most primitive modern-day molluscs known to man.[47]

Of especial note was the close similarity in overall appearance between this 20th century monoplacophoran species and its primeval fossil ancestors, suggesting that monoplacophorans had occupied much the same ecological niche throughout their lineage's many millions of years of existence. Indeed, because of its resemblance to one particular long-extinct genus, *Pilina*, when officially described in February 1957 by Danish zoologist Dr Henning Lemche it was dubbed *Neopilina galatheae* ('similar to *Pilina*, obtained by *Galathea*').[47]

Spoon-shaped and no more than 1.5 in long, all of the *Neopilina* shells, inhabited and uninhabited, were very fragile, semi-transparent, and extremely thin – with a shimmering mother-of-pearl inner surface, a yellowish-white outer shading, and a slightly slanted peak. The mollusc itself had a circular fleshy foot, similar to but smaller than that of a limpet. Yet unlike a limpet, or any other living species of mollusc known at that time, its body was divided internally into segments – a condition reminiscent of that in earthworms, ragworms, and leeches (collectively termed segmented worms or annelids). Zoologists considered this to be extremely exciting, for the following reason.[3,47]

The fertilised eggs of annelids and those of molluscs undergo the same basic pattern of division (known as spiral cleavage), and ultimately transform into almost identical larvae (of a type called a trochophore). These similarities have been interpreted by many zoologists as indicators of a close evolutionary relationship between these two animal phyla. As a consequence, the news that *Neopilina* was a primitive mollusc with annelid-like segmentation fuelled widespread

Neopilina galatheae – *its discovery in 1952 sensationally resurrected the monoplacophoran molluscs from over 350 million years of presumed extinction.*
(Geert Brovad)

speculation that monoplacophorans constituted a 'missing link' between other molluscs and the annelids, and that molluscs had descended from annelids.[347]

Of late, however, this theory has lost favour, and a new theory proposes that molluscs and annelids arose independently of one another, from a common ancestor. According to this, therefore, the presence of segmentation in annelids and in monoplacophorans is also of independent origin, not evolving until after the separate emergence of these two phyla from their shared ancestor.[3,47]

If the latter theory is correct, this reduces the significance of the segmentation exhibited by *Neopilina*, but its identity as a living monoplacophoran is still more than enough to make its discovery the most belated comeback of this century.[3,47-8]

It was not long before *Neopilina galatheae* was joined by a number of other present-day monoplacophorans. In December 1958, four specimens of a second species, christened *N. ewingi*, were dredged up from the Peru-Chile Trench off northern Peru by the research vessel *Vema* (owned by the Lamont Geological Observatory, of New York's Columbia University). This was followed in 1960 by the discovery of *N. valeronis*, hauled up from the Cedros Trench of Baja California, again by *Vema*. Seven years later, Peru's Trench offered up *N. bacescui* and *N. bruuni*.[18,48] All of these were deepwater species, brought up from 3000-6500 m (10,000-21,660 ft), but in 1976 this trend was broken by Dr J.H. McLean, who obtained a new, tiny species from depths of as little as 174 m (580 ft) on the Cortes

Ridge, off southern California. Similar finds were made in 1977 by Dr H.A. Lowenstam of the California Institute of Technology.[49] These finds show that *N. galatheae* is far from being the lone survivor of an otherwise long-vanished line that it was initially assumed to be.

Hutchinsoniella – an oddity from the ooze

In 1955, a wholly new crustacean subclass – dubbed Cephalocarida – was created by Dr Howard L. Sanders in order to accommodate some diminutive but quite extraordinary animals discovered in the mud and ooze at the bottom of New York's Long Island Sound. They were tiny, colourless, shrimp-like creatures no more than 4 mm (1.5 in) long; with a horseshoe-shaped head bearing two pairs of short antennae but lacking eyes; an elongate body composed of 19 segments (but not assembled into a thorax and an abdomen) of which the first nine each bore a pair of leaf-like limbs; and a terminal anal

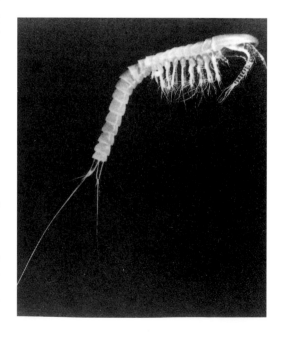

Hutchinsoniella macracantha – *possibly the world's most primitive crustacean, it was first documented in 1955.*
(Reproduction courtesy of the Smithsonian Institution)

segment that bore two pairs of tail-like appendages (one pair of which was extremely long). The undescribed species to which these curious specimens belonged was christened *Hutchinsoniella macracantha*, and caused a sensation in the zoological world – all because of the shape of its limbs.[50]

With every previously known species of present-day crustacean, the body's limbs consisted of two or more morphological types, each type having become specialised to fulfil a different function. With *Hutchinsoniella*, however, all nine pairs were virtually identical to one another, a condition comparable in the opinion of many researchers to that of the earliest ancestral crustaceans. And that was not all – for whereas the base of the limb in previously-known modern-day crustaceans often gave rise to two terminal appendages (such limbs are termed biramous), in *Hutchinsoniella* each limb's base gave rise to three such appendages (i.e. triramous), comparable to the limb structure of the ancient trilobites. All of this implies that *Hutchinsoniella* may be the most primitive crustacean alive today.[25,50]

A second cephalocarid species, lacking a pair of limbs on its eighth body segment, and obtained from San Francisco Bay in 1957, was formally documented in 1961. Named *Lightiella serendipita*, it was the first of a series of species belonging to this genus that turned up during the early 1960s. *Sandersiella acuminata* was described in 1965, its generic name commemorating the cephalocarids' discoverer, and at least two more *Sandersiella* species have been uncovered since then. In 1977, a new cephalocarid from New Zealand was *Chiltoniella elongata*, thus yielding a current total of at least nine new species in four genera, of which *Lightiella* is often separated from the others within a family of its own.[25]

Little is known of cephalocarid biology, but they appear to feed upon the tiny organic-rich particulate matter present within their habitat's thick mud. Unlike most other non-parasitic crustaceans, cephalocarids are hermaphroditic (developing both male and female sexual systems), rather than having separate sexes.[25]

Spelaeogriphaceans – cave-dwelling crustaceans from Cape Town

Sanders's description of the new crustacean subclass, Cephalocarida, had no sooner appeared in print before another new crustacean group came into being, this time to house a small, blind, transparent species from South Africa. In 1956, a series of specimens representing this hitherto unknown crustacean was obtained by members of the South African Spelaeological Association from a pool at a depth of 110 ft, located inside a cavern known as Bat Cave, on Cape Town's Table Mountain. The specimens ultimately reached crustacean specialist Dr Isabella Gordon of the British Museum (Natural History), who recognised that the new species clearly belonged to the subclass Malacostraca (containing the familiar lobsters, crabs, shrimps, and prawns), but was sufficiently dissimilar from all of its other members to require a new taxonomic order.[25,51] In 1957, Gordon named this species *Spelaeogriphus lepidops* ('scale-eyed cave riddle'); its order was dubbed Spelaeogriphacea.[51]

Measuring no more than a few millimetres in length, the subterranean *Spelaeogriphus* has a long cylindrical body, superficially shrimp-like in appearance, bearing more than ten pairs of limbs that comprise several different morphological types, and an eyeless head equipped with two pairs of antennae (the posterior pair of which is well developed). Instead of eyes, it has only a pair of scale-like structures called ocular lobes, which lack visual components or pigments, so that the animal is undoubtedly blind.[25,51]

Curiously, this little crustacean combines features from several separate malacostracan groups, including the woodlouse-allied tanaidaceans, the mountain shrimps or anaspidaceans, and the thermosbaenaceans (see p. 216). Yet despite its taxonomic significance, it has attracted surprisingly little research interest; nor has there been much attempt to look for additional species. In 1974, however, the fossil crustacean *Acadiocaris novascotica*, housed until then within the order Syncarida, was recognised by crustacean expert Dr W. Frederick Schram to be a spelaeogriphacean.[25,51]

Flecker's sea-wasp – beware the tentacles of death

Except for its rounded apex, the 3-4-in-high bell of the Australian sea-wasp jellyfish *Chiropsalmus quadrigatus* is virtually cuboidal in shape. This is a characteristic of most of the species sharing its taxonomic group (nowadays widely treated as a separate class, distinct from the true jellyfishes or scyphozoans), so they are collectively termed cubomedusans or box jellies. For many years, there have been a number of cases reported from northern Australian waters involving swimmers and bathers stung very severely (sometimes fatally) by jellyfishes that leave weals in their victims' flesh and inflict such intense agony that death has sometimes ensued within minutes. Investigations suggested that a cubomedusan species was the most

likely culprit, but as these are almost transparent it proved very difficult to obtain a conclusive identification. However, as one such species – *C. quadrigatus* – was definitely known to frequent these waters, in the absence of precise data, science assumed that this was probably the creature responsible, until a case occurred that exposed the real offender.[52-3]

On 20 January 1955, at 9.35 a.m., a five-year-old boy was swimming in the sea at Cardwell, north Queensland, when he was stung by a jellyfish and died shortly afterwards. The manner of stinging was of the type hitherto assumed to be due to *C. quadrigatus*, but on this occasion there was actually some physical evidence to consider too. Tentacles from his attacker were found in the boy's hair; moreover, his mother had observed the jellyfish responsible. The following day, zoologist Dr Hugo Flecker instigated a series of nettings in the expanse of sea where the boy had been attacked, in the hope that its assailant would still be there. The nettings resulted in the capture of several box jellies, which were closely examined. Their tentacles appeared to be the same as those found in the boy's hair, and his mother stated that the jellies themselves were of the same type as her son's attacker. All of this was obviously very important, but most important of all was that the species to which these jellies belonged was not the familiar *C. quadrigatus*. Instead, they proved to be of a species wholly unknown to science until then, superficially like *C. quadrigatus* but differing from it significantly with regard to certain specific anatomical details.[52-3]

In 1956, Dr R.V. Southcott, a jellyfish researcher who had examined the specimens after receiving them from Dr Flecker, christened this newly-exposed species *Chironex fleckeri* – known popularly as Flecker's sea-wasp, and the sole member of a new genus.[52]

With a bell up to 7 in tall at maturity, but otherwise resembling *C. quadrigatus* externally, the virtually transparent *Chironex* has several unique anatomical features, including its lobe-shaped gonads (reproductive organs); those of *C. quadrigatus* and other cubomedusans are leaf-shaped. At each lower corner of its cuboidal bell is a bunch of tentacles, faintly tinged with mauve; each tentacle can measure up to 1 ft long prior to any active extension induced by the box jelly itself, and is encircled by rings of devastatingly effective stinging cells called nematocysts. Analyses of these cells and the poison that they release upon contact, not to mention the harrowing cases on record involving the stinging of humans by this species, confirm that Flecker's sea-wasp is unquestionably the world's most dangerous jellyfish.[52-4]

Its venom is cardiotoxic, acting upon the victim's heart, and is so potent that according to one Australian scientist: '...only a bullet kills faster'. Worst of all, however, is the degree of pain that it inflicts. Wielding an armoury of almost 40 million nematocysts, *Chironex* is capable of eliciting the most horrific, excruciating pain known to mankind – so terrible that even before its victim has died (in cases of extensive stinging), he/she has been driven to the point of raving insanity by the indescribable agony of the stings.[52-4]

Fortunately, a toxoid for active immunisation is now available; but there is a simple (if unusual) way of avoiding the stings of *Chironex*. Despite their formidable effect, its nematocysts do not have great powers of penetration, so swimmers can actually withstand brushing against its tentacles – if they are wearing an all-embracing, loosely-fitting swimsuit made from ladies' panty hose. This odd costume has thus become the unlikely 'uniform' of lifeguards working in offshore waters frequented by *Chironex*, where, needless to say, it is acknowledged that an unusual swimsuit is infinitely preferable to an agonising death.[54]

Gnathostomulids – an overlooked phylum

Zoologists with a specialised knowledge of the flatworm phylum (Platyhelminthes – housing such notorious species as tapeworms, liver flukes, and many other parasites) had been aware since the 1920s of a small group of ostensibly simple creatures known as gnathostomulids ('jaw mouths'). Rather than parasitising other animals, however, these tiny, worm-like creatures lead innocuous, inconspicuous lives buried in the thick black ooze at the bottom of the sea. Indeed, as they seem perfectly able to spend their entire lives completely submerged within this slimy sludge it is likely that they respire anaerobically (without oxygen), an impressive feat that many bacteria but few animals can accomplish.[55]

Even so, with transparent bodies no more than 1 mm long the gnathostomulids remained undescribed by science until as recently as 1956, when Göttingen zoologist Dr Peter Ax published the findings of his detailed studies concerning them – with far-reaching results.[56]

His investigations drew comparisons between the gnathostomulids and the turbellarian flatworms – the only platyhelminth class of predominantly non-parasitic species – and likened them to certain turbellarians lacking an internal body cavity (i.e. acoelomate), as the bodies of gnathostomulids are also totally solid throughout. Overall, however, they seemed

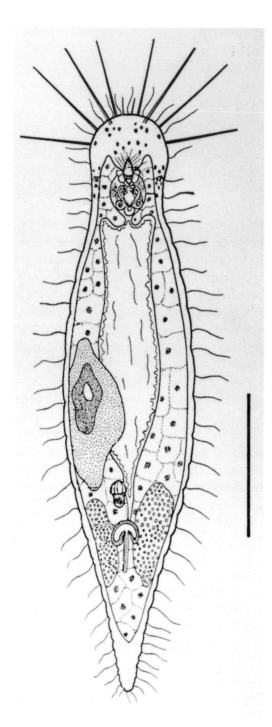

A gnathostomulid, Valvognathia pogonostoma – *the taxonomic significance of these tiny ooze-dwelling animals was not realised until 1969.* (Scale bar 0.1 mm) *(Dr Reinhardt Kristensen)*

sufficiently discrete to warrant separate categorisation, and so in 1960 he formally assigned them to a new, specially-created taxonomic class within the flatworm phylum.[57]

Less than a decade later, moreover, they acquired even greater taxonomic significance. The last time that an entirely new phylum of animals had been established was in 1944, to house the pogonophorans (see p. 221); this had raised the total number of modern-day animal phyla to 33. Resulting from his examinations of gnathostomulids, in 1969 Dr R. Riedl announced that these constituted a valid, independent phylum too. This was because he had discovered that these onetime overlooked and understudied creatures embodied an exceptional combination of characteristics drawn from two totally separate levels of morphological complexity within the animal kingdom.[58]

On the one hand, their acoelomate body, lack of an anus, and hermaphroditic reproductive system drew comparisons with various turbellarians – animals relatively low on the scale of structural, evolutionary development. On the other hand, they also possessed sophisticated sensory bristles, a well-formed head and jaws in most species, and a range of specific cellular details that were characteristic of some much more advanced animal groups, such as 'wheel'-bearing creatures called rotifers, and related organisms called gastrotrichs. Consequently, Riedl's recommendation was accepted by science, and Gnathostomulida, the thirty-fourth phylum of modern-day animals, was added to the zoological register.[55,58]

Glory of the sea

Throughout the history of shell collecting, the most sought-after species has always been the glory of the sea *Conus gloriamaris*, one of the many species of cone shell, but totally without peers as the most coveted prize of all – conchology's *crème de la crème*.

The reason for its near-legendary status is twofold. Firstly, it is an exquisite species. Its slender shell attains a height of up to 8 in, and bears an extremely graceful spire, composed of several almost straight whorls and elevated much higher than the spire of most other cone species. Equally elegant is its shell's patterning, for its entire surface, of pale background colour, bears a fine filigree of tiny triangular reticulations, overlain by four or five darker spiral bands of varying degrees of visibility. Once seen, the glory of the sea cone is never forgotten. Secondly, it has always been famed for its great rarity, with fewer than a dozen specimens known prior to the 20th century.[59-60]

Indeed, 1896 saw the discovery of what seemed destined to be the very last specimen of the glory of the sea cone ever collected, because in spite of numerous searches and enquiries within the conchological fraternity during the years that followed, no additional find was made – until 1957, when a specimen was discovered off Corregidor Island in the Philippines. The glory of the sea had finally resurfaced, quelling widespread fears that it had become extinct. Nothing could have been further from the truth, in fact, for since then quite a number have been obtained from the waters east of New Guinea – so that although in absolute terms it is still a rare species, compared to its former status it is no longer quite so scarce. In any event, its aura of romance and desirability remains to allure future generations of shell collectors worldwide.[59-60]

In 1959, another of conchology's celebrated rarities reappeared, when several specimens of the impressive bull conch *Strombus taurus* were collected by R.C. Willis

in the Marshall Islands – the first time that this species had been reported since its description in 1875.[60]

Stygiomedusa – extraordinary entity from the stygian depths

On 18 October 1959, the research vessel *Sarsia* was cruising off Santander in northern Spain's Bay of Biscay, collecting deepsea animals on behalf of the Development Commission's Fisheries Research Biomedical Unit, when their Isaac Kidd pelagic net brought to the surface a spectacular new denizen of the deep. Dredged up from a depth of at least 10,000 ft, it was a large jellyfish, deep brownish-red and plum in colour, with a bell (umbrella) of firm composition and a diameter of roughly 20 in.[61]

Following its capture, it was closely examined by Dr F.S. Russell of Plymouth's Marine Biological Association, who recognised that it was a member of the semaeostome order of jellyfishes, but was sufficiently different from all known semaeostomes to warrant the creation of a new genus. Semaeostomes are named after the four lobe-like structures termed oral arms that extend down from their mouth (manubrium). In the case of the *Sarsia* specimen, these arms were enormously elongate, superficially resembling tentacles and attaining a length of around 5.5 ft. In contrast, whereas most semaeostomes also have a fringe of long, true tentacles encircling their bell's rim, the *Sarsia* individual had none.

Most interesting of all: whereas sexual reproduction in most semaeostomes involves the shedding of eggs and sperm into the sea for external fertilisation, the new jellyfish was viviparous, i.e. its young develop internally and are born alive (rather than encased inside eggs). This was revealed by the presence of fully-developed young jellyfishes inside each of the adult's four specialised brood chambers that protrude into its stomach cavity.[61]

Later in 1959, Dr Russell prepared a short paper in which he named this brood-caring, live-bearing surprise *Stygiomedusa fabulosa*, likening its lightless, deepsea home to the inky blackness of Greek mythology's fabled River Styx, and emphasising the extraordinary nature of the jellyfish itself. This was followed in 1960 by a detailed morphological description, prepared jointly by Russell and Dr W.J. Rees of the British Museum (Natural History), where the *Sarsia* example now resides as the type specimen of *S. fabulosa*.[61]

On 3 May 1962, a specimen of what appeared to be a new species of *Stygiomedusa* was caught at a depth of 3160-3260 ft in the Gulf of Guinea, about 100 miles northwest of the Congo Estuary. The most important feature that appeared to differentiate it from *S. fabulosa* was the layout of its radial canals. These canals are actually fine tubes that radiate outwards to the edge of the jellyfish's bell from its centrally-located stomach (gastric cavity). In *S. fabulosa*, these canals did not combine with one another over their entire length, and were readily discerned. By contrast, those of the Guinea *Stygiomedusa* specimen were totally obscured. Thus in 1967 French marine biologist Dr R. Repelin designated the latter as the type specimen of a new species – *S. stauchi*.[62]

Also in 1962, a second undeniable specimen of *S. fabulosa* was recorded, this time from Greenland, but sadly it was not preserved.[63] Nine years later, however, on 24 June 1971, the research vessel *Sarsia* obtained another *S. fabulosa*; and this one was preserved. It had been caught in a

region of the Bay of Biscay near to where the species' type specimen had been captured, but this time at a depth of only 4000-4660 ft.[64]

On 1 July 1972, yet another *Stygiomedusa* was procured. It had been captured by the research vessel *Chain*, about 745 miles north of the Azores in the north Atlantic, at a depth of 2500 ft, and proved to be of special significance. With a bell diameter of 56 in, it was the largest *Stygiomedusa* on record; but of much greater importance, it was undeniably intermediate in appearance between specimens of *S. fabulosa* and the single, type specimen of *S. stauchi*. Consequently, zoologists now consider *S. fabulosa* to be more variable morphologically than previously suspected, discounting *S. stauchi* as a separate species and reclassifying its type as merely a distinctive individual of *S. fabulosa*.[65]

White-toothed cowry – rediscovering the world's most valuable seashell

In the opinion of many shell collectors, the most valuable shell is that of the white-toothed cowry, and in view of its remarkable history this distinction is well-deserved. The type specimen of this species, of unknown provenance, was purchased in May 1828 from G.B. Sowerby by naturalist W.P. Broderip, who formally described it later that year. He named it *Cypraea leucodon* – after the white colouration of the tooth-like projections fringing its shell's aperture, and by which it could be readily distinguished from other cowry species. In 1837, with no additional specimen of *C. leucodon* reported, Broderip's entire shell collection was purchased by the British Museum's trustees. In so doing, the museum gained a shell that was destined to become one of the most famous in conchological history, because in spite of every effort made by shell collectors throughout the world to locate more *C. leucodon* specimens, not a single one was obtained.[60,66]

Over a century passed by in this way, until some experts began to wonder if *C. leucodon* really was a genuine species, or just a freakish form of some more familiar cowry. But in 1960, conchologists were startled to learn that a second specimen had been in existence for many years, in the collections of the Boston Society of Natural History, but with its true identity hitherto unrecognised. This find supported the status of *C. leucodon* as a valid species, but as the Boston specimen's origin was unknown, its species' provenance remained a mystery – until 1965. In that year, shell expert S. Peter Dance examined some photos of two shells that had been taken from the stomach of a fish caught in the Philippines' Sulu Sea – and realised that one of the shells was a perfect *C. leucodon*. After 137 years, the riddle of the white-toothed cowry had finally been solved.[60]

This history recalls that of another rare cowry. In 1903, Fulton's cowry *C. fultoni* was described from a specimen taken out of the stomach of a fish caught off South Africa's Natal coast; and most specimens obtained since have also been found inside fishes.[60,67]

Exposing the invisible irukandji

Generations of bathers and swimmers in the shallow seawater off Australia's northern coasts have been very severely stung during

Irukandji – the unpleasant effects of its stinging cells were well known to medical science several decades before its species' identity was exposed by zoology. (Dr Karl Shuker)

this country's summer months (December to February) by a mystery creature that in many ways seemed more akin to a phantom than to any form of corporeal animal. Known as the irukandji, after the Irukandji aboriginal tribe that formerly lived on the coast north of Cairns, Queensland (in whose shallow waters irukandji incidents most commonly occur), it was never seen, and eluded capture even in fishing nets of the finest mesh. Yet it left its victims in no doubt whatsoever of its physical reality.[53,68]

The first indication of an irukandji sting is a sharp prickling sensation in the area of the victim's flesh that has come into direct contact with the creature. This is followed a few minutes later by the appearance of 'goose-flesh' and then by a much more extensive region of reddening. Deceptively, this vanishes fairly swiftly afterwards, leaving the skin looking normal once more – but after 20 minutes or so, excruciating backache begins, followed by overall

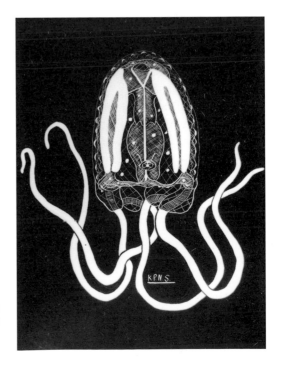

weakness, sudden (often intense) abdominal pains and contractions, headache, sweating, and sometimes laboured breathing, culminating in violent spasms of coughing and vomiting that can last for some hours if the victim is left untreated. To date, there have been no documented fatalities, but as can be appreciated from the above description the effects of an irukandji sting are nonetheless quite devastating, and require intravenous injection of pethidine for effective control. The characteristic set of symptoms engendered by such a sting has been well known in medical circles for at least 60 years, and since 1952 it has been officially referred to as the irukandji syndrome.[53,68]

Yet for many years the irukandji itself eluded every attempt made to discover its identity or to snare a specimen – though this is not too surprising really. After all, how could anyone capture a creature that could not be seen, and that could not be trapped in a net?[53,68]

The answer to this dilemma came in 1961. For much of the 1950s, Cairns marine biologist Dr John H. Barnes had been investigating box jellies (cubomedusans), and had been particularly keen to ascertain the identity of the irukandji. In an attempt to capture one, he had been employing a specially-constructed piece of apparatus that functioned by snapping shut on any fast-moving underwater creature that the operator wished to catch. Even so, this was still only a partial solution to the problem – needless to say, it could only be used on creatures that the operator could see, and the irukandji was famous for staying unseen.[53,68]

On 10 December 1961, however, the irukandji made a fatal mistake, which cost it its scientific anonymity. On that day, Barnes was exploring the shallow sea off Queensland's Palm Beach, when suddenly something small swam right in front of his face. Even at such close range, Barnes was unable to spot the creature's body, but he could discern some thin, white tentacles, and so quickly brought his 'catcher' into operation and deftly snapped it shut on the unidentified sea animal. It proved to be an exceedingly small, transparent box jelly, of a type hitherto unknown to him.[53,68]

Little more than 0.5 in across its bell, it was rather unusual in appearance because its bell resembled a rounded rectangle in shape, quite unlike the characteristic cuboidal version possessed by most other box jellies. Moreover, whereas other box jellies sported an entire bunch of tentacles at each of the four lowermost corners of their bell's cube, each of the lowermost corners of this creature's rectangular bell bore only a single tentacle, thus adding up to just four in total, each measuring no more than 16-20 in long.[53,68]

Clearly this was an important new species, but could it also be the legendary irukandji? Certainly its transparent body would ensure that it remained unseen by swimmers, and its minute size would enable it to pass through fine-meshed nets – but there was only one way to determine conclusively whether or not it was truly the irukandji. So Barnes stoically applied its tentacles directly onto his own skin, to record the effect. And sure enough, he experienced the well-documented, diagnostic irukandji syndrome. The experiment was repeated on various brave volunteers, and they too experienced those very same symptoms. The mystery was solved – science finally had a specimen of the elusive irukandji.[53,68]

Later that same day, a small fish that seemed to be in some way afflicted was scooped out of the water near the original irukandji's site of capture, and when examined it was found to be attached to an irukandji, which Barnes also preserved. Others were then captured at later dates, and in 1965 the type specimen and one other were passed by Barnes to Australian jellyfish expert Dr R.V. Southcott, who described their species in 1967. He named it *Carukia barnesi* – commemorating Dr Barnes's valiant determination to expose the irukandji's identity, and recognising its morphological singularities by housing it in a new genus.[69]

The secret of why the irukandji is so notoriously effective as a stinging organism has now been revealed. Its formidable stinging cells (nematocysts) are not just confined to its tentacles as with most jellyfishes – instead, there is also a generous sprinkling of wart-like nematocyst clusters all over its bell. In view of this devastating arsenal, it is fortunate that the irukandji does not reside permanently in Queensland's coastal waters; it is primarily an oceanic species, only invading the coasts if swarms are diverted by an appropriate combination of topographical features, prey, and water temperatures offshore.[53,68-9]

An enormous earwig from St. Helena

People who mistakenly believe in the unfounded old wives' tale that earwigs take a particular delight in entering the ears of the unwary have nothing to fear from *Labidura herculeana* – unless they have exceptionally large ears. Attaining a formidable total length (for an earwig) of 2.5-3 in, this robust resident of the South Atlantic island of St. Helena is the world's largest species of earwig, and has a highly unusual history.

It was officially described and named as long ago as 1798, by the famous Danish entomologist Fabricius, but somehow it later became confounded with the much smaller and more familiar shore earwig *L. riparia*, and thereafter received no further attention from science. For almost two centuries it was as if Fabricius's giant earwig had never existed, with his description of it long since forgotten.[6,70]

Model of St Helena giant earwig, flanked by the 2-man Project Hercules team, and Paul Pearce-Kelly (right) of London Zoo.
(Zoo Operations Ltd)

In 1962, while seeking bird bones in the sands of St. Helena's Prosperous Bay, ornithologists N.P. Ashmole and D.F. Dorward discovered some dried, tail-end pincers from what must have been some form of enormous earwig – as confirmed by zoologist Arthur Loveridge, to whom they were given. These were subsequently examined by a number of other zoologists, all of whom assumed that they must be from a wholly new species, never before documented by science. And so it was christened *L. loveridgei*, honouring the man who had first studied its remains.[71] From their condition, they seemed to be of recent origin (i.e. they were not fossilised), inciting speculation that this species might still be alive. In 1965, a team of entomologists arrived at St. Helena to look for it – and discovered quite a few, inhabiting deep burrows hidden beneath heavy boulders at Horse Point Plain (near Prosperous Bay), but that was not all that they found.[6,70]

Back home, researching these specimens, they uncovered details concerning the long-forgotten giant earwig *L. herculeana*, and realised that this was the very same species as the newly-described *L. loveridgei*. And so, in accordance with the rules of nomenclatural precedence in relation to scientific names, the latter version was suppressed, and '*L. herculeana*' was reinstated as the species' official scientific name.[70]

Tragically, however, the issue of what it should be called may now be somewhat academic. Searches since the 1960s have failed to locate any living specimens, either at Horse Point Plain or anywhere else on the island. The most recent search was made in spring 1988 by Project Hercules – a two-man expedition launched by London Zoo, comprising Dave Clarke and Richard Veal. However, bearing in mind its predominantly subterranean lifestyle, it is not impossible that the giant earwig of St. Helena still survives, undetected by man.[72]

Midgardia – wrapping its arms around a world record

On 18 August 1969, while dredging in the Gulf of Mexico's southern region at a depth of 1500 ft, Texas A and M University's research vessel *Alaminos* collected a female starfish, bright red in colour, exceedingly large and extremely fragile. Both of these conditions were due to its twelve extremely long and slender arms, which yielded a maximum armtip-to-armtip span of just under 54.5 in – effortlessly surpassing that of any other starfish specimen on record. In stark contrast, it weighed less than 2.5 oz dry, and its central body disc was only just over an inch in total diameter – thereby creating the illusion of a bodiless sea monster bristling with endless serpentine arms.[73]

This, at least, may well have been the image that it conjured up in the mind of Maureen E. Downey of the Smithsonian Institution – because, on 29 February 1972, when she officially described this new species (sufficiently removed from all others to require its own genus), she christened it *Midgardia xandaros*. *Xandaros* is Greek for 'sea monster', and *Midgardia* is an allusion to the famous Midgard Serpent of Norse mythology, which encircled the entire world in its limitless coils.[73]

Despite a superficial similarity to some giant form of brittle star (ophiuroid), *M. xandaros* belongs to the brisingid starfish family, whose members only occur in deep water, thus making its type specimen's capture a notable event. A second specimen had been caught during the same dredge, but it broke into fragments before being brought to the surface.[73]

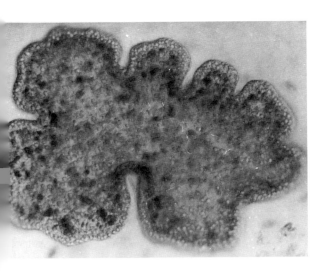

Placozoan, Trichoplax adhaerens – *the only member of an entire phylum, this enigmatic creature staged a welcome comeback in 1971.*
(Prof. Karl Grell)

Trichoplax – return of an enigma

One of the smallest yet most mysterious of all multicellular animals is a tiny creature known scientifically as *Trichoplax adhaerens,* but lacking a common name as even its very existence remains unknown to most people (including the majority of zoologists). Yet it is so different from all other animals that in 1971 its principal researcher, Prof. Karl G. Grell of Tübingen University, housed it within a phylum of its own – variously termed Phagocytellozoa or (most commonly) Placozoa. For convenience, this phylum's sole occupant is referred to in general terms as a placozoan – 'flat animal'. (A second species, discovered in the Gulf of Naples, was christened *Treptoplax reptans* by F.S. Monticelli in 1896, but has never been recorded again; most authorities today doubt that it is a genuinely distinct species.)[74]

Trichoplax was first discovered in 1883, when observed in the marine aquarium of Austria's Graz Zoological Institute, and was spasmodically recorded from other laboratory aquaria around the world in the years to come. But it had not been reported for a long time until it was formally rediscovered in 1971 by Dr Richard Miller, who observed it adhering to the walls of some seawater tanks at Philadelphia's Temple University.[74]

Structurally, *Trichoplax* is among the simplest of all multicelled animal forms – a flat, amorphous mass superficially resembling an oversized, grey-coloured amoeba that continually changes its shape, and measuring up to about 0.4 mm in diameter. Unlike the unicellular amoebae, however, its body is composed of several thousand cells, arranged in two clearly delineated layers (separated from each other by gelatinous fluid), which provide it with a distinct dorsal and ventral surface, but it lacks organs and tissues. Moreover, as it has neither a fixed front and rear end nor a left-hand and right-hand side, it can move in any direction – by crawling (juveniles can also swim).[55,74]

Reproduction can occur either by simple division of one animal into two (fission), or by the production of eggs subsequently fertilised by released sperm. Feeding seems to consist of enclosing any encountered algae or organic debris within a rapidly-formed pocket on its ventral surface. Presumably it then discharges enzymes into this pocket to initiate digestion, eventually absorbing the resulting 'soup' directly through its body surface, as it has no mouth. All in all, a truly exceptional species, whose rediscovery in 1971 was aptly referred to by Miller as 'the return of an enigma'.[55,74]

The no-eyed big-eyed wolf spider – an eight-legged contradiction from Kauai

In 1973, a most peculiar species of Hawaiian spider was described – currently known only

237

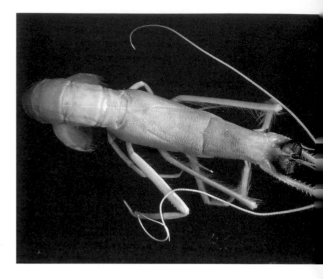

Neoglyphea inopinata – *overlooked for 67 years, in 1975 its type specimen revived a group of crustaceans previously believed extinct for 50 million years.* (*Dr Jacques Forest*)

from the deeper regions of Kauai's Koloa Cave and one other cave on this island's southeastern coast. Both caves consist of lava tubes resulting from an eruption of the volcano Koloa.[75]

Referred to scientifically as *Adelocosa anops*, this spelaean spider (sole member of its genus) delights in a very contradictory common name – the no-eyed big-eyed wolf spider. The reason for this etymological enigma stems from *Adelocosa's* membership of a scientific family of wolf spiders whose species are generally typified by very large, well-developed eyes, and are thus called big-eyed wolf spiders. In the case of *Adelocosa*, however, its ancestors apparently abandoned a traditional above-ground lifestyle in favour of a highly-specialised subterranean one – in which eyes were superfluous. Thus during the resulting evolution of this much-modified cave-dwelling species, they were eventually lost.[6,75]

Although made known to science only recently, this distinctive spider is quite familiar to Kauai's indigenous people, who call it *pe'e pe'e maka'ole*. It is easily identified by its long and semi-transparent, orange-coloured legs, its white abdomen, and its orange-brown cephalothorax (combined head-and-body section), as well as, of course, its lack of eyes. [6,75]

In 1991, many young specimens of *Troglodiplura lowryi*, a South Australian eyeless spider known before only from dried carcasses, were found alive in a Nullarbar Plain cave.[76]

Gascogne Gulf's living fossils

Despite their name and resemblance to underwater palm trees, sea lilies are definitely animals – known scientifically as crinoids and related to starfishes, sea urchins, brittle stars, and sea cucumbers. Once thought to have died out millions of years ago, the world's first living sea lily was discovered in 1755, in deep water off the Caribbean island of Martinique. Since then, many others have been obtained, belonging to more than 80 different modern-day species.

In 1973, a collection of marine specimens was made in southwestern France's Gascogne Gulf by the French research vessel *Thalassa*. Three years later, these were scrutinised by French biologist Dr Michel Roux from the University of South Paris, who found to his delight that amongst the collection's sea lilies were some examples that obviously belonged to the genus *Conocrinus*, previously known only from fossil forms. In short, not just a species, but a whole genus, of fossil sea lily had been restored to life.[77]

Furthermore, the examples were shown to belong to two separate *Concrinus* species, later named *C. cherbonnieri* and *C. cabiochi*, and proved remarkably similar to the fossil *Conocrinus* from southwestern France that dated back to the Eocene epoch, 54-36 million years ago. Additional studies disclosed that the modern-day *Conocrinus* species seemed to have been ousted from the gulf's muddy bottom by a more advanced sea lily, *Democrinus parfaiti*, but still survived at higher levels, at depths of 1000-1830 ft.[77]

Neoglyphea – rescuing its line from 50 million years of extinction

Among the vast assortment of marine specimens collected during summer 1908 in the vicinity of the Philippines by the oceanographic ship *Albatross,* was a small, pink, crab-like animal with large eyes. Caught on 17 July, it had been scooped up from the sandy bottom of the South China Sea, at a depth of 623 ft. It attracted little attention from scientists, but was dutifully preserved before taking its place alongside other *Albatross* specimens in the collections of zoological material housed in Washington's Smithsonian Institution.[78]

There it remained, un-named and unstudied, for the next 67 years, until in spring 1975 it captured the interest of two French scientists, Drs Jacques Forest and Michèle de Saint Laurent. And with good reason, because they recognised it to be a glyphid – a type of crustacean apparently ancestral to modern-day crabs, lobsters, and crayfishes, and believed until now to have died out around 50 million years ago. They named its species *Neoglyphea inopinata* ('unexpected near-glyphid'), and wondered if other specimens existed.[78]

The answer came a year later, when in March 1976 they succeeded in catching

nine specimens at a depth of approximately 660 ft in the same area as the provenance of the *Albatross* individual. Another 'living fossil' had entered the zoological annals.[79] As an unexpected bonus, *Neoglyphea* was found to harbour a new species of crustacean parasite, the copepod *Nicothoe tumulosa*, described in 1976 by biologist Dr R.F. Cressey.[80]

The Cooloola monster

The year 1976 also saw the discovery of a creature so extraordinary that it was initially assumed to be a man-made hoax (see this section's opening quote, p. 207). It was spotted by Queensland Museum researcher Ted Dahms amongst the insects collected in February by a colleague, V. Davies, in a pitfall trap set on the rainforest floor near Poona Lake, in southern Queensland's Cooloola National Park. Thus the new animal became known as 'the Cooloola monster'. An adult male, on first sight it resembled a very robust form of cricket. But detailed studies by orthopteran (cricket/grasshopper) specialist Dr David C.F. Rentz (of Canberra's Australian National Insect Collection) revealed it to be so overwhelmingly different from all others known, that it could not even be

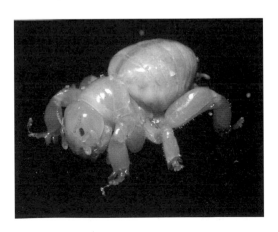

Penultimate instar of Cooloola monster (female) – this grasshopper is so extraordinary that its discovery in 1976 required the creation of a totally new taxonomic family.
(Dr David Rentz)

satisfactorily housed within any existing orthopteran family, let alone any genus or species. Hence a completely new family – Cooloolidae – had to be erected; and in 1980, the unique species that it housed was officially described, and named *Cooloola propator*.[81]

Other specimens have been collected, and used in morphological research that showed this important new insect to be most closely related to the ensiform orthopterans (the crickets and long-horned grasshoppers). Attaining a length of just over an inch in adult males, with its shovel-like head and limbs, very short antennae and near-sightless eyes, vestigial wings (absent altogether in females), and broad, powerful body (with prominently swollen abdomen in females), the Cooloola monster was quite evidently a burrower. Studies with living specimens verified this, disclosing that it inhabits the sandy, moist soil of Queensland's coastal rainforests, spending most of its time underground. As for food, its mouthparts' structure indicated a predatory existence, probably devouring other subterranean fauna.[81]

A vista of vestimentiferans – mankind's first view of the spectacular vent world

1977 has secured a momentous place in zoological history as the year that witnessed not just the disclosure of significant new species, but also the totally unexpected discovery of an entirely new world – a world never before seen by mankind.

The ocean bottom has traditionally been thought of as a barren, pitch-black zone never penetrated by the sun's life-giving light and warmth (and therefore virtually bereft of living organisms), a world perpetually maintained at icy temperatures throughout its vast expanse. Then in 1972, a huge rift valley on the stretch of seafloor about 210 miles northeast of the Galapagos Islands became the subject of a detailed oceanographic survey, which surprised geologists by revealing unexpected temperature variations across the valley. To explain this anomaly, it was postulated that in seafloor regions experiencing upwelling of magma (molten rock) during the creation of new oceanic crust, hot water may be rising through the seafloor via surface cracks or vents. But how could this hypothesis of hydrothermal activity be tested? There was only one way to settle the matter conclusively.[82]

And so, during February and March 1977 (and again in 1979) a team of scientists, led in 1977 by Dr John Corliss (from Oregon State University) and Dr Robert Ballard (from Massachusetts's Woods Hole Oceanographic Institution), travelled just over 8000 ft down through the sea to the Galapagos Islands' seafloor rift valley, transported in a 23-ft-long deep-diving submarine named *Alvin* which was owned by the U.S. Navy.[82]

Sure enough, they found their predicted hydrothermal vents – but that was not all. To their amazement, they also discovered that the vents supported a thriving animal community, teaming with an immense variety of forms of life – which in almost every case comprised species totally unknown to science. To quote team member Kathleen Crane: 'It was like a page out of the Jules Verne novel *20,000 Leagues Under the Sea*.'[82]

One vent was surrounded with blind yellow-white crabs (a new species ultimately named *Bythograea thermydron* and allocated its own taxonomic family),[83] plus white-shelled clams up to 1 ft long (a new species again, later dubbed *Calyptogena magnifica*, with bright-red, haemoglobin-laden tissues).[84] Another vent was populated with peculiar creatures resembling dandelions gone to seed, and attached to the sea bottom via a network of fine filaments; nicknamed 'dandelions' (and comprising yet another new species, christened *Thermopalia taraxaca*), these were siphonophores – relatives of the Portugese man o'war *Physalia*.[85]

One vent particularly rich in fauna (and aptly named 'the Garden of Eden' by the *Alvin* team) bore crabs, clams, 'dandelions', squat lobsters (galatheids), limpets, amber-coloured mussels, thread-like enteropneusts nicknamed 'spaghetti worms' (a new species, dubbed *Saxipendium coronatum*[86]), plus the hydrothermal vents' pièce de resistance – great clusters of 8.5-ft-long, tube-dwelling worms.[82]

Even by the vent world's own exceptional standards for remarkable fauna, these worms were extraordinary. Thousands of their tall, vertical tubes clustered around the vent, and from the top of each tube a spectacular, vivid red plume of petal-like tentacles emerged – yielding a breathtaking display so reminiscent of magnificent flowerbeds that the 1979 expedition referred

to another vent bearing these tubes as 'the Rose Garden'.[82,87]

Specimens were collected for comprehensive laboratory examination. Nothing like these tubicolous vent worms had ever been seen before, and it soon became clear that their unique external appearance was more than matched by their internal anatomy. Painstaking dissection and microscopical studies of every aspect of their morphology were carried out at the Smithsonian Institution, headed by its Curator of Worms, Dr Meredith Jones.[82,87]

When taken out of its tube, each of these worms was found to possess four distinct body regions. Uppermost was the striking plume (whose red colouration was due to the presence of haemoglobin), in turn composed of numerous tentacles and attached to a central support. Beneath it was the vestimentum, a solid body region largely composed of muscle and connective tissue, and bearing wing-like projections externally. Internally, it housed the worm's brain, and possessed a dorsal chamber into which the worm's genital aperture opened; the sexes, incidentally, were separate in this species. At its lowermost end the vestimentum connected to the trunk, the third body region, which contained the worm's single ventral nerve cord, dorsal and ventral blood vessels, the gonad (egg- or sperm-producing organ) and gonoducts, plus a very curious structure termed the trochosome (well-supplied with blood vessels, and proving to be a great mass of closely-packed bacteria). The final portion of the worm's body was the opisthosome, a segmented region bearing bristle-like structures called setae, and terminating in a rounded knob.[87]

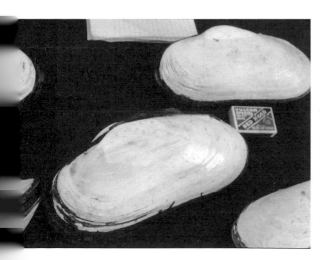

Giant vent clams – up to 1 ft long, from the Galapagos hydrothermal vent system. (Prof. John Edmond)

If all of that were not strange enough, this peculiar worm – surely as alien as any life form from outer space – provided an extra surprise. It lacked a digestive system – having neither mouth nor gut. It also lacked any vestige of eyes or comparable structures (though in view of its lightless habitat on the ocean floor, this is less startling).[87]

Jones's studies revealed that the tubicolous vent worm's closest relatives were none other than *Lamellibrachia barhami* and *L. luymesi*, those remarkable, afrenulate species of pogonophoran (see p. 223) comprising the taxonomic order Vestimentifera, in which Jones placed this giant cousin from the vent world, when he formally described it in 1980, naming it *Riftia pachyptila* ('thick-plumed rift dweller').[87] Moreover, by 1985 he had elevated Vestimentifera from a mere order within the phylum Pogonophora to an entirely separate phylum in its own right, emphatically underlining its three known species' fundamental distinction from all other animals.[88] (Most other workers, however, prefer to retain Vestimentifera within Pogonophora, albeit as a separate class.)

Returning to its anatomy, as *Riftia* has neither gut nor mouth, how does it feed? Its plume's large surface area and numerous tentacles, each richly supplied with blood vessels, probably enable it to function as an efficient organ for the absorption of organic molecules from the surrounding seawater. Direct absorption across the worm's body surface within its tube is also likely. It may well obtain nutrients from its internal, trochosomal bacteria too. But what of the other members of the vent fauna? What were they feeding on?[87]

Until the discovery of the vent world, all known life forms on Earth ultimately obtained their energy from the sun. Plants and certain bacteria harnessed sunlight to manufacture their own food, in the form of carbohydrates – a process termed photosynthesis. Herbivorous organisms obtained their energy by eating these photosynthesising species, and carnivorous organisms obtained theirs by devouring the herbivores. The vent world's discovery, however, unveiled the operation of a radically new, autonomous energy chain, one that was completely independent of the sun. Instead of sunlight, the energy source being used was chemical energy – released during the combination of sulphates with hydrogen to yield hydrogen sulphide, a process occurring when sulphate-laden warm water rising up through the seafloor's crust makes contact with the cold, oxygenated water present at the vents' openings. The released energy was being utilised by sulphur-oxidising bacteria to manufacture their own food. In turn, they were being eaten by larger life forms, which were themselves being preyed upon by others, and so on.[82]

In more recent times, hydrothermal vent systems have also been discovered elsewhere. One, further north than the Galapagos version, is sited on a zone called the East Pacific Rise, and is distinguished by its impressive chimney-shaped vents – some belching out smoky water rich in metals, others releasing creamy water. Vents of the Galapagos type are also present here, plus many new animal species, including vestimentiferans, strange 4-in-long pink worms termed Pompeii worms, a very primitive short-stalked barnacle *Neoverruca brachylepadoformis*, and a living Palaeozoic-type scallop *Bathypecten vulcani*.[82,89]

One hundred and twenty miles south of Mexico's Baja California, the sea floor has many pagoda-like vents, which are visited by three species of endemic vent fishes, all completely new to science. Two of these,

Thermarces cerberus (also reported from the Galapagos rift system) and *T. andersoni,* are eelpouts – slender, eel-like species measuring just under 1 ft long, with pinkish-white skin and small prickly teeth; the third, *Bythites hollisi,* is allied to the cusk-eels (ophidiids).[90] Interestingly, in the vent system of the Philippines' Mariana Trench vestimentiferans are replaced by large hairy snails – yet another new species.[91]

A recent development is the discovery that decomposing whale carcases on the seafloor may be serving as 'stepping stones' for vent world animals, enabling them to migrate across regions of the floor that would otherwise be too inhospitable for their passage. As whale carcases release sulphur compounds during their disintegration, these compounds would feed the sulphur-oxidising bacteria characterising hydrothermal vents, and in turn provide the larger vent world creatures with their sustenance.[92]

Evidently, there is a great deal of fundamentally significant biological knowledge to be gleaned from this revolutionary ecosystem residing in lightless splendour on the ocean bottom. How ironic, then, that while man has been fascinated for so long by the possibility of new life forms existing on extraterrestrial worlds in outer space, this new world has been awaiting discovery here on his own planet.

Vaceletia – all sphinctozoans are not the same

First appearing in the Carboniferous Period (345-280 million years ago), the sphinctozoans constituted an odd group of segmented, sponge-like animals that seemingly died out over 200 million years later, at the end of the Cretaceous Period, without giving rise to any modern-day descendants. This palaeontological presumption was decisively disproven in April 1977, however, when several dozen specimens of a living sphinctozoan species were recovered by the French oceanographic vessel *Suroît* just off the Iles Glorieuses, a collection of tiny islets north of the Mozambique Channel. This provided scientists with a unique chance to uncover the precise relationship of sphinctozoans to other animal forms.[93]

With at least some of the fossil species, palaeontologists had obtained what appeared to be insurmountable proof from anatomical and other comparisons that their correct taxonomic position was alongside the calcareous sponges (class Calcarea). Yet when Dr J. Vacelet – a researcher at the Endoume marine station (Marseilles) – studied this newly-disclosed 'living fossil', which she named *Neocoelia crypta,* she came to a very different conclusion. Her findings strongly implied that, albeit a genuine sphinctozoan, it was actually more closely related to the sclerosponges (p. 211) than to the calcareous ones.[93]

If neither party were wrong, how could this paradox be resolved? Vacelet's studies suggested to her an acceptable solution – namely, that the sphinctozoans comprised a diphyletic group. That is to say, instead of all sphinctozoans sharing a common ancestry there were really two, totally distinct lines, traditionally classed together because of superficial similarities in morphology but actually having separate origins from one another. One of these lines had shared its ancestry with the calcareous sponges, whereas the other had shared its ancestry with the sclerosponges. This demonstrates well that however painstaking the form taken by palaeontological work on fossilised animal specimens, only a living

Yager, from Virginia's Old Dominion University, was responsible for the creation of a ninth.[96]

A keen novice diver, with fellow biologist and diving instructor Dennis Williams she had been exploring Lucayan Cavern – a pitch-black, water-filled cave beneath the island of Grand Bahama – when the beam of light from her underwater torch disclosed a myriad of tiny specks flitting in every direction through the surrounding water. At first she assumed that they were simply dust particles, but closer observation revealed that they were minute life forms. One tiny worm-like animal seemed particularly unusual – a very graceful but totally blind swimmer measuring 0.4 in long, with a series of paired, oar-like limbs, a slender body, and very long antennae – so she carefully captured it in a plastic collecting bottle.[96]

Upon her return, she took the strange little creature to cave biologist Dr John Holsinger for identification. To say that he was delighted with it would be putting it mildly. The tiny animal in her bottle was a crustacean, but so unlike any other species known that it became sole member of a new genus, family, order, and subclass. Named *Speleonectes lucayensis* by Dr Yager in 1981, this extraordinary species became known as a remipede ('oar-footed') after its most noticeable characteristic; its subclass was named Remipedia.[96]

Other remipedes have since been discovered. In February 1992, Dr Yager informed me that the current total stands at nine – seven from the Bahamas, one from Mexico, and one from the Canary Islands. This last-mentioned species is particularly interesting, bearing in mind that it occurs

representative can offer conclusive evidence for their correct taxonomic categorisation.[93]

In 1982, *Neocoelia* was renamed *Vaceletia* ('*Neocoelia*' had already been used for another animal); and in 1984, it was recorded for the first time from the western Pacific.[94]

In 1979 Vacelet described *Cryptosyringa membranophila*, a peculiar tetractinomorph sponge from underwater Jamaican caves, and associated with some very unusual membranous structures. A brand new family was needed to accommodate it.[95]

Remipedes – oar-footed crustaceans rowing into zoological history

The discovery of *Hutchinsoniella* in the 1950s (see p. 226), brought the total of modern-day subclasses of crustacean to eight. In late 1979, U.S. biologist Dr Jill on the very opposite side of the Atlantic from all of the others – thereby revealing that the remipedes have a much wider distribution range than first suspected. Discovered in Lanzarote's underwater lava tunnel of Jameos del Agua, and described in 1984, it received the intriguing scientific name *Morlockia ondinae* – morlocks were subterranean entities in H.G. Wells's novelette *The Time Machine*, and Ondine was a water nymph.[25,97]

Incidentally, since the late 1970s many authorities elevate Crustacea from a class to a phylum, with all of its former subclasses (including Remipedia) thus becoming classes.

Tambusisi tree-nymph – a ghostly giant from Sulawesi

Idea comprises a genus of Asian, forest-dwelling butterflies known as tree-nymphs. With their large, black-and-white, semi-transparent wings capable only of sustaining a weak, fluttering flight, these delicate insects have a ghostly, disembodied appearance that has inspired fanciful myths and superstitions throughout their distribution range.[6,98]

Some tree-nymphs, such as the Moluccan *I. idea*, can attain very sizeable wingspans, up to 5.5 in. Yet even these were dwarfed by the monstrous examples that were sometimes seen flitting high overhead by the team of young explorers trekking across Mount Tambusisi's southwestern slopes, during an Operation Drake expedition to the southeast Asian island of Sulawesi (Celebes) in March 1980. As they seemed much too large to be specimens of *I. blanchardii*, the only species of tree-nymph

known to inhabit Sulawesi, every effort was made to secure some for identification and study – but each attempt met with failure. Consequently, when two of these immense *Idea* fluttered into view on 10 March, just as the team was about to pack up camp and move to another section of the island, they instantly found themselves being pursued *en masse* by a flurry of flailing butterfly nets brandished by every member of the expedition in the vicinity, until one of the two, a female, was successfully captured by the team's entomological expert, Major Anthony Bedford Russell.[98]

Not only did it belong to a completely new species, which Bedford Russell named *Idea tambusisiana*, the giant Tambusisi tree-nymph, but with a massive wingspan of 6.5 in, it was also one of the largest butterflies ever to be recorded by science, as well as the first new species of tree-nymph to be described for 97 years.[6,99]

King bee – buzzing back

Although it hardly compares with the gigantic versions beloved by science-fiction film producers, the world's largest bee nonetheless attains a very respectable total

King bee (with honey bee for comparison, left) - the world's biggest bee, discovered in 1859 but not seen again until 1981.
(Dr Adam Messer)

length of 1.75 in (more than twice the size of the familiar *Bombus* bumblebees of field and garden). Commonly called the king bee, it was first discovered in 1859, when naturalist Alfred Russell Wallace collected a female specimen on the Indonesian island of Bacan, in the north Moluccas.[6,100]

Except for its pale cheeks (genae), and a white band encircling the front edge of its abdomen, it was predominantly black in colour, with long, smoky wings, and was readily distinguished from all other bees not only by its huge size, but also by its enormous mandibles – formidable plier-shaped mouthparts projecting forwards and outwards like a pair of sturdy, ebony antlers, and accompanied by an equally enlarged labrum or 'upper lip'. This extraordinary insect was sent to the British Museum (Natural History), and its species was described in 1861, when it was named *Chalicodoma pluto*. A short time later, a second female was obtained – after which, despite its notable size, the king bee proved to be expertly adept at remaining concealed, because it was not reported again for over a century.[6,100]

In February 1981, entomologist Dr Adam Messer was studying the insect life on the Moluccan island of Halmahera. During a visit one day to some primary lowland forest about 5 miles southeast of Kampung Pasir Putih, he was startled to see two enormous bees, busily engaged in gathering resin from tree trunks, by loosening it using their immensely large mandibles and then scraping it up, bulldozer-style, with the long labrum, until a solid ball of resin was produced. Closer inspection revealed beyond any doubt that these were female king bees. Further observations by Messer led to this species' discovery on the island of Soasiu (Tidore) as well, and to its rediscovery on Bacan. Messer also

uncovered the secret of its surprising success at concealment – unlike so many other species of bee, it does not build its own nests, but shares those of various forms of tree-inhabiting termite.[6,100]

Equally important was his capture of some male king bees, the first ever recorded. At just under 1 in long, they were smaller than the females. Similarly, their mandibles and labrum were shorter, and their cheeks were rufous, not white.[6,100]

Lastly, anyone finding the concept of a 1.75-in bee somewhat traumatic will be comforted to learn that the extra-large size of the king bee's body is not paralleled by the potency of its sting. In fact, because its sting is not barbed, it is actually less painful than that of many much smaller and more familiar bee species.[6,100]

The tantalising tantulocarids

In 1975, biologist Dr K-H. Becker described a bizarre little creature found as an external parasite on several deepsea copepod crustaceans. Their parasite was itself a crustacean, but an extremely unusual one – little more than a sac of organs equipped at one end with piercing mouthparts. Some minuscule limbs are present behind these in the larval form (tantulus), but are shed at its exoskeleton's final moult before attaining the adult, reproductive stage. There are no limbs comparable to other crustaceans' abdominal limbs.[25,101]

Becker named this highly modified species *Basipodella harpacticola*, and classed it as an aberrant copepod. However, when a similar species, *Deoterthron dentatum*, was described in 1980, comparisons of the two in relation to other crustaceans suggested that they were more closely allied to the barnacles. This controversy was resolved in 1983, when further studies concluded that

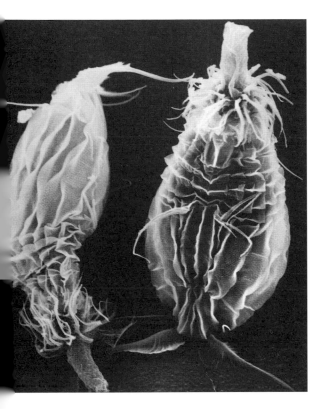

Larvae of Nanaloricus mysticus – *the first loriciferan known to science, it was described in 1983, and required a completely new phylum to accommodate it.* (*Dr Reinhardt Kristensen*)

these perplexing parasites, together with some obscure forms documented as long ago as 1903, warranted their own crustacean subclass, Tantulocarida.[25,101]

Loricifera – a prediction come true

Giving one's name to an uncommonly ugly form of animal larva may not be everyone's idea of obtaining scientific immortality, but it is nonetheless an effective way to achieve this – especially when that larva's species is so utterly different from all others that a completely new *phylum* has to be created to accommodate it.

Its story began in 1961 when, as a student at Washington's National Museum of Natural History, Dr Robert Higgins predicted the existence of a remarkable little creature unlike any known to science at that time. By an ironic twist of fate, in May 1974 he

actually found a real-life specimen of his hitherto hypothetical creature – but failed to recognise it for what it was. Instead, he deemed it to be nothing more than a larval priapulid worm.[102]

The following year, however, another specimen was found, this time by Danish zoologist Dr Reinhardt Møbjerg Kristensen, from the University of Copenhagen. Yet as bad luck would have it, the tiny animal was destroyed during its preparation for transmission electron microscopy. Happily, between 1976 and 1979 Dr Kristensen discovered some larvae in shell gravel obtained from depths of 330-365 ft outside western Greenland's Godhavn Harbour. And finally, in April 1982, an adult turned up – completely by accident.[102]

Kristensen had obtained a huge sample of shell gravel from a depth of 83-100 ft during field work at the Marine Biological Station in Roscoff, France, and was in a hurry to examine the minute creatures living between the gravel particles, as this was his last day there before leaving for Denmark. Consequently, instead of employing the usual sophisticated but somewhat protracted techniques for dislodging animals from the particles, he simply washed the gravel in freshwater. The change in salt concentration experienced by the tiny marine organisms in the gravel shocked them into loosening their grip on its particles, and they could then be collected in the surrounding water. Among the creatures obtained in this way was an adult of Higgins's postulated animal form, plus others from every stage in its life history. Shortly afterwards, specimens belonging to a slightly different species were obtained from Greenland gravel samples, using this same technique.[102]

By now, Kristensen and Higgins had learnt about each other's interest in these mysterious minute creatures, and had teamed up to work on them. They discovered that the individual (a larva) collected by Higgins in 1974 was indeed of the same group, but sufficiently different from Kristensen's species to warrant separation within a new genus and family. As for the creatures *in toto*, true to Higgins's expectations they required a brand new phylum. In 1983, Kristensen named it Loricifera, and formally described its first species, the Roscoff one, which he christened *Nanaloricus mysticus*.[102]

A tiny creature, no more than 0.23 mm (0.009 in) long, with a fairly squat body and a head section bearing a collar of radiating spines, it leads a sedentary existence – quite unlike its free-swimming larva, whose striated, pear-shaped body has a rear pair of flipper-like appendages. Anatomically, the species combines features from several different phyla, but is characterised by a unique mouth, comprising a long tube that can be retracted completely within the creature's body in a manner not previously recorded from any other type of animal.[102]

As for Higgins, although he did not have the honour of describing the first real-life species of his conjectured creature he was given an unusual consolation prize – ever afterwards, the basic larval type produced by loriciferans would be officially referred to as the Higgins larva. Higgins's reaction to this accolade was to comment: 'I'm very pleased of course, even though it is such an ugly creature.' Twenty-two years after his student prognostication, his hypothetical animal was hypothetical no longer.[102]

Incidentally, in 1986 Higgins was able to describe the species to which his lost specimen belonged; its scientific name is *Pliciloricus enigmaticus*, and it is just one of eight new species that Higgins and Kristensen described within a single paper. The other seven species are: *P. dubius, P. gracilis, P. orphanus, P. profundus, Rugiloricus carolinensis, R. cauliculus,* and *R. ornatus*.[103] In 1988, Kristensen described another important new species, *P. hadalis* – the first loriciferan recorded from fine sediment (red clay), from a depth (8260 m) great enough to be included within the hadal bathymetric zone, and from the western Pacific.[104]

Most recently, in February 1992, I was both delighted and honoured to be informed by Dr Kristensen that he would be naming a new species of loriciferan after me; he currently has nearly 70 undescribed species in his collection.[104]

Sea daisy – a driftwood-derived novelty

In the early summer of 1985, biologist Dr Bruce Marshall at New Zealand's National Museum was studying some tiny marine snails, obtained from crevices in samples of driftwood collected at the sea bottom around the country's coasts. The first samples had been gathered on 9 July 1983, just west of Hokitika, South Island, at a depth of about 3800 ft, with further samples having been obtained between April and May 1985, off Castlepoint, North Island, at depths of 3523-4027 ft. Among the snail specimens contained within these were some small starfishes too, so in August 1985 three echinoderm specialists called by to take them for study. When they examined the vessels containing the starfishes, however, they noticed that some much smaller, unfamiliar-looking animals were also present.[105]

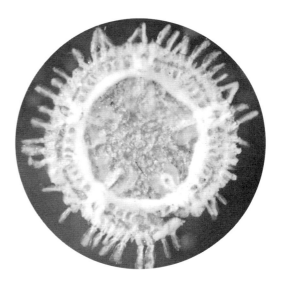

Sea daisy Xyloplax medusiformis – *its discovery in 1985 added a new class of echinoderms to the zoological inventory.*
(Dr Alan Baker)

To most observers, these minute mysteries, none more than 9 mm in total diameter, would seem to be nothing more exciting than some form of miniature jellyfish medusa. Conversely, the echinoderm experts – Drs Alan Baker and Helen E.S. Clark (from New Zealand's National Museum) and Francis W.E. Rowe (from Sydney's Australian Museum) – recognised them to be the zoological find of a lifetime.[105]

The new species that they represented soon became known as the sea daisy, and in June 1986 it was officially named *Xyloplax medusiformis* – 'medusa-like plated animal found on wood'. Belying its superficial outward appearance, however, the tiny creature was not a jellyfish at all, but a new member of the echinoderm phylum. Previously, there had been five classes of modern-day echinoderm; now, thanks to the salvaged samples of driftwood, there was a sixth – a newly-created class christened Concentricycloidea, with the sea daisy *Xyloplax* as its sole occupant.[105]

Although the sea daisy betrays its echinoderm identity via such characteristics as a calcite-based skeleton, a body structure founded upon a basically five-rayed (pentamerous) configuration, and peculiar little appendages called tube-feet, it also has several features that readily delineate it from all previously-described members of the phylum.[105]

For example, the perimeter of its disc-shaped, plated body bears a fringe of petal-like spines (the reason why it became known as the sea daisy). For hydrostatic purposes, its body contains two, concentric water-containing rings (hence its class's name, Concentricycloidea) instead of just a single ring like other echinoderms. The sea daisy's underside is covered by a thin membrane, through which it probably absorbs all its nutrients and excretes all its waste products, as it has neither a mouth nor an anus (it does not have a stomach either). And its tube feet are aligned in a single ring around the edge of its body's underside, instead of in five or more pairs of rows radiating outwards from the centre of its underside (like the spokes of a wheel) in the style of all other echinoderms.[105] Its overall structural anatomy indicates that the sea daisy is most closely related to the starfishes and brittle stars, although it has no arms of its own.[105]

In 1988, the three echinoderm specialists who described *X. medusiformis* brought to scientific attention a second species of sea daisy, which they christened *X. turnerae*. This was based upon specimens obtained from wooden plates that had been submerged for 12-40 months in the Tongue of the Ocean, east of Andros Island, Bahamas, at a depth of just over 6885 ft. Its most striking differences from *X. medusiformis* are its stomach, which the latter species lacks, and its apparent oviparity (*X. medusiformis* is viviparous).[106]

Back to 1985, this was also the year in which Dr Michel Roux described a quite exceptional 'living fossil', five specimens of which had been obtained at depths of 5000-6660 ft off the Mascarene island of Reunion in the Indian Ocean during 1982. This was a species of stalked sea lily named *Guillecrinus reunionensis*, and what makes it so significant is that it comprises the very first modern-day representative of the sea lily subclass Inadunata – believed until then to be wholly extinct since the Palaeozoic Era, which ended 225 million years ago.[107]

Exsul singularus – reappearance of the world's rarest fly

The year 1987 ended on an entomological high note, with the return of a handsome species of fly – one that spurns the traditional buzzing bluebottle image in favour of a mighty 2-in-long body, and a pair of enormous, butterfly-like wings of shimmering, white-edged ebony hue, which heat up in sunlight, enabling it to take flight. Named *Exsul singularus*, this attractive insect had not been reported since 1941, but reappeared alive and well 46 years later in the Homer Tunnel, Dunedin, in the southernmost region of New Zealand's South Island. Its discoverer was a five-year-old boy – Jamie Morris, who lives close to the tunnel. The specimen that he captured was photographed and conclusively identified by entomologists – no doubt with great excitement, as *E. singularus* is generally considered to be the world's rarest fly. To date, it is only known from adult specimens; its larval form has never been documented.[108]

Ants in the plants, and Australian Amazonians

Sometimes, notable invertebrate finds can be made in the most surprising places. One day in 1989, Kathryn Fuller, president of the U.S.A. division of the World Wide Fund For Nature (WWF), happened to notice some ants running across her desk in her Washington office. By good fortune, Harvard University zoologist Prof. E.O. Wilson, a renowned authority on ants and author of a newly-completed definitive tome on the ants of the world, was visiting Fuller at that time, so she asked him to identify her desk's tiny trespassers. To his great surprise, they did not seem to correspond to any species on record. Eager to learn more about them, Wilson and Fuller investigated their origin, and discovered that they had come from a colony in a potted plant behind the desk. Some worker specimens were collected, and later, when back at Harvard, Wilson also received some soldier specimens from Fuller. Currently awaiting formal classification, their species appears to belong to the Neotropical *Pheidole* genus, and may indeed be new to science.[109]

In spring 1991, bulldozing work on a building site in Sydney, Australia, was abandoned after workers discovered that it was inhabited by some highly unexpected occupants. Most people are familiar with the sight of millipedes scuttling along the ground on their multitude of legs, for there are numerous species found throughout the world. In contrast, only a single species of aquatic, freshwater millipede has been recorded – from the blackwater swamps of the Amazon River in Brazil – or at least this was true until the bulldozers' discovery in Sydney, because during their preliminary work they encountered a colony of pin-sized freshwater millipedes. Currently awaiting formal description and naming, this new aquatic species offers hope that other undisclosed relatives await discovery elsewhere.[110]

The biggest Spanish dancer in the world?

In stark contrast to their morphologically unappealing land-dwelling relatives, the sea slugs or nudibranchs offer eyewitnesses a visual extravaganza – each species presenting such a dazzling pageant of sumptuous hues and so flamboyant a bouquet of plume-like gills that it could readily be mistaken for a surrealistic, sea-dwelling bird of paradise. There are numerous species, of worldwide distribution, and until very recently the largest on record was the northwestern Pacific's *Tochuina tetraqueta*, up to 1 ft long.

In May 1990, however, artist Tamara Double was diving in the Red Sea, near to Djibouti's Les Sept Frères islands, when she saw some huge sea slugs almost twice as long as *T. tetraqueta*, each bearing six branches of deep red, profusely-plumed gills, and undulating its pinkish-red mantle edges like a flamenco dancer. They seemed to be a giant form of the aptly-named Spanish dancer *Hexabranchus sanguineus*, not believed to exceed 9 in long in the Red Sea. Double thus captured one, which is now being studied by Dr Nathalie Yonow at Swansea University to discover if it is indeed an outsized Spanish dancer, or an exciting new species in its own right. Others have been seen near Fiji and in the South China Sea.[111]

Platasterias latiradiata – rise and fall of a living fossil

When recalling major zoological discoveries, few books devote much space to invertebrate examples (except for the living monoplacophoran molluscs *Neopilina*), but one such example that has featured in several recent works is a case involving the resurrection of a supposedly long-extinct subclass via a modern-day species whose true identity had not previously been recognised. When I researched this case, however, I discovered that in reality this creature's claim to fame as a major 'living fossil' had been conclusively refuted in the scientific literature. Yet as so often happens in cases of this type, whereas the truth had received little publicity outside its own specific field, the fallacy was still being recycled in popular-format and formal zoological works alike. Hence I have chosen to bring this invertebrate section to a close by presenting the full history of the 'living fossil that never was', from discovery to denouement.

The most familiar members of the phylum Echinodermata are the starfishes, which have traditionally been divided into two subclasses – Euasteroidea (the true starfishes), housing all of the modern-day species; and Somasteroidea, known only from fossil species dating back to the early Ordovician Period, some 400 million years ago. During the 1960s, however, Somasteroidea experienced a most unexpected (albeit temporary) renaissance.

The seeds for this had been sown some years earlier, when Prof. H. Barraclough Fell, a starfish expert from New Zealand's Victoria University, had become interested in the obscure species *Platasterias latiradiata* from Mexico's Pacific coast, described in 1871 but still virtually unknown. After studying the meagre amount of published data concerning its structural anatomy, he began to wonder whether it really was a true starfish after all, because it seemed to exhibit certain features more comparable to those of somasteroids than eusasteroids – including petal-shaped arms whose skeletal components resembled rod-like structures called virgalia (possessed by somasteroids but not by euasteroids).[112-13]

Yet to satisfy himself totally, Fell needed to examine a specimen of this enigmatic echinoderm – which immediately posed a problem, as earlier enquiries to museums in Mexico had failed to elicit one. Undaunted, he contacted Alisa M. Clark, Curator of Echinoderms at the British Museum (Natural History), and promptly received a portion of an arm from a preserved *Platasterias*. From his study of this vital material, it became apparent to him that the arm's ventral skeleton was indeed constructed from virgalia-like rods, and other anatomical features likewise seemed to substantiate a somasteroid identity for it.[112-13]

Thus, in December 1961 Fell announced that *Platasterias* was a living somasteroid, thereby resurrecting an entire subclass of echinoderms from 400 million years of extinction.[112] In 1962, he published details of his structural analysis of *Platasterias* and his conclusions in several scientific journals, which attracted appreciable zoological interest.[113]

By 1966, however, doubts regarding the somasteroid affinities of *Platasterias* had begun to be voiced. Dr F. Jensenius Madsen, of Copenhagen's Zoological Museum, opined that the virgalia of somasteroids were not as significant as previously thought. The skeleton of euasteroids is composed of bone-like knobs called ossicles, and Madsen considered the virgalia to be nothing more than ventrolaterally-sited versions of these, thereby reducing their taxonomic value. From this, he postulated that *Platasterias* was merely an aberrant member of the starfish genus *Luidia*, and that its petal-shaped arms were simply an adaptation for life on an unsteady sandy seafloor.[114] His opinion gained support from other researchers (notably Dr D.B. Blake) investigating ossicle structure in starfishes; so by the early 1970s *Platasterias* was not only reclassified as a euasteroid, but was also renamed *Luidia latiradiata*[115] – thereby jettisoning the subclass Somasteroidea back into Ordovician obscurity.

THE FUTURE

Speculations and Stop Press

The borderland of zoology is very extensive; the number of animals still to be discovered on this small planet is much greater than is popularly realised or science is willing to advertise. Nor are all of these microscopic worms or tiny, obscure tropical beetles... A notion has somehow gained popular credence that the surface of the earth is now fully explored and for the most part well known and even mapped. There was never a greater misconception.

IVAN T. SANDERSON – MORE "THINGS"

Those lines are as true today – in the first half of this century's closing decade – as they were in 1969, when Sanderson's book, *More "Things"*, was published. Naturally, it would be impossible to predict the remainder of the 1990s' inventory of major new and rediscovered animals. Yet in view of such remarkable very recent finds as the onza, Vu Quang ox, Yemen monitor, Thai giant stingray, and mainland Javan rhinos, it may well include the names of at least a few of the many exciting forms documented in the numerous books and articles dealing with cryptozoological animals (officially referred to as cryptids).

Of course, some cryptids may simply be based upon misidentifications of known native animals, or of exotic species that have escaped from captivity. To give just a single example: for several months in 1988 and early 1989, sightings of a strange lynx-like creature were frequently reported from the Ludlow area of Shropshire, England, but these were officially discounted as misidentifications of foxes or feral domestic cats – until February 1989. This was when farmer Norman Evans found near to his home the dead body of an Asian jungle cat

Felis chaus, a relatively large, lynx-like species not native to Britain. It had apparently been killed by a car, and was found to be a captive-bred escapee that had been living in the Ludlow countryside for a considerable time.

Conversely, there are many cryptids that genuinely seem to be undiscovered or officially extinct species. Currently comprising the world's most controversial creatures – those whose very existence has yet to be formally accepted by science (in spite of substantiation by eyewitness accounts, photographs, and sometimes even a preserved specimen or two) – they are very varied in type. They range from such famous, extensively-investigated examples as North America's bigfoot (*Gigantopithecus?*), the Himalayan yeti (terrestrial orang utan?), sea serpents (a motley assemblage of strange seals, primitive whales, giant eels, and aquatic reptiles?), lake monsters (ditto?), and the Congolese mokele-mbembe (living dinosaur?), to such little-investigated mystery beasts as the New Guinea devil pig (palorchestid diprotodont?), Chad's 'mountain tiger' (sabre-tooth?), the crowing crested cobra (African mystery snake),

If this book can not only sweep away the dusty, discredited fallacy that this century has been conspicuously devoid of zoological surprises, but also serve as a tangible rebuff to anyone denying that the future may hold many more surprises, then it will more than successfully have achieved all of my ambitions for it.

tatzelworm (large, unidentified Swiss lizard), Timor Sea ground shark (giant wobbegong?), and Bahamian lusca (gigantic cirrate octopus?).

Today, these are animals of ambiguity; tomorrow, they could be taking their places alongside the okapi, Komodo dragon, Congo peacock, coelacanth, vestimentiferans, megamouth, Jerdon's courser, onza, and all of the many other zoological success stories of the 20th century. Similarly, although the vast majority of new and rediscovered animals will nonetheless be relatively small, seemingly trivial ones, there is no reason why some of these should not prove in reality to be as significant in scientific stature as the loriciferans, Selevin's dormouse, *Neoglyphea*, irukandji, *Burramys*, po'o-uli, sea daisies, *Neopilina*, pogonophorans, Cooloola monster, and *Indostomus*.

Provided that the expanses of tropical rainforest still remaining can be comprehensively explored before mankind succeeds in its terrifying attempts to destroy them, provided that the vast volumes of ocean, sea, lake, and river can be investigated before mankind succeeds in polluting them thoroughly, or – in a more optimistic vein – provided that all types of habitat can not only be searched but also be conserved for the foreseeable future, there can really be no doubt whatsoever that many additional new and rediscovered animals of note will be added to these pages in the decades to come.

Indeed: to keep this book's coverage of such animals as current as possible, a stop press section now follows, containing brief news concerning the latest finds and developments.

STOP PRESS

Reviving the desert warthog

Although only a single living species of warthog, *Phacochoerus aethiopicus*, is recognised by zoologists today, a century ago the warthogs of South Africa's Cape Province were deemed by some to comprise a separate species. These have long since died out, but following his studies on the few specimens preserved in museums, ungulate researcher Dr Peter Grubb disclosed in 1991 that a widely-separated population of warthogs thriving in Somalia and northern Kenya belongs to this 'lost', second species, and that the latter is indeed of distinct taxonomic status, for which he has proposed 'desert warthog' as a suitable English name.

ANON. (1991). Closet skeleton brought to life. *BBC Wildlife*, 9 (October): 682-3.

A surviving species of stegodont elephant?

During February and March 1992, renowned explorer Colonel John Blashford-Snell led an expedition to a remote valley in the Bardia region of western Nepal in search of 'giant elephants' reported by the local people. Two such beasts, both adult bulls, were eventually encountered and photographed, and their heights were estimated to be 11 ft 3 in at the shoulder – taller than the biggest-ever Asian elephant *Elephas maximus* recorded until then. But this was not all. Each bore two very large domes on its forehead, and a distinctive nasal bridge – features not exhibited by

Nepalese giant elephant – freak Asian elephant or surviving stegodont?
(Nick Brown)

255

normal Asian elephants, but which were characteristics of a primitive extinct elephant known as *Stegodon.*

The ancestor of today's African and Asian elephants (and also of the mammoths), it supposedly died out over a million years ago. Recently, however, Canadian palaeontologist Dr Clive Coy has speculated that Nepal's giant elephants might actually be surviving relatives of *Stegodon,* but only a thorough study of their cranial and dental morphology can determine whether or not this very exciting possibility is true.

BLASHFORD-SNELL, J. (1992). Honey Blossom gets her mammoth. *Mail on Sunday – YOU Magazine* (London), 7 July: 40-42; FIELDING, N. (1993). The elephant that time forgot. *Mail on Sunday* (London), 23 May.

Unmasking the Tyne petrel

Since 1988, several strange storm petrels with dark rumps and forked tails have been spied each summer in northeastern England, and sometimes even ringed. Dubbed Tyne petrels, they were believed for a time to comprise a species new to science, but DNA fingerprinting techniques revealed in 1992 that they were Swinhoe's petrels, *Oceanodroma monorhis,* an eastern Asiatic species not previously recorded from the North Atlantic.

ANON. (1990). Seabird capture fuels debate over unknown species. *Daily Telegraph* (London), 9 July; ANON. (1992). Tests uncover bird mystery. Ibid., 14 December.

The invisible kiwi

One brown kiwi looks very much like another – but their genetic profiles tell a very different story. A recent study of brown kiwis in New Zealand discovered that certain upland populations are so different genetically from those elsewhere that they fully warrant classification as a distinct species in their own right, set apart from the traditional species of brown kiwi, *Apteryx australis.* The reason that they have not previously been differentiated from the latter is that their genetic differences are ones that do not noticeably affect their outward morphology, i.e. their taxonomic characteristics are 'invisible'. The new kiwi is being referred to at present as the tokoeka kiwi, utilising a Maori name for it.

ANON. (1993). Kiwi discovery. *Wild About Animals,* (August): 25.

Pygmy bluetongue – regurgitating a rediscovery

When herpetologist Graham Armstrong opened up the gut of a squashed snake (killed by a car) spotted by him on a road near Burra, South Australia, in late October 1992, he found inside the corpse of a pygmy bluetongue skink *Tiliqua adelaidensis,* a lizard believed extinct since 1959. The area where he saw the snake was duly searched, and a colony of pygmy bluetongues was uncovered, from which some were then sent to Adelaide Zoo for breeding.

ANON. (1992). Road kill reveals lizard not extinct. *Portland Press Herald* (Portland – U.S.A.), 28 December.

Cave realms and vent worlds

In 1991, Romanian biospeleologist Serban Sarbu announced that the Movile Cave in southern Romania housed a unique cave fauna of primitive 'living fossils' containing at least 14 species new to science, including archaic snails, amphipod and isopod crustaceans, and springtails.

And the existence of an enormous system of hydrothermal vents on the Atlantic's floor about 800 miles southwest of the Azores, bearing a diverse array of fauna including giant *Riftia* tube worms and hairy snails, was revealed in March 1993 by a team of scientists aboard the research ship *RRS Charles Darwin*.

DURBANA, D. (1992). La caverne des fossiles vivants. *Science et Vie,* No. 903 (December): 74-79; ANON. (1993). Boffins find huge springs underwater. *Express and Star* (Wolverhampton), 11 March.

A living graptolite?

Comprising a once-diverse group of colonial, polyp-budding hemichordates related to the modern-day pterobranchs, those fossil marine invertebrates known as graptolites were traditionally believed to have died out entirely by the end of the Carboniferous Period.

On 27 February 1989, specimens of a hitherto unknown pterobranch were collected at a depth of 830 ft near the New Caledonian island of Lifou by the submersible *Cyanea* during the French Calsun Expedition. When these were examined by Prof. Noel Dilly of St. George's Hospital Medical School, London, he recognised that this new species, which he named *Cephalodiscus graptolitoides,* bore spines reminiscent of a spine-like structure called the nema – a characteristic of many graptolites. Following his studies, moreover, he considered that the overall similarity between this species and graptolites was such that there seemed no reason why it should not be classed as a bona fide living graptolite. After 300 million years, have these famously fossilised animals finally been resurrected? Watch this space!

*DILLY, P.N. (1993). *Cephalodiscus graptolitoides* sp. nov. A probable extant graptolite. *Journal of Zoology,* 229 (January): 69-78.

A last word

It was in 1886, within his book *Mythical Monsters*, that naturalist Charles Gould asked: 'Can we suppose that we have at all exhausted the great museum of nature? Have we, in fact, penetrated yet beyond its antechambers?' The wealth of major new and rediscovered animals so far unveiled during the 20th century, as documented in this present book, emphatically verifies that by 1886 we had indeed far from exhausted that peerless museum. And if only a small proportion of the extraordinary animals currently documented within the bulging files of cryptozoology are found in the future, these will more than adequately demonstrate that, more than a hundred years on from Gould's enquiry, we are still positioned far from that museum's inner sanctum. How much closer our steps will take us towards this depends not only upon how willing science is to seek those creatures still hidden from its view, but also upon how willing its disciples are to recognise that even an extensive, widely-respected knowledge of science is still infinitely less than omniscience. A wise scientist does not take pride in how much he knows, but rather takes heed of how little he knows.

APPENDIX

The Scientific Classification of Animals

Taxonomy, the scientific process of classifying animals (and all other living organisms), employs a hierarchial system of categories. At the base of this hierarchy is the most important taxonomic category of all – the species. Although it has been defined in a number of different ways, a species is considered by most authorities to comprise one or more populations of organisms whose members can readily interbreed with one another to yield viable, fertile offspring. In some cases, such populations may actually be separated from one another by physical geographical boundaries, such as a mountain range, river, sea, or some other topographical barrier; but if members from these populations are brought together and found to be capable of mating with one another to yield fit progeny, they are still classed as members of the same species. For example, the red foxes of Britain, continental Europe, and North America are separated from each other geographically, but if brought together will all freely interbreed to produce fertile, fit offspring – hence they are all considered to belong to one and the same species. Members of populations belonging to *different* species can sometimes mate too, and even occasionally produce offspring, but these are usually sterile, and are known as hybrids.

It was the famous 18th century Swedish botanist Linnaeus (Carl Linné) who first devised the binomial system of nomenclature still used today in scientific classification, a system that provides every species with its own unique two-part name, its scientific name. This is generally of Latin or Greek origin (or both), as these were the universal languages of scholars worldwide in the time of Linnaeus, and is always printed in italics.

For example, the wolf's scientific name is *Canis lupus; lupus* is the wolf's specific or trivial name, and *Canis* is its generic name or genus (plural: genera). By devising the binomial system, Linnaeus created a means by which a species mentioned in any given book, scientific paper, article, etc, could be instantly identified by the reader, regardless of the language in which the publication had been written. The problem with common names is that they change – often radically – from one language to another.

For instance, the species of bird that we refer to in Britain as the common gull is known in America as the mew gull, in France as the ash-grey gull (goéland cendré) and in Germany as the storm gull (Sturmmöwe) – four fundamentally different names. As scientific names stay exactly the same in all languages, however, this species' binomial name in Britain, America, France, Germany and everywhere else is *Larus canus*, thereby eliminating any inter-linguistical ambiguities.

Whereas specific names always begin with a small (lower case) letter, genera always begin with a capital (upper case) letter.

258

Moreover, if a given genus is referred to more than once within a single passage or section of a publication, it is often abbreviated after the first instance of usage to its initial letter. For example, once the wolf's name has been given as *Canis lupus,* for the remainder of the passage or section in question it can be referred to simply as *C. lupus.*

The genus is the group in which closely related species are housed together. Consequently, as the wolf, domestic dog, coyote, and golden jackal, for instance, are all closely related, their scientific names are: *Canis lupus, C. familiaris, C. latrans,* and *C. aureus* respectively. Rather more distantly related to these species – but very closely related to each other – are the fox species, such as the red fox, swift fox, kit fox, and sand fox. These therefore share a different genus, *Vulpes,* thus becoming *Vulpes vulpes, V. velox, V. macrotis,* and *V. pallipes* respectively.

In the same way that closely related species are housed together within the same genus, closely related genera are housed together within the same family. In the case of the wolf, domestic dog, red fox, swift fox, dhole, bushdog, Cape hunting dog, fennec, and all other dogs, this is the dog family, known scientifically as Canidae. Similarly, closely related families are housed together within the same order – the next category on the ascending hierarchy of scientific classification – and further progression upwards in the hierarchy follows the same approach. That is, closely related orders are housed together within the same class, closely related classes within the same phylum (plural:phyla), and, reaching the apex of the hierachy, closely related phyla within the same kingdom. In the case of animals, the 36 animal phyla are housed together within the kingdom Animalia; the

plant phyla are housed within the kingdom Plantae; the fungi phyla within the kingdom Fungi, and so on.

To illustrate the hierarchial approach to the scientific classification of animals, Table 1 (see over) comprises a complete classification of the wolf, from species to kingdom. And to demonstrate the diversity of animal life, a complete classification of the animal kingdom down to the level of individual classes (for the major phyla) is provided in Table 2 (see over). It will be seen from these that the higher the level within the hierarchy the animals are, the less closely related and more diverse they will be. For example, two animal species housed within separate classes of the same phylum are less closely related to one another and are (usually) more different in appearance from one another than are two species housed within separate orders of the same class. Put another way, a pheasant and a wolf are visibly less closely related to one another than are a pheasant and a sparrow.

Sometimes, to facilitate classification (especially when dealing with taxonomically complex animal groups), additional categories, prefixed by 'sub' or 'super', are inserted between existing ones. Thus, the category of subfamily is sometimes used, inserted between genus and family; so too is the category of superfamily, inserted between family and order. This in turn leads us to one final but important category, the subspecies – because even a species can be subdivided, if it consists of several geographically separate populations that can be readily distinguished from one another in some way (e.g. visually, aurally, behaviourally).

Each such population is termed a subspecies of that species. In nature, the subspecies of any given species are, by definition, separated from one another geographically, so that interbreeding cannot usually occur – but if individuals of separate subspecies are deliberately brought together, they will breed and produce viable, fertile offspring (thereby revealing that, despite their distinguishing features, they do indeed belong to the same species, rather than comprising separate species in their own right).

In scientific classification, subspecies have trinomial (three-part) names. All subspecies within a given species share the first two names, but each has its own unique third name, to distinguish it from the other subspecies. For instance, the wolf is split into many different subspecies, which include the timber wolf *Canis lupus lycaon*, the Texas grey wolf *C. l. monstrabilis*, the Himalayan wolf *C. l. chanca*, and the European wolf *C. l. lupus*.

Table 1: **Scientific Classification of the Wolf *Canis lupus***

KINGDOM:	Animalia (Animals)	Other kingdoms include: Plantae (plants), Fungi (fungi).
PHYLUM:	Chordata (chordates)	Other phyla within the kingdom Animalia include: Mollusca (molluscs), Platyhelminthes (flatworms), Uniramia (insects and relatives), Echinodermata (spiny-skinned animals), Porifera (sponges).
CLASS:	Mammalia (Mammals)	Other classes within the phylum Chordata include: Aves (birds), Osteichthyes (bony fishes), Reptilia (reptiles), Ascidiacea (sea squirts), Amphibia (amphibians).
ORDER:	Carnivora (majority of flesh-eating mammals)	Other orders within the class Mammalia include: Cetacea (toothed and toothless whales), Marsupialia (pouched mammals), Chiroptera (bats), Primates (primates, including man), Proboscidea (elephants), Rodentia (rodents), Artiodactyla (even-toed ungulates).
FAMILY:	Canidae (dogs)	Other families within the order Carnivora include: Felidae (cats), Mustelidae (weasels and relatives), Hyaenidae (hyaenas), Ursidae (bears and giant panda).
GENUS:	*Canis* ('typical' dogs)	Other genera within the family Canidae include: *Vulpes* (foxes), *Cuon* (dhole), *Lycaon* (hunting dog), *Chrysocyon* (maned wolf), *Speothos* (bushdog), *Fennecus* (fennec).
SPECIES:	*lupus* wolf, (i.e. *Canis lupus*)	Other species within the genus *Canis* include: *Canis niger* (red wolf), *C. latrans* (coyote), *C. aureus* (golden jackal) *C. familiaris* (domestic dog).

Table 2: **The 36 Phyla of the Animal Kingdom (including the classes of the major phyla)**

N.B. – There is still much disagreement regarding animal classification: the following table follows the version most widely accepted. Also: until the mid-1970s, the classes of the phyla Chelicerata, Uniramia, and Crustacea were grouped together within a single phylum, Arthropoda ('jointed-legged animals'); in that system, the present-day classes of Crustacea were treated merely as subclasses. Abbreviation: a.k.a. = also known as.

1	PHYLUM: **CHORDATA** – Chordates (with a notochord at some developmental stage)		
	Class: Mammalia	–	mammals
	Class: Aves	–	birds
	Class: Reptilia	–	reptiles
	Class: Amphibia	–	amphibians
	Class: Osteichthyes	–	bony fishes; a.k.a. Pisces
	Class: Chondrichthyes	–	cartilaginous fishes; a.k.a. Selachii
	Class: Agnatha	–	jawless fishes
	Class: Leptocardii	–	lancelets
	Class: Thaliacea	–	salps
	Class: Larvacea	–	larvaceans
	Class: Ascidiacea	–	sea squirts
2	PHYLUM: **HEMICHORDATA** – Hemichordates		
	Class: Pterobranchia	–	pterobranchs
	Class: Enteropneusta	–	acorn worms
3	PHYLUM: **CHAETOGNATHA** – Arrow worms		
4	PHYLUM: **ECHINODERMATA** – Spiny-skinned animals		
	Class: Holothuroidea	–	sea cucumbers
	Class: Echinoidea	–	sea urchins
	Class: Ophiuroidea	–	brittle stars
	Class: Asteroidea	–	starfishes
	Class: Concentricycloidea	–	sea daisies
	Class: Crinoidea	–	sea lilies and feather stars
5	PHYLUM: **BRYOZOA** – Moss animals; a.k.a. **ECTOPROCTA** and **POLYZOA**		
6	PHYLUM: **PHORONIDA** – Phoronid worms		
7	PHYLUM: **BRACHIOPODA** – Lamp shells		
8	PHYLUM: **TARDIGRADA** – Water bears		

9   PHYLUM: **PENTASTOMIDA** – Tongue worms; a.k.a. **LINGUATULIDA**

10   PHYLUM: **CRUSTACEA** – Crustaceans (biramous arthropods)

Class: Malacostraca	–	crabs, lobsters, shrimps, woodlice, amphipods
Class: Cirripedia	–	barnacles
Class: Branchiura	–	fish 'lice'
Class: Copepoda	–	copepods
Class: Tantulocarida	–	tantulocarids
Class: Remipedia	–	remipedes
Class: Mystacocarida	–	mystacocarids
Class: Ostracoda	–	seed shrimps
Class: Branchiopoda	–	fairy shrimps, brine shrimps, water 'fleas'
Class: Cephalocarida	–	cephalocarids

11   PHYLUM: **CHELICERATA** – Chelicera-jawed arthropods

Class: Pycnogonida	–	sea spiders; a.k.a. Pantopoda
Class: Arachnida	–	spiders, scorpions, ricinuleids, ticks, mites
Class: Merostomata	–	king (horseshoe) crabs

12   PHYLUM: **UNIRAMIA** – Uniramous arthropods

Class: Insecta	–	insects; a.k.a. Hexapoda
Class: Collembola	–	springtails
Class: Symphyla	–	symphylans
Class: Pauropoda	–	pauropods
Class: Chilopoda	–	centipedes
Class: Diplopoda	–	millipedes

13   PHYLUM: **ONYCHOPHORA** – Velvet worms

14   PHYLUM: **MOLLUSCA** – Molluscs

Class: Cephalopoda	–	squids, octopuses, vampire squid, nautilus
Class: Scaphopoda	–	elephant tusk shells
Class: Bivalvia	–	two-shelled molluscs; a.k.a. Lamellibranchia
Class: Gastropoda	–	single-shelled 'seashells', slugs, snails
Class: Polyplacophora	–	chitons
Class: Aplacophora	–	solenogasters
Class: Monoplacophora	–	monoplacophorans (including *Neopilina*)

15   PHYLUM: **ECHIURA** – Spoon worms

16   PHYLUM: **PRIAPULIDA** – Priapulid worms

17   PHYLUM: **SIPUNCULA** – Peanut worms

18   PHYLUM: **POGONOPHORA** – Beard worms and vestimentiferans

19   PHYLUM: **ANNELIDA** – Segmented (Ringed) worms
          Class: Hirudinea   –   leeches
          Class: Oligochaeta   –   earthworms and pond worms
          Class: Polychaeta   –   marine bristleworms

20   PHYLUM: **GNATHOSTOMULIDA** – Gnathostomulid worms

21   PHYLUM: **ACANTHOCEPHALA** – Thorny-headed worms

22   PHYLUM: **ROTIFERA** – Wheel animalcules

23   PHYLUM: **ENTOPROCTA** – Entoprocts; a.k.a. **KAMPTOZOA**

24   PHYLUM: **LORICIFERA** – Loriciferans

25   PHYLUM: **KINORHYNCHA** – Kinorhynch worms; a.k.a. **ECHINODERA**

26   PHYLUM: **NEMATOMORPHA** – Horsehair worms

27   PHYLUM: **NEMATODA** – Round worms
          Class: Phasmida   –   round worms with phasmids
                              (sensory organs)
          Class: Aphasmida   –   round worms lacking phasmids

28   PHYLUM: **GASTROTRICHA** – Gastrotrich worms

29   PHYLUM: **NEMERTEA** – Ribbon worms; a.k.a. **RHYNCHOCOELA**

30   PHYLUM: **PLATYHELMINTHES** – Flatworms
          Class: Cestoidea   –   true tapeworms, a.k.a. Eucestoda
          Class: Cestodaria   –   fluke-like tapeworms
          Class: Digenea   –   internal parasitic flukes
          Class: Monogenea   –   external parasitic flukes
          Class: Turbellaria   –   turbellarians

31   PHYLUM: **CTENOPHORA** – Comb jellies

32   PHYLUM: **CNIDARIA** – Stinging-celled animals
          Class: Anthozoa   –   sea anemones, soft corals, hard corals
          Class: Cubozoa   –   box jellies
          Class: Scyphozoa   –   true jellyfishes
          Class: Hydrozoa   –   hydras, sea firs, siphonophores

33   PHYLUM: **PLACOZOA** – Placozoans (only one species, *Trichoplax adhaerens*)

34   PHYLUM: **MESOZOA** – Mesozoans

35   PHYLUM: **PORIFERA** – Sponges
          Class: Demospongiae   –   demosponges
          Class: Sclerospongiae   –   coralline sponges (sclerosponges)
          Class: Hexactinellida   –   six-rayed sponges
          Class: Calcarea   –   calcareous sponges

36   PHYLUM: **PROTOZOA** – Single-celled animals (amoebae, ciliates, flagellates, etc)

BIBLIOGRAPHY

In all of the following reference lists, each asterisked (*) reference is a paper comprising a given species' formal scientific description.

Abbreviations: *A.M.N.H.* = *Annals and Magazine of Natural History; B.B.M.H.S.Z.* = *Bulletin of the British Museum (Natural History) - Zoology; B.B.O.C.* = *Bulletin – British Ornithologists Club; C.R.A.S.* = *Comptes Rendus de l'Académie des Sciences; O.c.* = *Op. cit.; P.B.S.W.* = *Proceedings of the Biological Society of Washington; P.Z.S.L.* = *Proceedings of the Zoological Society of London; R.Z.B.A.* = *Revue de Zoologie et la Botanique Africaines; S.G.N.F.B.* = *Sitzungsberichte Gesellschaft Naturforschender Freunde zu Berlin.*

Section 1: THE MAMMALS

1   THOMAS, O. (1900). The white rhinoceros on the Upper Nile. *Nature,*, 62 (18 December): 599; *LYDEKKER, R. (1908). The white rhinoceros. *The Field*, 111 (22 February): 31.

2   HEUVELMANS, B. (1958). *On the Track of Unknown Animals*. Rupert Hart-Davis (London).

3   WENDT, H. (1959). *Out of Noah's Ark*. Weidenfeld & Nicolson (London); SHUKER, K.P.N. (Consultant) (1993). *Secrets of the Natural World* (Vol. 11 of *Quest For the Unknown*). Reader's Digest (Pleasantville).

4   STANLEY, H.M. (1890). *In Darkest Africa.* Sampson Low (London).

5   JOHNSTON, H. (1901). The okapi. Newly-discovered beast living in Central Africa. *McClure's Magazine*, 17 (September): 497-501.

6   JOHNSTON, H. (1900). Letter from, containing an account of a supposed new species of zebra inhabiting the Congo forest. *P.Z.S.L.*, (20 November): 774-5.

7   SCLATER, P.L. (1900). Exhibition of, and remarks upon, two bandoliers made from the skin of a supposed new species of zebra. *Ibid.*, (18 December): 950; *SCLATER, P.L. (1901). On an apparently new species of zebra from the Semliki Forest. *Ibid.*, (5 February): 50-2.

8   BURTON, M. & BURTON, R. (Eds.) (1968-70). *Purnell's Encyclopedia of Animal Life* (6 vols). BPC (London).

9   SCLATER, P.L. (1901). Exhibition of water-colour painting of okapi, and extracts of letter written by Sir Harry Johnston. *P.Z.S.L.*, (7 May): 3-6; LANKESTER, E.R. (1901). Exhibition of two skulls and the skin of the new mammal, the okapi. *Ibid.*, (18 June): 279-81; LANKESTER, E.R. (1902). On Okapia, a new genus of *Giraffidae* from Central Africa. *Transactions of the Zoological Society of London*, 16: 279-307.

10 GRZIMEK, B. (Ed.) (1972-5). *Grzimek's Animal Life Encyclopedia* (13 vols). Van Nostrand Reinhold (London).

11 BRIDGES, W.M. (1937). Okapi comes to the zoological park. *Bulletin of the New York Zoological Society*, 40 (September-October): 135-47.

12 JOHNSTON, H. (1901). The five-horned giraffe. *The Times* (London), 20 June; THOMAS, O. (1901). On the five-horned giraffe obtained by Sir Harry Johnston near Mount Elgon. *P.Z.S.L.*, (19 November): 474-83.

13 ROTHSCHILD, M. (1983). *Dear Lord Rothschild*. Hutchinson (London).

14 *THOMAS, O. (1901). On the more notable mammals obtained by Sir Harry Johnston in the Uganda Protectorate. P.Z.S.L., (21 May): 85-90; KINGDON, J. (1977). *East African Mammals. An Atlas of Evolution in Africa*. Vol. IIIA. Academic Press (London).

15 *MATSCHIE, P. (1903). Ueber einen Gorilla aus Deutsch-Ostafrika. *S.G.N.F.B.*, No. 6 (9 June): 253-9.

16 GROVES, C. (1970). Population systematics of the gorilla. *Journal of Zoology*, 161: 287-300.

17 *ELLIOT, D.G. (1913). *A Review of the Primates*. American Museum of Natural History (New York).

18 HEUVELMANS, B. (1980). *Les Bêtes Humaines d'Afrique*. Plon (Paris).

19 ALLEN, G.M. (1942). *Extinct and Vanishing Mammals of the Western Hemisphere*. American Committee For International Wild Life Protection (Washington D.C.).

20 DAY, D. (1989). *The Encyclopedia of Vanished Species*. Universal Books (London).

21 *PRENTISS, D.W. (1903). Description of an extinct mink from the shell-heaps of the Maine coast. *Proceedings of the U.S. National Museum*, 26: 887-8.

22 *MILLER, G.S. (1903). Seventy new Malayan mammals. *Smithsonian Miscellaneous Collections*, 45: 1-73.

23 SHUKER, K.P.N. (1991). *Extraordinary Animals Worldwide*. Robert Hale (London).

24 *PETERS, W. (1873). Ueber *Dinomys*, eine merkwueridge neue Gattung der stachelschweinartigen Nagethiere aus den Hochgebirgen von Peru. *Auszug Monatsberichte der Konigl.-preuss. Akademie der Wissenschaften zu Berlin*, (10 July): 551-2.

25 GOELDI, E.A. (1904). On the rare rodent *Dinomys branickii* Peters. *P.Z.S.L.*, (7 June): 158-65.

26 RIBEIRO, A. de M. (1919). *Dinomys pacarana*. Arch. Escola Superiore Agricultura e Medicina Veterinário, 2: 13-15; ANTHONY, H.E. (1921). New mammals from British Guiana and Colombia. *American Museum Novitates*, No. 19: 6-7; SANBORN, C.C. (1931). Notes on *Dinomys*. *Publications of the Field Museum of Natural History (Zoology Series)*, 18: 149-55.

27 *THOMAS, O. (1904). On *Hylochoerus*, the forest-pig of Central Africa. *P.Z.S.L.*, (15 November): 193-9.

28 ANON. (1909). Forest hog from the Upper Congo. *The Field*, 114: 193.

29 *THOMAS, O. (1904). New *Callithrix, Midas, Felis, Rhipidomys*, and *Proechimys* from Brazil and Ecuador. *A.M.N.H.*, (Series 7), 14: 188-96; RIBEIRO, A. de M. (1912). Zwei neue Affen unserer Fauna. *Rundschau*: 21-3.

30 HILL, W.C.O. (1957). *Primates. Comparative Anatomy and Taxonomy. Volume III: Pithecoidea - Platyrrhini.* Edinburgh University Press (Edinburgh).

31 *MATSCHIE, P. (1905). Eine Robbe von Laysan. *S.G.N.F.B.*: 254-62.

32 STONEHOUSE, B. (1985). *Sea Mammals of the World.* Penguin (Middlesex).

33 DENIS, A. (1963). A new seal. *Animals*, 3 (24 December): 57.

34 *GOELDI, E.A. (1907). On some new and insufficiently known species of marmoset monkeys from the Amazonian region. *P.Z.S.L.*: 88-99.

35 *BONHOTE, J.L. (1907). On a collection of mammals made by Dr Vassal in Annam. *Ibid.*: 3-11; *TIEN, D.V. (1960). Sur une nouvelle espèce de *Nycticebus* au Vietnam. *Zoologischer Anzeiger*, 164: 240-3; ANNANDALE, N. (1908). An unknown lemur from the Lushai Hills, Assam. *P.Z.S.L.*, (17 November): 888-9.

36 *MILLER, G.S. & HOLLISTER, N. (1921). Twenty new mammals collected by H.C. Raven in Celebes. *P.B.S.W.*, 34, 93-104; MUSSER, G.C. & DAGOSTO, M. (1987). The identity of *Tarsius pumilus*, a pygmy species endemic to the montane forests of central Sulawesi. *American Museum Novitates*, No. 2867 (12 March): 1-53.

37 *ANDREWS, R.C. (1908). Description of a new species of *Mesoplodon* from Canterbury Province, New Zealand. *Bulletin of the American Museum of Natural History*, 24: 205-15.

38 WATSON, L. (1985). *Whales of the World* (Rev. Edit.). Hutchinson (London).

39 LYDEKKER, R. (1910). A new African antelope. *The Times* (London), 23 September; *LYDEKKER, R. (1910). The spotted kudu. *Nature*, 84 (29 September): 397; LYDEKKER, R. (1910). The spotted kudu and the Arusi bushbucks. *The Field*, 116 (22 October): 798; LYDEKKER, R. (1911). On the mountain nyala, *Tragelaphus buxtoni*. *P.Z.S.L.*, (21 February): 348-53.

40 BROWN, L. (1969). Ethiopia's elusive nyala. *Animals*, 12 (December): 340-4.

41 *OUWENS, P.A. (1910). Contribution à la connaissance des mammifères de Celebes. *Bulletin de la Department d'Agriculture Indes Neerlandes*, 38: 1-7; GROVES, C.P. (1969). Systematics of the anoa (Mammalia, Bovidae). *Beaufortia*, 17 (7 November): 1-12.

42 FISHER, J., SIMON, N., & VINCENT, J. (1969). *The Red Book. Wildlife in Danger.* Collins (London).

43 *THOMAS, O. (1910). A new genus of fruit-bats and two new shrews from Africa. *A.M.N.H.* (Series 8): 6: 111-14; *THOMAS, O. (1915). New African rodents and insectivores, mostly collected by Dr C. Christy for the Congo Museum. *Ibid.*, 16: 146-52.

44 ALLEN, J.A. (1917). The skeletal characters of *Scutisorex* Thomas. *Bulletin of the American Museum of Natural History*, 37 (26 November): 769-84; BURTON, M. (1951). The hero shrew. *Illustrated London News*, 219 (17 November): 812.

45 *MORTON, S.G. (1849). Additional observations of a new living species of hippopotamus of Western Africa. *Journal of the Academy of Natural Sciences of Philadelphia* (Series 2), 1 (August): 3-11; LEIDY, J. (1852). On the osteology of the head of hippopotamus and a description of the osteological characters of a new genus of Hippopotamidae. *Ibid.*, (new series), 2 (7 May): 207-34.

46 MacALLISTER, A. (1873). On the visceral anatomy and myology of a young female hippopotamus which died in the Dublin Zoological Society. *Proceedings of the Royal Irish Academy*, 2: 494-500.

47 SCHOMBURGK, H. (1912). On the trail of the pygmy hippo. *Bulletin of the New York Zoological Society*, 16: 808-84; SCHOMBURGK, H. (1913). Distribution and habits of the pygmy hippopotamus. *Report of the New York Zoological Society*, 17: 113- 20.

48 NOWAK, R. (Ed.) (1991). *Walker's Mammals of the World* (5th Edit.). Johns Hopkins University Press (Baltimore).

49 *LAHILLE, F. (1912). Nota preliminar sobre una nueva especie de Marsopa del rio de la Plata (*Phocaena dioptrica*). *Anales del Museo Nacional de Buenos Aires*, 23: 269-78.

50 *TRUE, F.W. (1913). Description of *Mesoplodon mirum*, a beaked whale recently discovered on the coast of North Carolina. *Proceedings of the U.S. National Museum*, 45: 651-7.

51 *THOMAS, O. (1912). Two new genera and a new species of viverrine Carnivora. *P.Z.S.L.*, (19 March): 498-503; ANON. (1991). Photo first. *Wild About Animals*, (October): 14.

52 *ALLEN, J.A. (1919). Preliminary notes on African Carnivora. *Journal of Mammalogy*, 1: 25-6.

53 HART, J.A. & TIMM, R.M. (1978). Observations on the aquatic genet in Zaire. *Carnivore*, 1: 130-2.

54 PILLERI, G. (1979). The Chinese river dolphin (*Lipotes vexillifer*) in poetry, literature and legend. *Investigations Cetacea*, 10: 335-49; *MILLER, G.S. (1918). A new river-dolphin from China. *Smithsonian Miscellaneous Collections*, 68: 1-12.

55 KAIYA ZHOU (1988). The baiji. *In*: HARRISON, R. & BRYDEN, M.M. (Eds.), *Whales, Dolphins and Porpoises*. Merehurst (London). pp. 82-3.

56 *ALEXANDER, W.B. (1918). A new species of marsupial of the sub-family *Phalangerinae*. *Journal of the Royal Society of West Australia*, 4: 31-6.

57 TROUGHTON, E. (1965). *Furred Animals of Australia* (8th Edit.). Angus & Robertson (Sydney).

58 SALVADORI, F.B. & FLORIO, P.L. (1978). *Wildlife in Peril*. Westbridge Books (Newton Abbot).

59 *MONTANDON, G. (1929). Un singe d'apparence anthropoide en Amérique du Sud. *C.R.A.S.*, 188 (11 March): 815-17; LOYS, F. de. (1929). A gap filled in the pedigree of man? *Illustrated London News*, 174 (15 June): 1040.

60 SHUKER, K.P.N. (1989). *Mystery Cats of the World. From Blue Tigers to Exmoor Beasts.* Robert Hale (London).

61 *POCOCK, R.I. (1927). Description of a new species of cheetah (*Acinonyx*). *P.Z.S.L.*, (22 February): p. 18, and (6 April): 245-52; BOTTRIELL, L.G. (1987). *King Cheetah. The Story of the Quest.* E.J. Brill (Leiden).

62 GUGGISBERG, C.A.W. (1975). *Wild Cats of the World.* David & Charles (Newton Abbot).

63 *LONGMAN, H.A. (1926). New records of cetacea. *Memoirs of the Queensland Museum*, 8: 266-78.

64 AZZAROLI, M.L. (1968). Second specimen of the rarest living beaked whale. *Monitore Zoologico Italiano*, 2: 67-79.

65 MOORE, J.C. (1968). Relationships among the living genera of beaked whales. *Fieldiana Zoology*, 53: 209-98.

66 PITMAN, R.L. *et al.* (1987). Observations of an unidentified beaked whale (*Mesoplodon* sp.) in the eastern tropical Pacific. *Marine Mammal Science*, 3 (October): 345-52.

67 *GRANDIDIER, G. (1929). Un nouveau type de mammifère insectivore de Madagascar, le *Dasogale fontoynonti* G. Grand. *Bulletin de l'Académie Malgache* (new series), 11: 85-90.

68 MacPHEE, R.D.E. (1987). Systematic status of *Dasogale fontoynonti* (Tenrecidae, Insectivora). *Journal of Mammalogy*, 68: 133-5.

69 *SCHWARZ, E. (1929). Das Vorkommen des Schimpansen auf den linken Kongo-Ufer. *R.Z.B.A.*, 16: 425-6; SCHOUTEDEN, H. (1931). Quelques notes sur le chimpanze de la rive gauche du Congo, *Pan satyrus paniscus*. *Ibid.*, 20: 310-14.

70 SUSMAN, R.L. (Ed.) (1984). *The Pygmy Chimpanzee. Evolutionary Biology and Behavior.* Plenum Press (London).

71 MORRIS, R. & MORRIS, D. (1981). *The Giant Panda.* Kogan Page Ltd (London).

72 MILNE-EDWARDS, A. (1869). Extrait d'une lettre de même (M. l'Abbé David) datée de la principalité Thibetaine (independante) de Moupin, le 21 mars 1869. *Nouvelles Archives du Museum d'Histoire Naturelle (Bulletin)*, 5: 13.

73 MILNE-EDWARDS, A. (1870). Sur quelques mammifères du Thibet oriental. *Annales des Sciences Naturelles* (Series 5), 70: 341-2.

74 ROOSEVELT, T. & ROOSEVELT, K. (1929). *Trailing the Giant Panda.* Scribner's (New York).

75 HARKNESS, R. (1938). *The Baby Giant Panda.* Carrick & Evans (New York).

76 BELSON, J. & GILHEANY, J. (1981). *The Giant Panda Book.* Collins (London).

77 APPLETON, L. (1987). Who's that girl? It's Blue Sky! *Daily Mail* (London), 16 November.

78 LEONE, C.A. & WIENS, A.L. (1956). Comparative serology of carnivores. *Journal of Mammalogy*, 37: 11-23.

79 O'BRIEN, S. (1987). The ancestry of the giant panda. *Scientific American*, 257 (November): 82-7.

80 SHUKER, K.P.N. (1989). Mystery bears. *Fate*, 43 (April): 30-8.

81 HEUVELMANS, B. (1986). Annotated checklist of apparently unknown animals with which cryptozoology is concerned. *Cryptozoology*, 5: 1-26.

82 AHARONI, I. (1942). *Memoirs of a Hebrew Zoologist.* Am Oved Limited (Tel Aviv).

83 SIEGEL, H.I. (Ed.) (1985). *The Hamster. Reproduction and Behavior.* Plenum Press (London).

84 FINLAYSON, H.H. (1932). Rediscovery of *Caloprymnus campestris* (Marsupialia). *Nature*, 129 (11 June): 871.

85 ANON. (1933). [Shepherd's beaked whale reports.] *Hawera Star* (Hawera - New Zealand), 9 November and 12 December.

86 *OLIVER, W.R.B. (1937). *Tasmacetus shepherdi*: a new genus and species of beaked whale from New Zealand. *P.Z.S.L.*, (4 May): 371-81.

87 HEUVELMANS, B. (1968). *In the Wake of the Sea-Serpents.* Rupert Hart-Davis (London).

88 PODUSCHKA, W. (1975). Solenodon story. *Wildlife*, 17 (March): 108-11.

89 MILLER, G.S. (1930). Three small collections of mammals from Hispaniola. *Smithsonian Miscellaneous Collections*, 82: 1-10.

90 KEMF, E. (1988). Fighting for the forest ox. *New Scientist*, 118 (30 June): 51-3.

91 *URBAIN, A. (1937). Le kou prey ou boeuf gris Cambodgien. *Bulletin de la Société de France*, 62 (8 June): 305-7.

92 GRIGSON, C. (1988). Complex cattle. *New Scientist*, 119 (4 August): 93-4.

93 COOLIDGE, H.J. (1940). The Indo-Chinese forest ox or kouprey. *Memoirs of the Museum of Comparative Zoology, Harvard College*, 54 (August): 417-531.

94 SITWELL, N. (1970). Is this the rarest animal in the world? *Animals*, 13 (November): 306-7.

95 FITTER, R. (1976). The kouprey survives. *Oryx*, 13 (July): 249; ANON. (1980). Kouprey alive, well, and protected. *Ibid.*, 15 (July): 238.

96 ANON. (1988). The cow quest. *BBC Wildlife*, 6 (November): 635.

97 *BELOSLUDOV, B.A. & BASHANOV, V.S. (1939). A new genus and species of rodent from the Central Kazakstan. *Uchenye Zaipiski Kazakkskii Universitet Alma-Ata Biol.*, 1: 81-6; BASHANOV, V.S. & BELOSLUDOV, B.A. (1941). A remarkable family of rodent from Kazakhstan, U.S.S.R. *Journal of Mammalogy*, 22 (14 August): 311-15.

98 JOHNSON, D.H. (1948). A rediscovered Haitian rodent, *Plagiodontia aedium*, with a synopsis of related species. *P.B.S.W.*, 61 (16 June): 69-76.

99 *MILLER, G. (1927). The rodents of the genus *Plagiodontia*. *Proceedings of the U.S. National Museum*, 72: 1-8.

100 *ALLEN, G.M. (1917). An extinct Cuban *Capromys*. *Proceedings of the New England Zoological Club*, 6 (28 March): 53-6.

101 *BARBOUR, T. (1926). A remarkable new bird from Cuba. *Ibid.*, 9: 73-5; *BARBOUR, T. & PETERS, J.L. (1927). Two more remarkable new birds from Cuba. *Ibid.*, 9: 95-7.

102 *VARONA, L.S. (1970). Descripcion de una nueva especia de *Capromys* del sur de Cuba. *Poeyana Instituto de Biologia, Cuba* (Series A), No. 74: 1-16.

103 BURTON, J. & PEARSON, B. (1988). *Collins Guide to the Rare Mammals of the World.* Collins (London).

104 ANON. (1991). [Hutias rediscovered.] *Oryx*, 25 (July): 133.

105 *VARONA, L.S. & GARRIDO, O.H. (1970). Vertebrados de los Cayos de San Felipe, Cuba, incluyendo una nuevo especie de jutia. *Poeyana Instituto de Biologia, Cuba* (Series A), No. 75.

106 *VARONA, L.S. (1970). Subgenero y especie nuevas de *Capromys* (Rodentia: Caviomorpha) para Cuba. *Poeyana Instituto Zool. Acad. Cienc. de Cuba*, 194: 1-33.

107 McWHIRTER, R. & McWHIRTER, N. (Eds.) (1974). *The Guinness Book of Records* (21st Edit.). Guinness Superlatives (London); McWHIRTER, N. (Ed.) (1978). *The Guinness Book of Records* (25th Edit.). Guinness Superlatives (London).

108 DAVIES, G. & BIRKENHÄGER, B. (1990). Jentink's duiker in Sierra Leone: evidence from the Freetown Peninsula. *Oryx*, 24 (July): 143-6.

109 *KRUMBIEGEL, I. (1949). Der Andenwolf - ein neuentdecktes Grosstier. *Umschau*, 49: 590-1; KRUMBIEGEL, I. (1953). Der "Andenwolf", *Dasycyon hagenbecki* (Krumbiegel, 1949). *Säugetierkundliche Mitteilungen*, 1: 97-104.

110 DIETERLEN, I. (1954). Über den Haarbau des Andenwolfes, *Dasycyon hagenbecki* (Krumbiegel, 1949). *Ibid.*, 2: 26-31; CABRERA, A. (1957). Catalogo de los mamiferos de America del Sur. 1. (Metatheria - Unguiculata - Carnivora). *Revista - Museo Argentino de Ciencas Naturales Rivadavia (Zoologia)*, 4: 1- 307.

111 *SANBORN, C.C. (1951). Two new mammals from southern Peru. *Fieldiana Zoology*, 31: 473-7.

112 *IZOR, R.J. & TORRE, L. de la (1979). A new species of weasel (*Mustela*) from the highlands of Colombia, with comments on the evolution and distribution of South American weasels. *Journal of Mammalogy*, 59: 92-102.

113 SCHREIBER, A. *et al.* (1989). *Weasels, Civets, Mongooses, and Their Relatives*. IUCN (Gland - Switzerland).

114 YAMADA, M. (1954). An account of a rare porpoise *Feresa* from Japan. *Scientific Reports of the Whales Research Institute*, 9: 59-88.

115 *MIKHALEV, Yu. A. *et al.* (1981). The distribution and biology of killer whales in the southern hemisphere. *Report of the International Whale Commission*, 31: 551-65.

116 *BERZIN, A.A. & VLADIMIROV, V.L. (1983). A new species of killer whale (Cetacea, Delphinidae) from the Antarctic waters. *Zoologicheskii Zhurnal*, 62: 287-95; BIGG, M.A., *et al.* (1987). *Killer Whales, a Study of Their Identification, Genealogy and Natural History in British Colombia and Washington State*. Phantom Press and Publications (Nanaimo).

117 *HEIM de BALSAC, H. (1954). Un genre inedit et inattendu de mammifère (Insectivore Tenrecidae) d'Afrique Occidentale. *C.R.A.S.*, 239: 102-4; *de WITTE, G-F & FRECHKOP, S. (1955). Sur une espèce encore inconnue de mammifère africain, *Potamogale ruwenzorii*, sp. n. *Bulletin - Institut Royal des Sciences Naturelles de Belgique*, 31: 1-11.

118 GEE, E.P. (1964). *The Wild Life of India*. Collins (London).

119 *KHARJURIA, H. (1956). A new langur (Primates: Colobidae) from Goalpara District, Assam. *A.M.N.H.* (Series 12), 9: 86-9.

120 *T'AN PANG-CHIEH (1957). Rare catches by Chinese animal collectors. *Zoo Life*, 12 (Winter): 61-3; NAPIER, J.R. & NAPIER, P.H. (1967). *A Handbook of Living Primates*. Academic Press (New York).

121 *FRASER, F.C. (1956). A new Sarawak dolphin. *Sarawak Museum Journal*, 7: 478-503.

122 *NISHIWAKI, M. & KAMIYA, T. (1958). A beaked whale *Mesoplodon* stranded at Oiso Beach, Japan. *Scientific Reports of the Whales Research Institute*, 13: 53-83.

123 DERANIYAGALA, P. (1963). Mass mortality...and a new beaked whale from Ceylon. *Spolia Zeylandica*, 29: 79-84; MOORE, J.C. & GILMORE, R.M. (1965). A beaked whale new to the western hemisphere. *Nature*, 205 (20 March): 1239-40.

124 *NORRIS, K.S. & McFARLAND, W.N. (1958). A new harbor porpoise of the genus *Phocoena* from the Gulf of California. *Journal of Mammalogy*, 39: 22-39.

125 *HAYMAN, R.W. (1958). A new genus and species of West African mongoose. *A.M.N.H.* (Series 13), 1: 448-52.

126 SCHLITTER, D.A. (1974). Notes on the Liberian mongoose, *Liberiictis kuhni* Hayman, 1958. *Journal of Mammalogy*, 55 (May): 438-42; TAYLOR, M.E. (1992). The Liberian mongoose. *Oryx*, 26 (April): 103-6.

127 ANON. (1959). Protection for "friendly" monster. *Guardian* (Manchester), 4 March; ANON. (1961). Camera captures unknown ape. *Popular Science Monthly*, 179 (July): 83; SHUKER, K.P.N. (Consultant) (1993) *Man and Beast* Reader's Digest (Pleasantville)

128 HILL, W.C.O. (1963). The ufiti: the present position. *Symposia of the Zoological Society of London*, 10: 57-9.

129 BLYTH, E. (1863). *Catalogue of the Mammalia in the Museum of the Asiatic Society*. (Calcutta); BAILEY, F.M. (1912). Journey through a portion of south-eastern Tibet and the Mishmi Hills. *Geographical Journal*, 39: 334-47; DOLLMAN, J.G. (1932). Mammals collected by Lord Cranbrook and Captain F. Kingdom Ward in Upper Burma. *Proceedings of the Linnaean Society of London*, 145: 9-11.

130 *HAYMAN, R.W. (1961). The red goral of the North-East Frontier region. *P.Z.S.L.*, 136: 317-24.

131 HLA AUNG, S. (1967). Observations on the red goral...at Rangoon Zoo. *International Zoo Yearbook*, 7: 225-6.

132 *POCOCK, R.I. (1914). Description of a new species of goral (*Nemorhaedus*) shot by Captain F.M. Bailey. *Journal of the Bombay Natural History Society*, 23: 32-3.

133 GROVES, C.P. & GRUBB, P. (1985). Reclassification of the serows and gorals (*Nemorhaedus*: Bovidae). *In*: LOVARI, S. (Ed.), *The Biology and Management of Mountain Ungulates*. Croom Helm (London). pp. 45-50.

134 *SCHALDACH, W.J. & McLAUGHLIN, C.A. (1960). A new genus and species of glossophagine bat from Colima, Mexico. *Contributions to Science, Los Angeles*, No. 37: 1-8.

135 PIZZEY, G. (1963). Lost and found. *Animals*, 2 (26 November): 626-8; WILKINSON, H.E. (1961). The rediscovery of Leadbeater's possum, *Gymnobelideus leadbeateri* McCoy. *Victorian Naturalist*, 78: 97-102.

136 *MOORE, J.C. (1963). Recognizing certain species of beaked whales of the Pacific Ocean. *American Midland Naturalist*, 70: 396-428.

137 SCHAEFER, E. (1937). Über das Zwergblauschaf (*Pseudois* spec. nov.) und das Grossblauschaf (*Pseudois nahoor* Hdgs.) in Tibet. *Zoologische Garten*, 9: 263-78; *HALTENORTH, T. (1963). Klassifikation der Säugetiere: Artiodactyla. *Handbüche der Zoologie*, 8: 1-167.

138 GROVES, C.P. (1978). The taxonomic status of the dwarf blue sheep (Artiodactyla; Bovidae). *Säugetierkundliche Mitteilungen*, 26: 177-83.

139 ANON. (1968). New mammal discovered. *Animals*, 10 (March): 501-3.

140 *IMAIZUMI, Y. (1967). A new genus and species of cat from Iriomote, Ryukyu Islands. *Journal of the Mammalogical Society of Japan*, 3: 75-106.

141 WURSTER-HILL, D.H. *et al.* (1987). Banded chromosome study of the Iriomote cat. *Journal of Heredity*, 78: 105-7.

142 ANON. (1975). Iriomote cat survey finds a new pig. *Wildlife*, 17 (February): 87-8.

143 JACKSON, P. (1989). New cat discovered. *Cat News*, No. 10 (January); LOXTON, H. (1990). *The Noble Cat*. Merehurst (London).

144 FITTER, R. (1968). *Vanishing Wild Animals of the World*. Midland Bank/Kaye & Ward (London).

145 DECHAU, C-P. (1990). Rainforest yields 'extinct' lemur. *New Scientist*, 125 (27 January): 33.

146 WODZICKI, K. & FLUX, J.E.C. (1967). The rediscovery of the white-throated wallaby on Kawau island. *Australian Journal of Science*, 29: 429-30.

147 SEEBECK, J. (1967). Burramys - only known from fossils. *Animals*, 10 (October): 271-2; TROUGHTON, E. (1967). Broom's pygmy possum. *Proceedings of the Royal Zoological Society of New South Wales* (for 1966-67): 20-4.

148 MORCOMBE, M.K. (1967). The dibbler - unseen for 83 years. *Animals*, 10 (October): 273-4; MORCOMBE, M.K. (1967). The rediscovery after 83 years of the dibbler *Antechinus apicalis* (Marsupialia, Dasyuridae). *Western Australian Naturalist*, 10: 103-11; DICKMAN, C. (1986). Return of the phantom dibbler. *Australian Natural History*, 22 (winter): 33.

149 *HEUVELMANS, B. (1969). Note préliminaire sur un spécimen conservé dans la glace d'une forme encore inconnue d'hominidé vivant: *Homo pongoides* (sp. seu subsp. nov.). *Bulletin de l'Institut Royal des Sciences Naturelles de Belgique*, 45: 1-24; SANDERSON, I.T. (1969). Preliminary description of the external morphology of what appeared to be the fresh corpse of a hitherto unknown form of living hominid. *Genus*, 25: 249-78; HEUVELMANS, B. & PORCHNEV, B. (1974). *L'Homme de Neanderthal est Toujours Vivant*. Plon (Paris).

150 TESSIER-YANDELL, J. (1971). Rediscovery of the pygmy hog. *Animals*, 13 (December): 956-8.

151 MALLINSON, J. (1989). *In Search of Endangered Species*. David & Charles (Newton Abbot).

152 *MISHRA, A.C. & SINGH, K.N. (1978). Description of *Haematopinus oliveri* sp. nov. (Anoplura: Haematopinidae) parasitizing *Sus salvanius* in India. *Bulletin of the Zoological Survey of India*, 1: 167-9.

153 *HILL, J.E. (1974). A new family, genus and species of bat (Mammalia: Chiroptera) from Thailand. *B.B.M.N.H.Z.*, 27: 301-36.

154 ANON. (1985). The world's smallest mammal. *World Wildlife News*, (spring): 5.

155 GOULD, A.B. (1986). Smallest mammal still at large. *BBC Wildlife*, 4 (November): 566-7.

156 *THONGLONGYA, K. (1972). A new genus and species of fruit bat from South India (Chiroptera: Pteropodidae). *Journal of the Bombay Natural History Society*, 69: 151-8; WATKINS, M. (1993). Second sight. *BBC Wildlife*, 11 (August): 59; GOULD, E. (1978). Rediscovery of *Hipposideros ridleyi*. *Biotropica*, 10: 30-2.

157 WETZEL, R.M. *et al.* (1975). *Catagonus*, an "extinct" peccary, alive in Paraguay. *Science*, 189 (1 August): 379-81; WETZEL, R.M. (1977). The Chacoan peccary *Catagonus wagneri* (Rusconi). *Bulletin of Carnegie Museum of Natural History*, No. 3: 1-36; WETZEL, R.M. (1981). The hidden Chacoan peccary. *Carnegie Magazine*, 55: 24-32.

158 ANON. (1988). Chacoan peccary project. *Oryx*, 22 (April): 120.

159 MITTERMEIER, R.A., MACEDO-RUIZ, H. de, & LUSCOMBE, A. (1975). A woolly monkey rediscovered in Peru. *Oryx*, 13 (January): 41-6.

160 ANON. (1982). Monkey discovered. *Wildlife*, 24 (May): 164.

161 *ARCHER, M. (1975). *Ningaui*, a new genus of tiny dasyurids (Marsupialia) and two new species, *N. timealeyi* and *N. ridei*, from arid Western Australia. *Memoirs of the Queensland Museum*, 17: 237-49; ANON. (1975). Animal like a womble is new find. *The Times* (London), 13 January.

162 *KITCHENER, D.J. *et al.* (1983). A taxonomic appraisal of the genus *Ningaui* Archer (Marsupialia: Dasyuridae), including description of a new species. *Australian Journal of Zoology*, 31: 361-70.

163 *SPENCER, W.B. (1908). Description of a new species of *Sminthopsis*. *Proceedings of the Royal Society of Victoria* (Series 2), 21: 449-51.

164 DAVEY, K. (1983). *Our Arid Environment*. Reed (New South Wales).

165 ANON. (1981). 'Extinct' rodent found in desert. *Globe & Mail* (Toronto), 21 September; ANON. (1982). Rare marsupial found. *Oryx*, 16 (October): 313.

166 ANON. (1977). Survey team finds new rock wallaby. *Wildlife*, 19 (November): 491; *MAYNES, G.M. (1982). A new species of rock wallaby, *Petrogale persephone*...from Proserpine, Central Queensland. *Australian Mammalogy*, 5: 47-58.

167 *MENZIES, J.I. (1977). Fossil and subfossil fruit bats from the mountains of New Guinea. *Australian Journal of Zoology*, 25: 329-36.

168 HYNDMAN, D. & MENZIES, J.I. (1980). *Aproteles bulmerae* (Chiroptera: Pteropodidae) of New Guinea is not extinct. *Journal of Mammalogy*, 61: 159-60; ANON. (1993). Rediscovery of a fruit bat. *Oryx*, 27 (July): 144.

169 WOOD, G.L. (1982). *The Guinness Book of Animal Facts and Feats* (3rd Edit.). Guinness Superlatives (London).

170 MATTHEWS, P. & McWHIRTER, N. (Eds) (1992). *The Guinness Book of Records* 1993. Guinness Publishing (London).

171 ANON. (1989). New species of deer in China. *Oryx*, 23 (April): 109.

172 *GROVES, C.P. & GRUBB, P. (1982). The species of muntjac (genus *Muntiacus*) in Borneo: unrecognized sympatry in tropical deer. *Zoologische Mededelingen*, 56:

203-16; PUTMAN, R. (1988). *The Natural History of Deer.* Christopher Helm (London).

173 ANON. (1978). Giant civet rediscovered. *Oryx,* 14 (October): 309; ANON. (1979). The 'arboreal dog' reappears. *World Wildlife News,* (summer): 5.

174 *SEEBECK, J.H. & JOHNSTON, P.G. (1980). *Potorous longipes... a new species from eastern Victoria. Australian Journal of Zoology,* 28: 119-34.

175 PERRIN, W.F. *et al.* (1981). *Stenella clymene,* a rediscovered tropical dolphin of the Atlantic. *Journal of Mammalogy,* 62 (August): 583-98.

176 KINGDON, J. (1986). An embarrassment of monkeys. *BBC Wildlife,* 4 (February): 52-7.

177 REDMOND, I. (1986). New monkey puzzle. *Ibid.,* 2 (August): 384; ANON. (1988). Monkey makes its debut. *New Scientist,* 118 (23 June): 31.

178 *HARRISON, M.J.S. (1988). A new species of guenon (genus *Cercopithecus*) from Gabon. *Journal of Zoology,* 215 (July): 561-75.

179 *THYS VAN DEN AUDENAERDE, F.E.T. (1977). Description of a monkey- skin from east-central Zaire as a probably new monkey species (Mammalia, Cercopithecidae). *Revue de Zoologie Africaine,* 91: 1000-10.

180 *SCHWARZ, E. (1932). Der Vertreter der Diana-Meerkatze in Zentral- Afrika. *R.Z.B.A.,* 21: 251-4.

181 *POCOCK, R.I. (1907). A monographic revision of the monkeys of the genus *Cercopithecus.* *P.Z.S.L.:* 677-746.

182 *GROVES, C.P. & LAY, D. (1985). A new species of the genus *Gazella* (Mammalia: Artiodactyla: Bovidae) from the Arabian Peninsula. *Mammalia,* 49: 27-36; SCOTT, M. (1986). Gazelle comes out of the cupboard. *BBC Wildlife,* 4 (August): 378.

183 BURTON, J.A. (1988). No yeti yet. *Ibid.,* 3 (October): 461; ZHOU GUOXING. (1987). The big wildman and the little wildman. *Ibid.,* 5 (September): 442-4.

184 ZHOU GUOXING. (1984). Morphological analysis of the Jiulong Mountain "manbear" (wildman) hand and foot specimens. *Cryptozoology,* 3: 58-70.

185 GREENWELL, J.R. (1985). Groves joins editorial board. *ISC Newsletter,* 4 (winter): 10; TISDALE, L. (1986). Hair today, gone tomorrow. *BBC Wildlife,* 4 (May): 206-7.

186 *AYRES, J.M. (1985). On a new species of squirrel monkey, genus *Saimiri,* from Brazilian Amazonia (Primates, Cebidae). *Papeis Avulsos de Zoologia,* 36: 147-64; ANON. (1986). New monkey from old. *BBC Wildlife,* 4 (January): 10.

187 GREENWELL, J.R. (1986). Onza specimen obtained - identity being studied. *ISC Newsletter,* 5 (spring): 1-6; GREENWELL, J.R. (1987). Is this the beast the Spaniard saw in Montezuma's zoo? *BBC Wildlife,* 6 (July): 354-9.

188 TINSLEY, J.R. (1987). *The Puma: Legendary Lion of the Americas.* Texas Weston Press (El Paso); MARSHALL, R. (1961). *The Onza.* Exposition Press (New York); DOBIE, J.F. (1935). *Tongues of the Monte.* Doubleday, Doran, & Co (New York); SHUKER, K.P.N. (1986). Cryptoletter [onza]. *ISC Newsletter,* 5 (winter): 11.

189 GREENWELL, J.R. (1985). Two new onza skulls found. *Ibid.,* 4 (winter): 5-6.

190 GREENWELL, J.R. (1988). Onza identity still unresolved. *Ibid.,* 7 (winter): 5-6.

191 *MEIER, B. et al. (1987). A new species of *Hapalemur* from South East Madagascar. *Folia Primatologica,* 48: 211-15; CHERFAS, J. & DECHAU, C. (1988). Zoologist discovers new species of primate. *New Scientist,* 117 (28 January): 33.

192 *WOZENCRAFT, W.C. (1986). A new species of striped mongoose from Madagascar. *Journal of Mammalogy,* 67: 561-71

193 KIRBY, T. (1987). Rudimentary porcupine returns to earth. *BBC Wildlife,* 5 (March): 140-1.

194 ANON. (1992). New species of porcupine. *Oryx,* 26 (October): 198.

195 ANON. (1987). Sumatran rhino rediscovery. *Ibid.,* 21 (April): 120; RUSSELL, C. (1986). The rhino's return. *Daily Mail* (London), 22 October.

196 SCHALLER, G. et al. (1990). Javan rhinoceros in Vietnam. *Oryx,* 24 (April): 77-80.

197 *van DYCK, S. (1988). The bronze quoll, *Dasyurus spartacus* (Marsupialia: Dasyuridae), a new species from the savannahs of Papua New Guinea. *Australian Mammalogy,* 11: 145-56.

198 ANON. (1989). A new tree kangaroo. *Oryx,* 23 (July): 171; WOOD, G.L. (1989). Personal communication, 8 June.

199 ANON. (1988). New whale type found off Peru. *Cincinnati Enquirer* (Cincinnati), 19 December; ANON. (1989). Les grandes inconnues des océans. *Terre Sauvage,* No. 27 (March): 6; *REYES, J.C., MEAD, J.G., & WAEREBEEK, K. van (1991). A new species of beaked whale *Mesoplodon peruvianus* sp. n. (Cetacea: Ziphiidae) from Peru. *Marine Mammal Science,* 7 (January): 1-24.

200 SHUKER, K.P.N. (1991). Finding monsters from the deep. *Fate,* 44 (May): 94-5, 98-100.

201 JAMES, S. (1989). Toothless wonder. *Today* (London), 15 February: 20-1; PELLETIER, F-X. (1989). Les cousins d'eau donce. *Apnéa,* No. 20 (July-August): 46-8.

202 ANON. (1989). Golden-crowned lemur found in Madagascar. *New Scientist,* 121 (25 February): 41; *SIMONS, E. (1988). A new species of *Propithecus* (Primates) from northeast Madagascar. *Folia Primatologica,* 50: 143-51.

203 BELL, W. (1923). *The Wanderings of an Elephant Hunter.* Country Life (London).

204 *NOACK, T. (1906). Eine Zwergform des Afrikanischen Elefanten. *Zoologischer Anzeiger,* 29: 631-3; GREENWELL, J.R. (1990). New evidence supports existence of pygmy elephant. *ISC Newsletter,* 9 (spring): 1-6.

205 EISENTRAUT, M. & BÖHME, W. (1989). Gibt es zwei Elefantenarten in Afrika? *Zoo,* 32: 61-8.

206 SHUKER, K.P.N. (1990). The Kellas cat: reviewing an enigma. *Cryptozoology,* 9: 26-40; ANON. (1992). Mystery of the black cat. *Wild About Animals,* (June): 42.

207 *LORINI, M.L. & PERSSON, V.G. (1990). New species of *Leontopithecus* Lesson 1840 from southern Brazil (Primates: Callithricidae). *Boletin Museo Nacional Rio de Janeiro Zoologia,* No. 338: 1-14.

208 *MITTERMEIER, R.A. *et al.* (1992). A new species of

marmoset...from the Rio Maués region,...Central Brazilian Amazonia. *Goeldiana, Zoologia*, 14: 1-17.

209 *MENZIES, J.I. (1990). Notes on spiny bandicoots, *Echymipera* spp....from New Guinea and description of a new species. *Science in New Guinea*, 16: 86-98.

210 ANON. (1991). 'Extinct' armadillo comes out of its shell. *New Scientist*, 131 (10 August): 15.

211 ANON. (1993). New evidence confirms new Vietnam species. WWF-UK press release, 30 March; *VU VAN DUNG, MacKINNON, J. *et al* (1993). A new species of living bovid from Vietnam. *Nature*, 363 (3 June): 443-5.

212 GUILER, E. (1985). *Thylacine - the Tragedy of the Tasmanian Tiger*. Oxford University Press (Oxford); GREENWELL, J.R. (1985). Thylacine reports persist after 50 years. *ISC Newsletter*, 4 (winter): 1-5.

213 MOONEY, N. (1984). Tasmanian tiger sighting casts marsupial in new light. *Australian Natural History*, 21: 177-80.

214 ANON. (1990). Computers help to hunt the Tasmanian tiger. *New Scientist*, 125 (10 March): 24.

Section 2: THE BIRDS

1 *OGILVIE-GRANT, W.R. (1896). On a new species of bird from the island of Samar. *B.B.O.C.*, 6: 16-17.

2 *HARTERT, E. (1901). On new birds from the Solomon Islands. *Ibid.*, 12: 24-5.

3 BURTON, J.A. (Ed.) (1992). *Owls of the World* (3rd Edit.). Eurobook/Peter Lowe (London).

4 *ROTHSCHILD, W. (1903). On a new species of *Chalcurus*. *B.B.O.C.*, 13: 41-2.

5 DELACOUR, J. (1977). *The Pheasants of the World* (2nd Edit.). Spur Publications/World Pheasant Association (Hindhead).

6 JACOBSON, E. (1937). The alovot, a bird presumably living in the island of Simalur (Sumatra). *Temminckia*, 2: 159-60; SHUKER, K.P.N. (1990). A selection of mystery birds. *Avicultural Magazine*, 96 (spring): 30-40.

7 *ROTHSCHILD, W. (1903). Description of a new rail from Wake Island. *B.B.O.C.*, 13: 78.

8 GREENWAY, J.C. (1967). *Extinct and Vanishing Birds of the World* (2nd Edit.). Dover (New York); FULLER, E. (1987). *Extinct Birds*. Viking/Rainbird (London).

9 *OGILVIE-GRANT, W.R. (1906). On new species of birds from Formosa. *B.B.O.C.*, 16: 118-23.

10 FISHER, J., SIMON, N., & VINCENT, J. (1969). *The Red Book. Wildlife in Danger*. O.c.

11 *ROTHSCHILD, W. (1909). Description of a new bird from Africa. *Ibis*: 690-1.

12 COLLAR, N.J. & STUART, S.N. (1985). *Threatened Birds of Africa and Related Islands. The ICBP/IUCN Bird Red Data Book, Part 1* (3rd Edit.). ICBP & IUCN (London).

13 *STRESEMANN, E. (1912). Leucospar, gen. n. (*Sturnidae*). *B.B.O.C.*, 31: 4.

14 KING, W.B. (1981). *Endangered Birds of the World. The ICBP Bird Red Data Book*. Smithsonian Institution Press/ICBP (Washington); MOUNTFORT, G. (1988). *Rare Birds of the World*. Collins (London).

15 COCKER, M. (1990). SOS! Bali starling campaign. *World*, No. 38 (June): 8.

16 *KURODA, N. (1917). On one new genus and three new species of birds from Corea and Tsushima. *Tori*, No. 5 (Supplement): 1-6.

17 MADGE, S. & BURN, H. (1988). *Wildfowl*. Christopher Helm (London).

18 *LOWE, P. (1923). *Atlantisia*, gen. nov. *B.B.O.C.*, 43: 174-6; FRASER, M.W., DEAN, W.R.J., & BEST, I.C. (1992). Observations on the Inaccessible Island rail *Atlantisia rogersi*: the world's smallest flightless bird. *Ibid.*, 112: 12-22.

19 *DELACOUR, J. & JABOUILLE, P. (1924). New races of *Tropicoperdix, Hierophasis...Aethopyga*. *Ibid.*, 45: 28-35.

20 *CHAPIN, J. (1929). A new bowerbird of the genus *Xanthomelus*. *American Museum Novitates*, No. 367: 1-3.

21 GILLIARD, E.T. (1969). *Birds of Paradise and Bower Birds*. Weidenfeld & Nicolson (London).

22 *LÖNNBERG, E. (1931). A remarkable gull from the Gobi Desert. *Arkiv foer Zoologi*, 23B: 1-5; KITSON, A. (1980). *Larus relictus* - a review. *B.B.O.C.*, 100: 178-84.

23 *GRISCOM, L. (1929). Studies of the Dwight Collection of Guatemala birds. I. *American Museum Novitates*, No. 379: 1-13.

24 LaBASTILLE, A. (1991). *Mama Poc. The Account of a Species Extinction*. Norton (New York).

25 *BOULTON, R. (1932). A new species of tree partridge from Szechuan, China. *P.B.S.W.*, 45: 235-6; KING, B. & LI GUIYUAN. (1988). China's most endangered galliform. *Oryx*, 22 (October): 216-17.

26 HEUVELMANS, B. (1958). *On the Track of Unknown Animals*. O.c.; WENDT, H. (1959). *Out of Noah's Ark*. O.c.

27 CHAPIN, J.P. (1938). The Congo peacock. In: *Compte-Rendu du IX Congrès Ornithologique International* (Rouen). pp. 101-9.

28 *CHAPIN, J.P. (1936). A new peacock-like bird from the Belgian Congo. *R.Z.B.A.*, 29 (20 November): 1-6.

29 AUSTIN, O.L. & SINGER, J. (1961). *Birds of the World*. Hamlyn (London).

30 *MOLTONI, E. (1938). *Zavattariornis stresemanni* novum genus et nova species Corvidarum. *Ornithologische Monatsberichte*, 46: 80-3.

31 *BENSON, C.W. (1942). A new species and ten new races from southern Abyssinia. *B.B.O.C.*, 63: 8-19; BENSON, C.W. (1946). Notes on the birds of southern Abyssinia. *Ibis*, 88: 444-61.

32 RIPLEY, S.D. (1955). Anatomical notes on *Zavattariornis*. *Ibid.*, 97: 142-5; GOODWIN, D. (1976). *Crows of the World*. British Museum - Natural History (London).

33 LOWE, P.R. (1949). On the position of the genus *Zavattariornis*. *Ibis*, 91: 102-4.

34 HIDES, J.G. (1936). *Papuan Wonderland*. Blackie & Son (London).

35 *STONOR, C.R. (1939). A new species of bird of paradise of the genus *Astrapia*. *B.B.O.C.*, 59: 57-61.

36 *FOERSTER, F. & ROTHSCHILD, W. (1906). *Two New Birds of Paradise*. (Tring).

37 *ROTHSCHILD, W. & HARTERT, E. (1911). Preliminary

descriptions of some new birds from Central New Guinea. *Novitates Zoologiae*, 18: 159-60.

38 *RAND, A.L. (1940). Results of the Archbold Expeditions. No. 25. *American Museum Novitates*, No. 1072: 1-14.

39 *SALVADORI, T. (1896). Uccelli raccolti da Don Eugenio Dei Principi Ruspoli duvante l'ultimo suo viaggio nelle regioni dei Somali e dei Galla. *Annali del Museo Curico di Storia Naturale di Genova*, 16: 43-6.

40 MURPHY, R.C. & MOWBRAY, L.S. (1951). New light on the cahow, *Pterodroma cahow*. *Auk*, 68: 266-80.

41 *MURPHY, R.C. (1949). A new species of petrel from the Pacific. *Festschrift von Erwin Stresemann* (for 1949): 89-91.

42 MANN, R. (1990). Petrel explosion in South Pacific. *BBC Wildlife*, 8 (June): 360.

43 *OWEN, R. (1848). [Description of moho.] *Transactions of the Zoological Society of London*, 3: 347, 366.

44 BURTON, M. (1948). Unseen for fifty years and now rediscovered in New Zealand: the 'extinct' takahe... *Illustrated London News*, 213 (11 December): 658.

45 *MEYER, A.B. (1883). [Description of takahe.] *Abbildungen von Vogel-Skeletten*, 4-5: 34-7.

46 PHILLIPPS, W.J. (1959). The last (?) occurrence of Notornis in the North Island. *Notornis*, 8 (April): 93-4.

47 ORBELL, G.B. (1949). In search of the "extinct" takahe. *Illustrated London News*, 214 (1 January): 18-19; FALLA, R.A. (1949). *Notornis* rediscovered. *Emu*, 48: 316-22.

48 *SCHOUTEDEN, H. (1952). Un strigidé nouveau d'Afrique noire: *Phodilus prigoginei* nov. sp. *R.Z.B.A.*, 46: 423-8.

49 *SASSI, M. (1914). Einige neue Formen der innerafrikanischen Ornis aus der Kollektic Grauer. *Anzeiger - Akademie der Wissenschaften in Wien* (for 1914): 308-12; *CHAPIN, J.P. (1932). Fourteen new birds from tropical Africa. *American Museum Novitates*, No. 570: 1-18; *PRIGOGINE, A. (1960). Une nouvelle martinet du Congo. *R.Z.B.A.*, 62: 103-5; *PRIGOGINE, A. (1983). Un nouveau *Glaucidium* de l'Afrique Centrale (Aves, Strigidae). *Ibid.*, 97: 886-95.

50 OGILVIE, M. & OGILVIE, C. (1986). *Flamingos*. Alan Sutton (Gloucester).

51 WALTERS, M. (1980). *The Complete Birds of the World*. David & Charles (Newton Abbot).

52 WATSON, J. (1980). The case of the vanishing owl. *Wildlife*, 22 (April): 38-9.

53 *BENSON, C.W. (1960). The birds of the Comoro Islands: results of the British Ornithologists' Union Centenary Expedition 1958. *Ibis*, 103b (1 March): 5-106.

54 SCOTT, K. (1992). Sound out at last. *BBC Wildlife*, 10 (October): 12.

55 DAVEY, K. (1983). *Our Arid Environment*. O. c.

56 CONDON, H.T. (1962). [Rediscovery of the Eyrean grasswren.] *Emu*, 62.

57 HILL, R. (1967). *Australian Birds*. Thomas Nelson (London).

58 ANON. (1969). Not extinct after all. *Oryx*, 10 (December): 174.

59 SERVENTY, D.L. (1962). Die Wiederentdeckung von *Atrichornis clamosus* (Gould) in Westaustralien. *Journal für Ornithologie*, 103: 213-14; SERVENTY, V. (1975). The noisy

scrubbird calls again. In: *Our Magnificent Wildlife*. *Reader's Digest* (London). pp. 250-1.

60 MOREAU, R.E. (1964). The re-discovery of an African owl *Bubo vosseleri*. *B.B.O.C.*, 84: 47-52.

61 *RIPLEY, S.D. (1966). A notable owlet from Kenya. *Ibis*, 108: 136-7.

62 *HARTERT, E. (1907). On a new species of *Larvivora* from the Tsin- Ling Mountains, N. China. *B.B.O.C.*, 19: 50.

63 McCLURE, H.E. (1963). Is this one of the rarest birds in the world? *Malayan Nature Journal*, 17: 1857; McCLURE, H.E. (1964). A thrush rediscovered. *Animals*, 4 (2 June): 40.

64 COLLAR, N.J. & ANDREW, P. (1988). *Birds to Watch. The ICBP World Checklist of Threatened Birds*. ICBP (Cambridge).

65 ROBSON, C. (1989). Pheasants in Vietnam. *Garrulax*, 3: 2-3; EAMES, J.C., ROBSON, C., & WOLSTENCROFT, J.A. (1989). Pheasant surveys in Vietnam. *World Pheasant Association News*, No. 23 (February): 18-22; ANON. (1990). Pheasant rediscoveries. *Oryx*, 24 (October): 194; ANON. (1990). Making a meal of extinction. *New Scientist*, 128 (8 December): 18.

66 BARLOY, J-J. & CIVET, P. (1980). *Fabuleux Oiseaux*. Robert Laffont (Paris).

67 *WETMORE, A. (1964). A revision of the American vultures of the genus *Cathartes*. *Smithsonian Miscellaneous Collections*, 146: 1-18; MAYR, E. (1971). New species of birds described from 1956 to 1965. *Journal für Ornithologie*, 112: 302-16.

68 FALLA, R.A. (1967). An Auckland Island rail. *Notornis*, 14 (September): 107-113; WHITTEN, A. (1972). Not quite extinct. *Animals*, 14 (June): 254.

69 LOCKLEY, R. (1984). Poor old kakapo. *BBC Wildlife*, 2 (January): 8- 12; HELTON, D. (1989). May the kakapo for ever boom. *Ibid.*, 7 (October): 687.

70 *BENSON, C.W. & PENNY, M.J. (1968). A new species of warbler from the Aldabra Atoll. *B.B.O.C.*, 88: 102-8.

71 *LOWERY, G.H. & TALLMAN, D.A. (1976). A new genus and species of nine-primaried oscine of uncertain affinities from Peru. *Auk*, 93 (July): 415- 28.

72 *CASEY, T.L.C. & JACOBI, J.D. (1974). A new genus and species of bird from the island of Maui, Hawaii (Passeriformes: Drepanididae). *B.P. Bishop Museum Occasional Papers*, 24: 216-226; CASEY, T.L.C. (1975). Po'o-uli. Hawaii's newly discovered honeycreeper. *Wildlife*, 17 (June): 272-3.

73 *VIELLARD, J. (1976). Un nouveau témoin relictuel de la spéciation dans la zone mediterraneanne: *Sitta ledanti* (Aves: Sittidae). *C.R.A.S.*, 283D: 1193-5; BELLATRECHE, M. & CHALABI, B. (1990). Données nouvelles sur l'aire de distribution de la sittelle Kabyle *Sitta ledanti*. *Alauda*, 58: 95-7.

74 *O'NEILL, J.P. & GRAVES, G.R. (1977). A new genus and species of owl (Aves: Strigidae) from Peru. *Auk*, 94: 409-16; ANON. (1977). New owl in the Andes. *New Scientist*, 76 (3 November): 284.

75 *FLEMING, J.H. (1935). A new genus and species of flightless duck from Campbell Island. *Occasional Papers of the Royal Ontario Museum*, No. 1: 1- 3; ANON. (1977).

Flightless teal refound. *Oryx*, 14 (January): 22.

76 ANON. (1978). Rediscovered - after a century of 'extinction'. *Wildlife*, 20 (April): 151; MACEDO-RUIZ, H. de (1979). 'Extinct' bird found in Peru. *Oryx*, 15 (January): 33-7.

77 BOURNE, W.R.P. (1964). The relationship between the magenta petrel and the Chatham Island taiko. *Notornis*, 11: 139-44; ANON. (1978). Ornithologists identify new species of bird. *The Times* (London), 9 February.

78 SICK, H. (1979). Die Herkunft von Lear's Ara (*Anodorhynchus leari*) entdeckt! *Gefiederte Welt*, 103: 161-2; SICK, H. & TEIXEIRA, D.M. (1980). Discovery of the home of the indigo macaw in Brazil with notes on field identification of 'blue macaws'. *American Birds*, 34: 118-19, 122; LOW, R. (1984). *Endangered Parrots*. Blandford Press (Poole).

79 JUNIPER, A. (1990). A very singular bird. *BBC Wildlife*, 8 (October): 674-5.

80 *YAMASHINA, Y. & MANO, T. (1981). A new species of rail from Okinawa island. *Journal of the Yamashina Institute of Ornithology*, 13: 1-6.

81 STOKES, T. (1979). On the possible existence of the New Caledonian wood rail *Tricholimnas lafresnayanus*. *B.B.O.C.*, 99: 47-54; STOKES, T. (1980). Notes on the landbirds of New Caledonia. *Emu*, 80: 81-6.

82 *HUMPHREY, P.S. & THOMPSON, M.C. (1981). A new species of steamer duck (*Tachyeres*) from Argentina. *University of Kansas Museum of Natural History, Occasional Papers*, 95: 1-12.

83 ANON. (1981). Bird feared as extinct doing well in New Guinea. *Patriot-News* (Harrisburg - Pennsylvania), 11 November; DIAMOND, J.M. (1982). Rediscovery of the yellow-fronted gardener bowerbird. *Science*, 216 (23 April): 431-4.

84 *WESKE, J.S. & TERBORGH, J.W. (1981). *Otus marshalli*, a new species of screech-owl from Peru. *Auk*, 98: 1-7.

85 ANON. (1982). Owl rediscovered. *Wildlife*, 24 (January): 5.

86 MARTIN, B.P. (1987). *World Birds*. Guinness Books (London).

87 HENSHAW, H.W. (1902). *Birds of the Hawaiian Islands*. Thos. G. Thrum (Honolulu).

88 PYLE, R.L. & RALPH, C.J. (1982). The autumn migration. August 1- November 30, 1981. Hawaiian islands region. *American Birds*, 36: 221-3; PRATT, J.D. *et al.* (1987). *A Field Guide to the Birds of Hawaii and the Tropical Pacific*. Princeton University Press (Princeton).

89 *ROUX, J-P. et al. (1983). Un nouvel albatross *Diomedea amsterdamensis* n. sp. découvert sur l'île Amsterdam (37°50'S, 77°35'E). *Oiseau*, 53: 1-11.

90 WATLING, D. & LEWANAVANUA, R.F. (1985). A note to record the continuing survival of the Fiji (MacGillivray's) petrel *Pseudobulweria macgillivrayi*. *Ibis*, 127: 230-3; GREENWELL, J.R. (1985). Extinct landing. *ISC Newsletter*, 4 (summer): 8.

91 *FRY, C. & SMITH, D. (1985). A new swallow from the Red Sea. *Ibis*, 127: 1-6.

92 *RIDGELY, R.S. & ROBBINS, M.B. (1988). *Pyrrhura orcesi*, a new parakeet from southwestern Ecuador... *Wilson Bulletin*, 100 (June): 173-82.

93 *O'NEILL, J.P., MUNN, C.A., & FRANKE J., I. (1991). *Nannopsittaca dachilleae*, a new species of parrotlet from eastern Peru. *Auk*, 108: 225-9.

94 BHUSHAN, B. (1986). Rediscovery of the Jerdon's or double-banded courser *Cursorius bitorquatus* (Blyth). *Journal of the Bombay Natural History Society*, 83: 1-14.

95 DENNIS, J.V. (1968). Return of the ivory-bill. *Animals*, 10 (March): 492-7; ANON. (1969). An ivory-billed woodpecker. *Pursuit*, 2 (July): 49.

96 GREENWELL, J.R. (1986). Ivory-billed woodpecker found alive in Cuba. *ISC Newsletter*, 5 (summer): 3-5; KIRBY, T. (1986). The tick of a lifetime. *BBC Wildlife*, 4 (July): 342.

97 GOULD, A.B. (1986). Hot tip to a pitta. *Ibid.*, 4 (October): 502-3; COLLAR, N.J., ROUND, P.D., & WELLS, D.R. (1986). The past and future of Gurney's pitta *Pitta gurneyi*. *Forktail*, 1: 29-51.

98 ANON. (1989). [Rediscovery of Schneider's pitta.] *Oryx*, 23 (July): 167.

99 ANON. (1987). Weaver rediscovery. *Ibid.*, 21 (April): 116.

100 ANON. (1987). Rare woodpecker sighting. *Ibid.*, 21 (October): 256; ANON. (1988). Rediscovery of antwren. *Ibid.*, 22 (April): 119.

101 WOOD, G.L. (1982). *The Guinness Book of Animal Facts and Feats* (3rd Edit.). *O.c.*; RAXWORTHY, C.J. & COLSTON, P.R. (1992). Conclusive evidence for the continuing existence of the Madagascar serpent-eagle *Eutriorchus astur*. *B.B.O.C.*, 112: 108-11.

102 McRAE, J. (1989). Flying visits show up birds and scientists. *BBC Wildlife*, 7 (January): 12-13.

103 McKEAN, J. (1985). Birds of the Keep River National Park (Northern Territory), including the night parrot *Geopsittacus occidentalis*. *Australian Bird Watcher*, 11: 114-30; ANON. (1991). [Rediscovery of night parrot.] *New Scientist*, 129 (19 January): 64.

104 BURNHAM, O. (1991). Personal communication, 20 August; COLLAR, N.J. (1992). Personal communication, 12 March.

105 ANON. (1991). Cocha antshrike refound. *Oryx*, 25 (July): 133; ANON. (1992). Vanuatu still has its starling. *Ibid.*, 26 (April): 80; ANON. (1992). Rare pochard captured. *Ibid.*, 26 (April): 73. ANON. (1993). Flowerpecker rediscovery. *Ibid.*, 27 (July): 139.

106 LOW, R. (1990). *Macaws. A Complete Guide*. Merehurst (London); HOPPE, D. (1985). *The World of Macaws*. T.F.H. Publications (Neptune City); DECOTEAU, A.E. (1982). *Handbook of Macaws*. T.F.H. Publications (Neptune City).

107 SMITH, H. (1992). Who's a pretty rare Polly? *Mail on Sunday* (London), 29 March.

Section 3: THE REPTILES AND AMPHIBIANS

1 *BOULENGER, G.A. (1900). A list of the batrachians and reptiles of the Gaboon (French Congo), with descriptions of new genera and species. *P.Z.S.L.*, (8 May): 433-56.

2 PI, J.S. (1970). The hairy frog. *Animals*, 13 (October): 282-3; DURRELL, G. (1954). *The Bafut Beagles*. Rupert Hart-Davis (London).

3 *MOCQUARD, F. (1900). Diagnoses d'espèces nouvelles...de batraciens recueillis par M. Alluaud dans le sud de Madagascar. *Bulletin du Muséum d'Histoire Naturelle*: 345-8.

4 GRZIMEK, B. (Ed.) (1972-5). *Grzimek's Animal Life Encyclopedia* (13 vols). *O.c.*

5 *BOULENGER, G.A. (1903). Report on the batrachians and reptiles. *Fasciculi Malayensis Zoologiae*, 1: 131-76.

6 *SIEBENROCK, F. (1903). Ueber zwei seltene und eine neue Schildkröte des Berliner Museums. *Anzeiger der k-Akademie der Wissenschaften*, 40: 106-8.

7 *BOULENGER, G.A. (1906). Descriptions of new batrachians discovered by Mr. G.L. Bates in South Cameroon. *A.M.N.H.* (Series 7): 17: 317-23.

8 MATTHEWS, P. & McWHIRTER, N. (Eds.) (1992). *The Guinness Book of Records* 1993. *O.c.*

9 PI, J.S. (1985). Contribution to the biology of the giant frog (*Conraua goliath*, Boulenger). *Amphibia-Reptilia*, 6: 143-53.

10 *ANDERSSON, L.C. (1908). A remarkable new gecko from South Africa... *Jahrbücher des Nassauischen Vereins für Naturkunde*, 61: 299-306.

11 *BARBOUR, T. (1911). New lizards...from the Dutch East Indies, with notes on other species. *P.B.S.W.*, 24: 15-21.

12 HEUVELMANS, B. (1958). *On the Track of Unknown Animals*. *O.c.*

13 WENDT, H. (1959). *Out of Noah's Ark*. *O.c.*

14 *OUWENS, P.A. (1912). On a large Varanus species from the island of Komodo. *Bulletin du Jardin Botanique de Buitenzorg*, 2: 1-3.

15 ATTENBOROUGH, D. (1957). *Zoo Quest For a Dragon*. Lutterworth (London).

16 WOOD, G.L. (1982). *The Guinness Book of Animal Facts and Feats* (3rd Edit.). *O.c.*

17 BURDEN, W.D. (1928). *The Dragon Lizards of Komodo*. Putnam's Sons (New York).

18 KERN, J.A. (1968). Dragon lizards of Komodo. *National Geographic Magazine*, 134 (December): 872-80.

19 DIAMOND, J.M. (1987). Did Komodo dragons evolve to eat pygmy elephants? *Nature*, 326 (30 April): 832; MITCHELL, P.B. (1987). Here be Komodo dragons. *Ibid.*, 329 (10 September): 111.

20 AUFFENBERG, W. (1981). *The Behavioural Ecology of the Komodo Monitor*. University of Florida Press (Gainesville).

21 CROOK, I. & CROOK, G. (1972). New Zealand's rarest frog. *Animals*, 14 (April): 188-90.

22 *McCULLOUGH, A.R. (1919). A new discoglossid frog from New Zealand. *Transactions of the New Zealand Institute*, 51: 447-9.

23 *TURBOTT, E.G. (1942). The distribution of the genus *Leiopelma* in New Zealand with a description of a new species. *Transactions and Proceedings of the Royal Society of New Zealand*, 71: 247-53.

24 *AMARAL, A. (1921). Contribuiçao para o conhecimento dos ofidios do Brazil: Parte i Quatro noves espécies de serpentes brasileires. *Anexos das Memórias do Instituto de Butantan, Secçao de Ofiologia*, 1: 1-88; DITMARS, R.L. (1931). *Snakes of the World*. Macmillan (London).

25 MAY, J. & MARTEN, M. (1982). *The Book of Beasts*. Hamlyn (London).

26 HOGE, A.R. *et al*. (1960). Sexual abnormalities in *Bothrops insularis* (Amaral) 1921 Serpentes. *Memórias do Instituto de Butantan*, 29: 17-87.

27 OLIVER, J.A. (1958). The taipan, Australia's deadliest snake. *Animal Kingdom*, 61 (February): 23-6; COVACEVICH, J. & WOMBEY, J. (1976). Recognition of *Parademansia microlepidotus* (McCoy) (Elapidae), a dangerous Australian snake. *Proceedings of the Royal Society of Queensland*, 87: 29.

28 *AHL, E. et al. (1930). Beiträge zur Lurch- und Kriechtierfauna Kwangsi's. *S.G.N.F.B.*: 310-32.

29 *SCHMIDT, K.P. (1928). A new crocodile from New Guinea. *Field Museum Publications, Chicago* (Zoology Series 12), 247: 177-81.

30 *SCHMIDT, K.P. (1935). A new crocodile from the Philippine islands. *Chicago Field Museum of Natural History (Zoological Series)*, 20: 67-70.

31 GUGGISBERG, C.A.W. (1972). *Crocodiles*. David & Charles (Newton Abbot).

32 *LAFRENTZ, K. et al. (1930). Beiträge zur Herpetologie Mexikos. *Abhandlungen - Berlin Museum Naturwissenschaften*, 6: 91-161.

33 *DUNN, E.R. (1933). Amphibians and reptiles from El Valle de Anton, Panama. *Occasional Papers of the Boston Natural History Society*, 8: 65-79.

34 FISHER, J.; SIMON, N.; & VINCENT, J. (1969). *The Red Book. Wildlife in Danger*. *O.c.*

35 *MYERS, G.S. (1942). The black toad of Deep Springs Valley, Inyo County, California. *Occasional Papers of the Museum of Zoology, University of Michigan*, No. 460 (16 September): 1-13.

36 *CARR, A.F. (1939). *Haideotriton wallacei*, a new subterranean salamander from Georgia. *Occasional Papers of the Boston Natural History Society*, 8: 333-6.

37 *McCRADY, E. (1954). A new species of *Gyrinophilus* (Plethodontidae) from Tennessee caves. *Copeia* (for 1954): 200-6.

38 *MENDELSSOHN, H. & STEINITZ, H. (1943). A new frog from Palestine. *Ibid.*, (for 1943): 231-3.

39 DAY, D. (1989). *The Encyclopedia of Vanished Species*. *O.c.*

40 *STUART, L.C. (1941). A new species of *Xenosaurus* from Guatemala. *P.B.S.W.*, 54: 47-8; *TAYLOR, E.H. (1949). A preliminary account of the herpetology of the state of San Luis Potosi, Mexico. *Kansas University Science Bulletin*, 33: 169-215; *KING, W. & THOMPSON, F.G. (1968). A review of the American lizards of the genus *Xenosaurus* Peters. *Bulletin of the Florida State Museum (Biological Science)*, 12: 93-123.

41 *MYERS, G.S. & FUNKHAUSER, J.W. (1951). A new toad from southwestern Colombia. *Zoologica*, 36: 279-82.

42 *SIEBENROCK, F. (1901). Beschreibung einer neuen Schildkrötengattung aus der Familie *Chelydidae* von Australien: *Pseudemydora*. *Anzeiger der k-Akademie der Wissenschaften*, No. 22; WILLIAMS, E.E. (1958). Rediscovery of the Australian chelid genus *Pseudemydora* Siebenrock (Chelidae, Testudines). *Breviora*, No. 84: 1-8.

43 DUGES, A. (1888). La tortuga polifemo. *La Naturaleza*, 1: 146-7; *LEGLER, J.M. (1959). A new tortoise, genus *Gopherus* from Northcentral Mexico. *University of Kansas Publications, Museum of Natural History*, 11: 335-43.

44 GROOMBRIDGE, B. & WRIGHT, L. (1982). *The IUCN Amphibia-Reptilia Red Data Book. Part 1. Testudines. Crocodylia. Rhynchocephalia.* IUCN (Gland - Switzerland).

45 *TYLER, M.J. (1963). An account of collections of frogs from Central New Guinea. *Records of the Australian Museum*, 26: 113-30.

46 *NEILL, W.T. (1964). A new species of salamander, genus *Amphiuma*, from Florida. *Herpetologica*, 20: 62-6.

47 REYNOLDS, R.P. & MARLOW, R.W. (1982). Lonesome George, the Pinta Island tortoise. *Noticias Galapagos*, No. 37: 14-17.

48 *MYERS, C.W. *et al.* (1978). A dangerously toxic new frog (*Phyllobates*) used by Embera Indians of western Colombia with discussion of blowgun fabrication and dart poisoning. *Bulletin of the American Museum of Natural History*, 161: 309-65.

49 *LIEM, D.S. (1973). A new genus of frog of the family Leptodactylidae from SE. Queensland, Australia. *Memoirs of the Queensland Museum*, 16: 459-70; CORBEN, C.J., INGRAM, G.J., & TYLER, M.J. (1974). Gastric brooding: Unique form of parental care in an Australian frog. *Science*, 186: (6 December): 946-7; TYLER, M.J. (Ed.) (1983). *The Gastric Brooding Frog.* Croom Helm (Beckenham).

50 *MAHONEY, M., TYLER, M.J., & DAVIES, M. (1984). A new species of the genus *Rheobatrachus*... from Queensland. *Transactions of the Royal Society of Australia*, 108: 155-62; McDONALD, K.R. & TYLER, M.J. (1984). Evidence of gastric brooding in the Australian leptodactylid frog *Rheobatrachus vitellinus*. *Ibid.*, 108: 226; CHERFAS, J. (1984). Ulcer studies rescued by reincarnated frog. *BBC Wildlife*, 2 (April): 172-3.

51 INGRAM, G. (1991). The earliest record of the ?extinct platypus frog. *Memoirs of the Queensland Museum*, 30: 454.

52 AUFFENBERG, W. (1979). A monitor lizard in the Philippines. *Oryx*, 15 (January): 38-46.

53 ANON. (1979). Legless lizard rediscovered *Ibid.*, 15 (April): 126; DAVEY, K. (1983). *Our Arid Environment. O.c.*

54 ANON. (1979). New banded iguana. *Oryx*, 15 (January): 24; *GIBBONS, J.R.H. (1981). The biogeography of *Brachylophus* (Iguanidae) including the description of a new species, *B. vitiensis*, from Fiji. *Journal of Herpetology*, 15: 255-73; ANON. (1981). Fijians protect the crested iguana. *World Wildlife News*, (summer): 26-7.

55 *STORR, G.M. (1980). A new *Brachyaspis* (Serpentes: Elapidae) from Western Australia. *Record of the West Australian Museum*, 8: 397-9.

56 *SANCHIZ, F.B. & ADROVER, R. (1977). Anfibios fosiles del Pleistoceno de Mallorca. *Donana Acta Vertebratica*, 4: 5-25; MAYOL, J. & ALCOVER, J.A. (1981). Survival of *Baleaphryne* Sanchiz and Adrover, 1979 (Amphibia: Anura; Discoglossidae) on Mallorca. *Amphibia-Reptilia*, 1: 343-5.

57 *HENDERSON, J.R. (1912). Preliminary note on a new tortoise from south India. *Records of the Indian Museum*, 7:

217; GROOMBRIDGE, B., MOLL, E.O., & VIJAYA, J. (1982). Rediscovery of a rare Indian turtle. *Oryx*, 17 (July): 130-4.

58 CORKE, D. (1984). Maria Islands - home of the world's rarest snake. *World Wildlife News*, (spring): 8-9; ANON. (1986). [Couresse.] *Times Higher Education Supplement* (London), 17 August.

59 ANON. (1987). [Ensaf's giant gecko.] *New Scientist*, 113 (19 March): 19; *BALOUTCH, M. & THIREAU, M. (1986). A new species of gecko, *Eublepharis ensafi* (Sauria, Gekkonidae, Eublepharinae), from Khouzistan (southwestern Iran). *Bulletin Mensuel de la Société Linnéene de Lyon*, 55 (August): 281-8.

60 GRISMER, L.L. (1989). *Eublepharis ensafi* Baloutch and Thireau, 1986: A junior synonym of *E. angramainyu* Anderson and Leviton, 1966. *Journal of Herpetology*, 23: 94-5.

61 *BAUER, A. & RUSSELL, A.P. (1986). *Hoplodactylus delcourti* n. sp. (Reptilia: Gekkonidae), the largest known gecko. *New Zealand Journal of Zoology*, 13: 141-8; GREENWELL, J.R. (1988). World's largest gecko discovered. *ISC Newsletter*, 7 (spring): 1-4.

62 BAUER, & RUSSELL, A.P. (1987). *Hoplodactylus delcourti* (Reptilia: Gekkonidae) and the *kawekaweau* of Maori folklore. *Journal of Ethnobiology*, 7 (summer): 83-91; MAIR, W.G. (1873). Notes on Rurima rocks. *Transactions of the New Zealand Institute*, 5: 151-3; RAYNAL, M. & DETHIER, M. (1990). Lézards géants des Maoris...La vérité derrière la légende. *Bulletin Mensuel de la Société Linnéene de Lyon*, 59 (March): 85-91.

63 HELLABY, D. (1984). Giant geckos 'sighted' 20 years ago. *Dominion* (Wellington), 11 September; GRANT, P. (1990). Lizards live on radio. *BBC Wildlife*, 8 (June): 360; WHITAKER, A.H. & THOMAS, B.W. (1900). *Large Lizard Sightings in the Gisborne Region: Report on a National Museum Investigation.* National Museum of New Zealand (Wellington).

64 BURTON, J.A. (1986). Golden find on holy hill. *BBC Wildlife*, 4 (June): 262.

65 BÖHME, W. *et al.* (1987). Neuentdeckung einer Grossechse (*Sauria: Varanus*) aus der Arabischen Republik Jemen. *Herpetofauna*, 9 (February): 13-20; GREENWELL, J.R. (1989). T.V. show leads to reptile discovery. *ISC Newsletter*, 8 (winter): 5-6; *BÖHME, W. *et al.* (1989). A new monitor lizard (Reptilia: Varanidae) from Yemen, with notes on ecology, phylogeny and zoogeography. *Fauna of Saudi Arabia*, 10: 433-48.

66 ANON. (1989). Snake rediscovered on St. Vincent. *Oryx*, 23 (October): 226.

67 *BULLER, W.L. (1877). [(*Hatteria*) *Sphenodon guntheri*, sp. n., from Brothers Island, near Cook Strait, New Zealand...] *Transactions and Proceedings of the New Zealand Institute* (for 1876), 9: 317-325; BARTON, M. (1989). Brother's cousins. *BBC Wildlife*, 7 (December): 790.

68 DAUGHERTY, C.H. *et al.* (1900). Neglected taxonomy and continuing extinctions of tuatara (*Sphenodon*). *Nature*, 347 (13 September): 177-9.

69 GLEDHILL, R. (1990). Explorer may have found new

species. *The Times* (London), 8 May; RAXWORTHY, C. (1992). Personal communication, 19 July.

70 ANON. (1991). Jamaican iguana rediscovered. *Oryx*, 25 (July): 133.

71 *INGRAM, G. & CORBEN, C. (1990). *Litoria electrica*: a new treefrog from western Queensland. *Memoirs of the Queensland Museum*, 28: 475-8.

72 *MYERS, C.W., PAOLILLO O, A., & DALY, J.W. (1991). Discovery of a defensively malodorous and nocturnal frog in the family Dendrobatidae... *American Museum Novitates*, No. 3002 (7 March): 1-33; HARDING, K. (1992). The secrete weapon. *BBC Wildlife*, 10 (June): 12.

73 *BOUR, R. (1982). Contribution à la connaissance des tortues terrestres des Seychelles...et description d'une espèce nouvelle probablement originaire des îles granitiques et au bord de l'extinction. *C.R.A.S.*, 295 (20 September): 117- 22; ANON. (1983). An extinct tortoise rediscovered? *Oryx*, 17 (April): 61.

74 SWINGLAND, I. (1992). Personal communication, 11 February; ARNOLD, N. (1992). Personal communication, May.

Section 4: THE FISHES

1 *JORDAN, D.S. (1898). Description of a species of fish (*Mitsukurina owstoni*) from Japan, the type of a distinct family of lamnoid sharks. *Proceedings of the Californian Academy* (Series 3), 1: 199-201.

2 ELLIS, R. (1982). *The Book of Sharks* (Rev. Edit.). Robert Hale (London); STEEL, R. (1985). *Sharks of the World*. Blandford (Poole).

3 *REGAN, C.T. (1903). On a collection of fishes from the Azores. *A.M.N.H.* (Series 7), 12: 344-8.

4 GRZIMEK, B. (Ed.) (1972-5). *Grzimek's Animal Life Encyclopedia* (13 vols). *O.c.*

5 MARSHALL, N.B. (1961). A young *Macristium* and the ctenothrissid fishes. *B.B.M.N.H.Z.*, 7: 355-70; *BERRY, F.H. & ROBINS, C.R. (1967). *Macristiella perlucens*, a new clupeiform fish from the Gulf of Mexico. *Copeia* (for 1967): 46-50; ROSEN, D.E. (1971). The Macristidae, a ctenothrissiform family based on juvenile and larval scolepomorph fishes. *American Museum Novitates*, No. 2452: 1-22.

6 *PARR, A.E. (1933). Deep sea Berycomorphi and Percomorphi from the waters around the Bahama and Bermuda Islands. *Bulletin of the Bingham Oceanographic Collection*, 3: 1-51; JOHNSTON, R.K. (1974). A second record of *Korsogaster nanus* Parr. *Copeia* (for 1970): 758-60.

7 *TUCKER, D.W. (1954). Report on the fishes collected by S.Y. "Rosaura" in the North and Central Atlantic, 1937-38. Part I. Families Cacharhinidae, Torpedinidae, Rosauridae (Nov.)... *B.B.M.N.H.Z.*, 2: 163-214.

8 *REGAN, C.T. (1909). The Asiatic fishes of the family Anabantidae. *P.Z.S.L.*: 767-87.

9 *REGAN, C.T. (1909). Descriptions of three new freshwater fishes from South America. *A.M.N.H.*, 3: 234-5.

10 *SMITH, H.M. (1912). Two squaloid sharks of the Philippine Archipelago, with descriptions of new genera

and species. *Smithsonian Institution National Museum Proceedings*, 42: 677-85.

11 NELSON, J.S. (1984). *Fishes of the World* (2nd Edit.). John Wiley (New York); WHEELER, A. (1985). *The World Encyclopedia of Fishes*. Macdonald (London).

12 *FOWLER, H.W. & BALL, S.E. (1924). Descriptions of new fishes obtained by the Tanager Expedition of 1923 in the Pacific Islands west of Hawaii. *Proceedings of the Academy of Natural Science*, Philadelphia, 76: 269-74.

13 *PRASHAD, B. & MUCKERJI, D.D. (1929). The fish of the Indawgyi Lake and the streams of the Myitkyina District (Upper Burma). *Records - Indian Museum (Calcutta)*, 31: 161-223; BANISTER, K.E. (1970). The anatomy and taxonomy of *Indostomus paradoxus*... *B.B.M.N.H.Z.*, 19: 179-209.

14 *CHEVEY, P. (1930). Sur un nouveau silure géant du basin du Mékong *Pangasianodon gigas* nov. g., nov. sp. *Bulletin Société Zoologique de France*, 55: 536-42.

15 WOOD, G.L. (1982). *The Guinness Book of Animal Facts and Feats* (3rd Edit.). *O.c.*

16 *BEEBE, W. (1932). A new deep-sea fish. *Bulletin of the New York Zoological Survey*, 35: 175-7; BEEBE, W. (1934). *Half-Mile Down*. Harcourt, Brace (New York).

17 DEMBECK, H. (1965). *Animals and Men*. Natural History Press (Garden City).

18 *MYERS, G.S. (1936). A new characid fish of the genus *Hyphessobrycon* from the Peruvian Amazon. *P.B.S.W.*, 49: 115-16.

19 *MYERS, G.S. & WEITZMAN, S.H. (1956). Two new Brazilian fresh water fishes. *Stanford Ichthyological Bulletin*, 7: 1-4.

20 *HUBBS, C.L. & INNES, W.T. (1936). The first known blind fish of the family Characidae: a new genus from Mexico. *Occasional Papers of the Museum of Zoology, University of Michigan*, No. 342: 1-7.

21 HERISSE, J. (1965). Blind fish. *Animal Life*, No. 29 (January): 8-9; TEYKE, T. (1990). Morphological differences in neuromasts of the blind cave fish *Astyanax hubbsi* and the sighted river fish *Astyanax mexicanus*. *Brain, Behavior and Evolution*, 35: 23-30.

22 *CLARK, H.W. (1937). New fishes from the Templeton Crocker Expedition of 1934-5. *Copeia* (for 1937): 88-91.

23 COURTENAY-LATIMER, M. (1989). Reminiscences of the discovery of the coelacanth. *Cryptozoology*, 8: 1-11.

24 SMITH, J.L.B. (1956). *Old Fourlegs. The Story of the Coelacanth*. Longmans (London).

25 ANON. (1939). A coelacanth fish. *The Times* (London), 17 March.

26 *SMITH, J.L.B. (1939). A living fish of Mesozoic type. *Nature*, 143 (18 March): 455-6; SMITH, J.L.B. (1939). The living coelacanthid fish from South Africa. *Ibid.*, 143 (6 May): 748-50.

27 SMITH, J.L.B. (1941). A living coelacanthid fish from South Africa. *Transactions of the Royal Society of South Africa*, 28: 1-106.

28 *HUBBS, C.L. & BAILEY, R.M. (1947). Blind catfishes from Artesian waters of Texas. *Occasional Papers of the Museum of Zoology, University of Michigan*, No. 499 (28 April): 1-15.

29 SMITH, A. (1990). *Blind White Fish in Persia* (Rev. Edit.). Penguin (London).

30 *BRUUN, A.F. & KAISER, E.W. (1950). *Iranocypris typhlops* n. g., n. sp., the first true cave-fish from Asia. *Dan. Scient. Invest. Iran*, 4: 1-8; *TREWAS, E. (1955). A blind fish from Iraq, related to *Garra*. *A.M.N.H.* (Series 12), 8: 551-5.

31 *GREENWOOD, P.H. (1976). A new and eyeless cobitid fish (Pisces, Cypriniformes) from the Zagros Mountains. *Journal of Zoology*, 180: 129-37.

32 *CHU SINLUO & CHEN YINRUI. (1979). A new blind cobitid fish...from subterranean waters in Yunnan, China. *Acta Zoologica Sinica*, 25: 285-7.

33 *REGAN, C.T. (1925). New ceratioid fishes from the North Atlantic, the Caribbean Sea, and the Gulf of Panama collected by the 'Dana'. *A.M.N.H.* (Series 9), 15: 561-67.

34 GÜNTHER, K. & DECKERT, K. (1956). *Creatures of the Deep Sea*. George Allen & Unwin (London).

35 IDYLL, C.P. (1964). *Abyss. The Deep Sea and the Creatures That Live In It*. Constable (London).

36 *BRUUN, A. (1953). *Galatheas Jordomsejling*, Schultz Forl. (Copenhagen).

37 SMITH, J.L.B. (1953). The second coelacanth. *Nature*, 171 (17 January): 99-101; FOREY, P.L. (1988). Golden jubilee for the coelacanth *Latimeria chalumnae*. *Ibid.*, 336 (22/29 December): 727-32; GORR, T. *et al.* (1991). Close tetrapod relationships of the coelacanth *Latimeria* indicated by haemoglobin sequences. *Ibid.*, 351 (30 May). 394-7.

38 JACKMAN, B. (1972). The five figure fish. *Sunday Times* (London), 2 April.

39 FRICKE, H. (1988). Coelacanths. The fish that time forgot. *National Geographic Magazine*, 173 (June): 824-38.

40 *BERTELSEN, E. & MARSHALL, N.B. (1956). The Mirapinnati, a new order of teleost fishes. *Dana Report*, No. 42: 1-34.

41 *COHEN, D.M. (1958). *Bathylychnops exilis*, a new genus of argentinid fish from the North Pacific. *Stanford Ichthyological Bulletin*, 7: 47-52; PEARCY, W. *et al.* (1965). A 'four-eyed' fish from the deep-sea: *Bathylychnops exilis* Cohen, 1958. *Nature*, 207 (18 September): 1260-2; STEIN, D.L. & BOND, C.E. (1985). Observations on the morphology, ecology, and behaviour of *Bathylychnops exilis* Cohen. *Journal of Fish Biology*, 27: 215-28.

42 *CLAUSEN, H.S. (1959). Denticipitidae, a new family of primitive isospondylous teleosts from West African freshwater. *Videnskabelige Meddelelser fra Dansk Naturhistorisk Forening*, 121: 141-56; GREENWOOD, P.H. (1968). The osteology and relationships of the Denticipitidae, a family of clupeomorph fishes. *B.B.M.N.H.Z.*, 16: 213-73.

43 *MEES, G.F. (1961). Description of a new fish of the family Galaxiidae from Western Australia. *Journal of the Royal Society of Western Australia*, 44: 33-8; BANISTER, K.E. & CAMPBELL, A. (Eds.) (1985). *The Encyclopedia of Underwater Life*. George Allen & Unwin (London).

44 *GÉRY, J. (1964). Une nouvelle famille de poissons dulcaquicales africains: les Grasseichthyidae. *C.R.A.S.*, 259: 4805-7.

45 *ROBINS, C.R. & SYLVA, D.P. de (1965). The Kasidoroidae, a new family of mirapinniform fishes from the Western Atlantic Ocean. *Bulletin of Marine Science*, 15: 189-201.

46 *THORP, C.H. (1969). A new species of mirapinniform fish (family Kasidoroidae) from the Western Indian Ocean. *Journal of Natural History*, 3: 61-70.

47 SYLVA, D.P. de & ESCHMEYER, W.N. (1977). Systematics and biology of the deep-sea fish family Gibberichthyidae, a senior synonym of the family Kasidoroidae. *Proceedings of the California Academy of Sciences*, 41: 215-31.

48 *PARR, A.R. (1933). Deep sea Berycomorphi and Percomorphi from the waters around the Bahama and Bermuda Islands. *Bulletin of the Bingham Oceanographic Collection*, 3: 1-51.

49 HEUVELMANS, B. (1968). *In the Wake of the Sea-Serpents*. Rupert Hart-Davis (London).

50 NIELSEN, J.G. & LARSEN, V. (1970). Remarks on the identity of the giant Dana eel-larva. *Videnskabelige Meddelelser fra Dansk Naturhistorisk Forening*, 133: 149-57.

51 *CASTLE, P.H.J. (1959). A large leptocephalid (Teleostei, Apodes) from off South Westland, New Zealand. *Transactions of the Royal Society of New Zealand*, 87: 179-84.

52 SMITH, D.G. (1970). Notacanthiform leptocephali on the Western North Atlantic. *Copeia* (2 March): 1-8.

53 DUNFORD, B. (1976). Huge shark may be new species. *Star-Bulletin* (Honolulu), 17 November; TAYLOR, L.R. (1977). Megamouth, a new family of sharks. *Oceans*, 10: 46-7.

54 SOULE, G. 1981). *Mystery Monsters of the Deep*. Franklin Watts (New York).

55 *TAYLOR, L.R., COMPAGNO, L.J.V., & STRUHSAKER, P.J. (1983). Megamouth - a new species, genus, and family of lamnoid shark (*Megachasma pelagios*, family Megachasmidae) from the Hawaiian Islands. *Proceedings of the California Academy of Sciences*, 43 (6 July): 87-110.

56 GREENWELL, J.R. (1985). Second megamouth shark found. *ISC Newsletter*, 4 (spring): 5.

57 GREENWELL, J.R. (1991). Megamouth VI caught alive and studied. *Ibid.*, 10 (summer): 1-3.

58 GREENWELL, J.R. (1988). Third megamouth found. *Ibid.*, 7 (winter): 4; ANON. (1988). Megamouth leviathan. *New Scientist*, 119 (1 September): 30.

59 NAKAYA, K. (1989). Discovery of a megamouth shark from Japan. *Japanese Journal of Ichthyology*, 36: 144-6.

60 *DAILEY, M.D. & VOGELBEIN, W. (1982). Mixodigmatidae, a new family of cestode...from a deep sea, planktivorous shark. *Journal of Parasitology*, 68: 145-9.

61 *HEEMSTRA, P.C. & SMITH, M.M. (1980). Hexatrygonidae, a new family of stingrays (Myliobatiformes: Batoidea) from South Africa... *Ichthyological Bulletin of the J.L.B. Smith Institute of Ichthyology*, No. 43: 1-17; WHEELER, A. (1981). A new stingray from South Africa. *Nature*, 289 (22 January): 221.

62 STERRY, P. (1988). Up the Amazon without a puddle. *BBC Wildlife*, 6 (August): 422-5; HENDERSON, P.A. & WALKER, I. (1990). Spatial organization and population density of the fish community of the litter banks within a central Amazonian blackwater stream. *Journal of Fish Biology*, 37:

401-11; HENDERSON, P.A. (1991). Personal communication, 29 May.

63 GREENWELL, J.R. (1986). Giant fish reported in China. *ISC Newsletter*, 5 (autumn): 7-8; SHUKER, K.P.N. (1990). Lesser-known lake monsters. *Fate*, 43 (September): 75-86.

64 *MONKOLPRASIT, S. & ROBERTS, T.R. (1990). *Himantura chaophraya*, a new giant freshwater stingray from Thailand. *Japanese Journal of Ichthyology*, 37: 203-8.

65 ANON. (1991). Once-extinct fish found living in Mexico in disgusting pond. *Belleville News-Democrat* (Belleville - Illinois), 26 February.

66 TURNER, M. (1992). New fish species found in outback. *Courier-Mail* (Brisbane), 11 January.

67 ANON. (1953). Capture "living fossil" fish. *Science News Letter*, 63 (17 January): 38; LEY, W. (1959). *Exotic Zoology*. Viking Press (New York).

68 SYLVA, D. de (1966). Mystery of the silver coelacanth. *Sea Frontiers*, 12: 172-5; FRICKE, H. (1989). Quastie im Baskenland? *Tauchen*, No. 10 (October): 64-7; ANON. (1993). Des coelacanthes dans le golfe du Mexique? *Science et Vie*, No. 911, (August): 17-18; MAZIÈRE, F. (1969). *Mysteries of Easter Island*. Collins (London).

69 SCHLIEWEN, U., FRICKE, H., *et al* (1993). Which home for coelacanth? *Nature*, 363 (3 June): 405.

Section 5: THE INVERTEBRATES

1 CHUN, C. (1903). Ueber Leuchtorgane und Augen von Tiefsee-Cephalopoden. *Verhandlungen. Deutsche Zoologische Gesellschaft*, 13: 67-91.

2 DARWIN, C. (1877). *The Various Contrivances by Which Orchids are Fertilized by Insects* (2nd Edit.). John Murray (London); *ROTHSCHILD, W. & JORDAN, K. (1903). A revision of the lepidopterous family Sphingidae. *Novitates Zoologiae*, 9 (Suppl.): 1-972.

3 BURTON, M. & BURTON, R. (Eds.) (1968-70). *Purnell's Encyclopedia of Animal Life* (6 vols). *O.c.*

4 ANGIER, N. (1992). It may be elusive but moth with 15-inch tongue should be out there. *New York Times* (New York), 14 January.

5 *ROTHSCHILD, W. (1907). *Troides alexandrae* sp. n. *Novitates Zoologiae*, 14: 96.

6 WELLS, S.M., PYLE, R.M., & COLLINS, N.M. (1983). *The IUCN Invertebrate Red Data Book*. IUCN (Gland - Switzerland).

7 *AGASSIZ, A. & CLARK, H.L. (1907). Preliminary report on the Echini collected in 1906...by the U.S. Fish Commission Steamer "Albatross"... *Bulletin of the Museum of Comparative Zoology, Harvard College*, 51: 107-39.

8 *SILVESTRI, F. (1907). Descrizione di un nuovo genere di Insetti Apterigoti rapprasentante di un novo ordine. *Bollettino... Scuola Superiore di Agricoltura...*, 1: 296-311; HEALEY, I.N. (1978). Proturans. In: BEER, G. de *et al.* (Eds.), *Encyclopedia of the Animal World* (3 vols). Bay Books (London). pp. 1486-7.

9 *BRUNNER VON WATTENWYL, K. & REDTENBACHER, J. (1908). *Die Insektenfamilie der Phasmiden*. (Leipzig).

10 REITTER, E. (1961). *Beetles*. Hamlyn (London); KLAUSNITZER, B. (1983). *Beetles*. Exeter Books (New York); ZAHL, P.A. (1959). Giant insects of the Amazon. *National Geographic Magazine*, 115 (May): 632-69.

11 *HICKMAN, S.J. (1911). On *Ceratopora*, the type of a new family of Alcyonaria. *Proceedings of the Royal Society of London (B)*, 84: 195-200.

12 *HARTMAN, W.D. & GOREAU, T.F. (1970). Jamaican coralline sponges. *Symposia of the Zoological Society of London*, 25: 205-43.

13 *LISTER, J.J. (1900). *Astrosclera willeyana*, the type of a new family of sponges. *In*: WILLEY, A., *Zoological Results...* , 4: 459-82.

14 *KIRKPATRICK, R. (1908). On two new genera of recent pharetronid sponges. *A.M.N.H.*(Series 8), 2: 503-15.

15 *HARTMAN, W.D. & GOREAU, T.F. (1975). A Pacific tabulate sponge, living representative of a new order of sclerosponges. *Postilla*, No. 167: 1- 14.

16 *SILVESTRI, F. (1913). Descrizione di un nuovo ordine di Insetti. *Bollettino... Scuola Superiore di Agricoltura...*, 7: 193-209.

17 LINDENMAIER, W. (1972). *Insects of the World*. McGraw-Hill (New York).

18 GRZIMEK, B. (Ed.) (1972-5). *Grzimek's Animal Life Encyclopedia* (13 vols). *O.c.*

19 *WALKER, E.M. (1914). A new species of Orthoptera, forming a new genus and family. *Canadian Entomology*, 46: 93-8.

20 *GURNEY, A.B. (1961). Further advances in the taxonomy and distribution of the Grylloblattidae (Orthoptera). *P.B.S.W.*, 74: 67-76.

21 *CHUN, C. (1914). Cephalopoda from the "Michael Sars" North Atlantic Deep-Sea Expedition 1910. *Report of Scientific Research, "Michael Sars" North Atlantic Deep Sea Expedition*, 3: 1-28; NESIS, K.N. (1987). *Cephalopods of the World*. T.F.H. Publications (Neptune City).

22 *CHAPIN, E.A. (1921). Remarks on the genus *Hystrichopsylla* Tasch., with description of a new species. *Proceedings of the Entomological Society of Washington*, 23: 25-7; SCHEFFER, V.B. (1969). Super flea meets mountain beaver. *Natural History*, 78 (May): 54-5.

23 *KOEHLER, R. (1922). Ophiurans of the Philippine Seas and adjacent waters. *Bulletin of the U.S. National Museum*, 5: 1-486.

24 *MONOD, T. (1924). Sur un type nouveau de Malacostracé: *Thermosbaena mirabilis. Bulletin - Société Zoologique de France*, 49: 58-68.

25 SCHMIDT, W.L. (1973). *Crustaceans*. David & Charles (Newton Abbot); SCHRAM, F.R. (1986). *Crustacea*. Oxford University Press (Oxford).

26 *HAMPSON, G.F. (1926). *Descriptions of New Genera and Species of Lepidoptera...(Noctuidae) in the British Museum (Natural History)*. BMNH (London).

27 BÄNZIGER, H. (1969). The extraordinary case of the blood-sucking moth. *Animals*, 12 (July): 135-7.

28 BÄNZIGER, H. (1976). In search of the blood-sucker. *Wildlife*, 18 (August): 366-9.

29 *SPENGEL, J.W. (1932). *Planctosphaera pelagica. Scientific*

Results "Michael Sars" North Atlantic Deep-Sea Expedition, 5: 1-27; HORST, C.J. van der. (1936). Planctosphaera and tornaria. Quarterly Journal of Microscopical Science, 78: 605-13; HYMAN, L.H. (1959). The Invertebrates: Smaller Coelomate Groups. Vol. 5. McGraw-Hill (New York); DAMAS, D. & STIASNY, G. (1961). Les larves planctoniques d'entéropneustes. Mémoires de l'Académie Royale de Belgique Cl. Science, 15: 1-68.

30 HADFIELD, M.G. & YOUNG, R.E. (1983). Planctosphaera (Hemichordata: Enteropneusta) in the Pacific Ocean. Marine Biology, 73: 151-3.

31 *CALMAN, W.T. (1933). A dodecapodous pycnogonid. Proceedings of the Royal Society of London, 113B: 107-15.

32 SAVORY, T. (1964). Ricinuleids. Animals, 4 (18 August): 376-8.

33 FINNEGAN, S. (1935). Rarity of the archaic arachnids Podogona (Ricinulei). Nature, 136 (3 August): 186; SANDERSON, I.T. (1937). Animal Treasure. Macmillan (London).

34 *CLARK, J. (1934). Notes on Australian ants, with descriptions of new species and a new genus. Memoirs of the National Museum of Victoria, 8: 5- 20; TAYLOR, R.W. (1978). Nothomyrmecia macrops: A living-fossil ant rediscovered. Science, 201 (15 September): 979-85.

35 *PENNAK, R. & ZINN, D.J. (1943). Mystacocarida, a new order of Crustacea from intertidal beaches in Massachusetts and Connecticut. Smithsonian Miscellaneous Collections, 103: 1-11.

36 IVANOV, A.V. (1963). Pogonophora Academic Press (New York).

37 *CAULLERY, M. (1914). Sur les Siboglinidae, type nouveau d'invertebrés, recueilli par l'expédition du Siboga. C.R.A.S., 158: 2014; CAULLERY, M. (1948). Le genre Siboglinum Caullery 1914. In: GRASSÉ, P.P. (Ed.), Traité de Zoologie, 11: 494-9.

38 *USCHAKOW, P. (1933). Eine neue Form der Familie Sabellidae. Zoologischer Anzeiger, 104: 705.

39 JOHANSSON, K.E. (1939). Lamellisabella zachsi Uschakow, ein Vertreter einer neuen Tierklasse Pogonophora. Zoologiska Bidrag fran Uppsala, 18: 253-68.

40 BEKLEMISHEV, V.N. (1944). [Foundations of a Comparative Anatomy of Vertebrates.] (Moscow).

41 IVANOV, A.V. (1951). On the affiliation of the genus Siboglinum Caullery with the class Pogonophora. Doklady Akademii Nauk USSR, 76: 739-42.

42 BRATTSTÔM, H. & FAUCHAULD, K. (1961). Pogonophora in Norwegian inshore waters. Sarsia, 2: 51-2.

43 SOUTHWARD, E. (1961). Pogonophora. Siboga Expedition, 25(3): 1-22.

44 *WEBB, M. (1966). Lamellibrachia barhami, gen. nov., sp. nov. (Pogonophora), from the north-east Pacific. Bulletin of Marine Science, 19: 18-47; *LAND, J. van der. & NØRREVANG, A. (1975). The systematic position of Lamellibrachia (Annelida, Vestimentifera). Zeitschrift für Zoologische Systematik und Evolutionforschung, 1: 86-101.

45 *CHUN, C. (1903). Aus den Tiefen des Weltmeeres (2nd Edit.). G. Fischer Verlag (Jena).

46 PICKFORD, G.E. (1946). Vampyroteuthis infernalis Chun: an archaic dibranchiate cephalopod. I. Natural history and distribution. Dana Report, No. 29: 1-40.

47 *LEMCHE, H. (1957). A new living deep-sea mollusc of the Cambro-Devonian class Monoplacophora. Nature, 179 (23 February): 413-16; BARNES, R.D. (1987). Invertebrate Zoology (5th Edit.). W.B. Saunders (New York).

48 *CLARKE, A.M. & MENZIES, R.J. (1959). Neopilina (Vema) ewingi, a second living species of the Paleozoic class Monoplacophora. Science, 129 (17 April): 1026-7; HYMAN, L.H. (1967). The Invertebrates: Vol. VI, Mollusca I. McGraw-Hill (New York).

49 LOWENSTAM, H.A. (1978). Recovery, behaviour and evolutionary implications of live Monoplacophora. Nature, 272 (18 May): 231-2.

50 *SANDERS, H.L. (1955). The Cephalocarida, a subclass of Crustacea from Long Island Sound. Proceedings of the National Academy of Science, 41: 61-6; SANDERS, H.L. (1957). The Cephalocarida and crustacean phylogeny. Systematic Zoology, 6: 112-29.

51 *GORDON, I. (1957). On Spelaeogriphus, a new cavernicolous crustacean from South Africa. B.B.M.N.H.Z., 5: 31-47.

52 *SOUTHCOTT, R.V. (1956). Studies on Australian Cubomedusae, including a new genus and species apparently harmful to man. Australian Journal of Marine and Freshwater Research, 7: 254-80.

53 BARNES, J.H. (1966). Studies on three venomous Cubomedusae. Symposia of the Zoological Society of London, 16: 307-22.

54 WOOD, G.L. (1982). The Guinness Book of Animal Facts and Feats (3rd Edit.). O.c.

55 MARGULIS, L. & SCHWARTZ, K. (1988). Five Kingdoms (2nd Edit.). W.B. Saunders (New York).

56 AX, P. (1956). Die Gnathostomulida, eine rätselhafte Wurmgruppe aus dem Meeresand. Akademie der Wissenschaften und der Litteratur in Mainz. Abhandlungen der Mathematischen-Naturwissenschaftlichen Klasse, 8: 1-32.

57 AX, P. (1960). Die Entdeckung neue Organisationstypen im Tierreich. Die Neue Brehm Bücherei, Band 258 (Wittenberg).

58 RIEDL, R. (1969). Gnathostomulida from America. First record of the new phylum from North America. Science, 163: 445-452.

59 DANCE, S.P. (1966). Shell Collecting. Faber & Faber (London).

60 DANCE, S.P. (1969). Rare Shells. Faber & Faber (London).

61 *RUSSELL, F.S. (1959). A viviparous deep-sea jellyfish. Nature, 184 (14 November): 1527-9; RUSSELL, F.S. & REES, W.J. (1960). The viviparous scyphomedusa Stygiomedusa fabulosa Russell. Journal of the Marine Biological Association U.K., 39: 303-17.

62 REPELIN, R. (1967). Stygiomedusa fabulosa n. sp. Scyphomedusé géante des profondeurs. Cahiers. Office de la Recherche Scientifique et Technique d'Outre-Mer (Oceanographie), 5: 23-8.

63 ULRICH, W. (1972). Ein drittes Exemplar der grossen, viviparen Tiefseemeduse Stygiomedusa Russ... S.G.N.F.B., 12: 48-60.

64 CORNELIUS, P.F.S. (1972). Second occurrence of Stygiomedusa fabulosa (Scyphozoa). Journal of the Marine

Biological Association U.K., 52: 487-8.

65 HARBISON, G.R. et al. (1973). *Stygiomedusa fabulosa* from the North Atlantic: Its taxonomy, with a note on its natural history. *Ibid.*, 53: 615-17.

66 CLENCH, W.J. (1960). *Cypraea leucodon* Broderip, 1828. *Journal of the Malacological Society of Australia*, No. 4: 14-15.

67 *SOWERBY, B.B. (1903). Mollusca of South Africa. *Marine Investigations in South Africa*, 2: 213-32.

68 BARNES, J.H. (1964). Cause and effect in irukandji stingings. *Medical Journal of Australia*: 897-904.

69 *SOUTHCOTT, R.V. (1967). Revision of some Carybdeidae (Scyphozoa: Cubomedusae), including a description of the jellyfish responsible for the "irukandji syndrome". *Australian Journal of Zoology*, 15: 651-71.

70 LOVERIDGE, A. (1971). Giant earwig. *Animals*, 13 (March): 507.

71 ZEUNER, F.E. (1962). A subfossil giant dermapteran from St. Helena. *P.S.Z.L.*, 138: 651-3.

72 PEARCE-KELLY, P. (1988). Project Hercules update. *Zoo News*, (summer): 3.

73 *DOWNEY, M.E. (1972). Midgardia xandaros new genus, new species, a large brisingid starfish from the Gulf of Mexico. *P.B.S.W.*, 84 (29 February): 421-6.

74 MILLER, R.L. (1971). Observations on *Trichoplax adhaerens* Schulze 1883. *American Zoologist*, 11: 698-9; MILLER, R.L. (1971). *Trichoplax adhaerens* Schulze, 1883: return of an enigma. *Biological Bulletin*, 41: 374; IVANOV, A.V. (1973). *Trichoplax adhaerens*, a phagocytella-like animal. *Zoologischeskii Zhurnal*, 52: 1117-31; GRELL, K.G. & RUTHMANN, A. (1991). Chapter 2: Placozoa. In: HARRISON, F.W. (Ed.), *Microscopic Anatomy of Invertebrates, Volume 2: Placozoa, Porifera, Cnidaria, and Ctenophora.* Wiley-Liss, Inc (New York). pp. 13-27.

75 *GERTSCH, W.J. (1973). The cavernicolous fauna of Hawaiian lava tubes, 3. Araneae (Spiders). *Pacific Insects*, 15: 163-80.

76 ANON. (1991). Blind spiders are a sight for sore eyes. *Daily Telegraph* (London), 6 August.

77 *ROUX, M. (1976). Découverte dans le Golfe de Gascogne de deux espèces actuelles du genre cenozoïque *Conocrinus* (Echinodermes, Crinoïdes pédonculés). *C.R.A.S.*, 282D: 757-60; ANON. (1973). Des fossiles vivants dans le golfe de Gascogne. *La Recherche*, 8 (February): 161.

78 *FOREST, J. & SAINT LAURENT, M. de. (1975). Présence dans la faune actuelle d'un réprensentant du groupe mésozoïque des glyphéides: *Neoglyphea inopinata* gen. nov., sp. nov. (Crustacea Decapoda Glypheidae). *C.R.A.S.*, 281D: 155-8; SAINT LAURENT, M. de. & CHACE, F.A. (1976). *Neoglyphea inopinata*: a crustacean "living fossil" from the Philippines. *Science*, 192 (28 May): 884.

79 FOREST, J. & SAINT LAURENT, M. de. (1976). Capture aux Philippines de nouveaux exemplaires de *Neoglyphea inopinata* (Crustacea Decapoda Glypheidae). *C.R.A.S.*, 283D: 935-8; ANON. (1976). Fossil crustacean lives! *New Scientist*, 70 (27 May): 466.

80 *CRESSEY, R.F. (1976). *Nicothoe tumulosa*, a new siphonostome copepod parasite on the unique decapod

Neoglyphea inopinata... P.B.S.W., 89: 119-26.

81 ANON. (1978). Curious Australian cricket founds new family. *New Scientist*, 79 (7 September): 686; *RENTZ, D.C.F. (1980). A new family of ensiferous orthoptera from the coastal sands of southeast Queensland. *Memoirs of the Queensland Museum*, 20: 49-63.

82 CORLISS, J.B. & BALLARD, R.D. (1977). Oases of life in the cold abyss. *National Geographic Magazine*, 152 (October): 440-53; GROSVENOR, G.M. (1979). Strange world without sun. *Ibid.*, 156 (November): 680-8; BALLARD, R.D. & GRASSLE, J.F. (1979). Return to oases of the deep. *Ibid.*, 156 (November): 689-705; LIPSCOMB, J. (Producer) (1980). *Dive to the Edge of Creation* [a National Geographic TV documentary first screened (in U.S.A.) on 7 January 1980]. Stylus Video (London); HESSLER, R. (1981). Oasis under the sea - where sulphur is the staff of life. *New Scientist*, 81 (10 December): 741-7; BRIGHT, M. (1984). *Unlocking Nature's Secrets*. BBC (London); HESSLER, R. *et al.* (1988). Patterns on the ocean floor. *New Scientist*, 117 (24 March): 47-51.

83 *WILLIAMS, A.B. (1980). A new crab family from the vicinity of submarine thermal vents on the Galapagos Rift... *P.B.S.W.*, 93: 943-72.

84 *BOSS, K.J. & TURNER, R.D. (1980). The giant white clam from the Galapagos Rift, *Calyptogena magnifica* species novum. *Malacologia*, 20: 161-94.

85 *PUGH, P.R. (1983). Benthic siphonophores: a review of the family Rhodaliidae... *Philosophical Transactions of the Royal Society (B)*, 301: 165- 300.

86 *WOODWICK, K.H. & SENSENBAUGH, T. (1985). *Saxipendium coronatum*, new genus, new species (Hemichordata: Enteropneusta): The unusual spaghetti worms of the Galapagos rift hydrothermal vents. *P.B.S.W.*, 98: 351-65.

87 *JONES, M.L. (1980). *Riftia pachyptila*, new genus, new species, the vestimentiferan worm from the Galapagos Rift geothermal vents (Pogonophora). *Ibid.*, 93: 1295-1313; JONES, M.L. (1981). *Riftia pachyptila* Jones: Observations on the vestimentiferan worm from the Galapagos rift. *Science*, 213 (17 July): 333-6; JONES, M.L. (1984). The giant tube worms. *Oceanus*, 27: 47-52.

88 JONES, M.L. (1985). On the Vestimentifera, new phylum: six new species, and other taxa, from hydrothermal vents and elsewhere. *Bulletin of the Biological Society of Washington*, No. 6: 117-58.

89 *NEWMAN, W.A. & HESSLER, R. (1989). A new abyssal hydrothermal verrucomorphan (Cirripedia; Sessilia): The most primitive living sessile barnacle. *Transactions of the San Diego Society of Natural History*, 21 (15 February): 259-73; *SCHEIN-FATTON, E. (1985). Découverte sur la ride du Pacifique oriental à 13.N d'un Pectinidae (Bivalvia, Pteromorphia) d'affinités paléozoïques. *C.R.A.S.*, 301: 491-6.

90 *ROSENBLATT, R.H. & COHEN, D.M. (1986). Fishes living in deepsea thermal vents in the tropical eastern Pacific, with descriptions of a new genus and two new species of eelpouts (Zoarcidae). *Transactions of the San Diego Society of Natural History*, 21 (24 February): 71-9; *COHEN, D.M. *et*

al. (1990). Biology and description of a bythitid fish from deep-sea thermal vents in the tropical eastern Pacific. *Deep-Sea Research*, 37 (February): 267-83.

91 MacQUITTY, M. (1988). Sulphur on the menu cuisine for the hairy snail. *New Scientist*, 117 (24 March): 50.

92 SMITH, C.R. *et al.* (1989). Vent fauna on whale remains. *Nature*, 341 (7 September): 27-8.

93 *VACELET, J. (1977). Une nouvelle relique du secondaire: un réprésentant actuel des éponges fossiles sphinctozoaires. *C.R.A.S.*, 285D: 509-11; ANON. (1978). Une fossile vivant résout un problème de systématique. *La Recherche*, No. 85 (January): 46.

94 PICKETT, J. (1982). *Vaceletia progenitor*, the first Tertiary sphinctozoan (Porifera). *Alcheringa*, 6: 241-7; BASILE, L.L. *et al.* (1984). Sclerosponges, pharetronids, and sphinctozoans (relict cryptic hard-bodied Porifera) in the modern reefs of Enewetak Atoll. *Journal of Paleontology*, 58: 636-56.

95 *VACELET, J. (1979). Une éponge tétractinellide nouvelle des grottes sous marines de la Jamaïque, associées à des membranes étrangrés. *Bulletin. Museum Nationale d'Histoire Naturelle (Zool. Biol. Ecol. Anim.)*, No. 1: 33-9.

96 *YAGER, J. (1981). Remipedia, a new class of crustacean from a marine cave in the Bahamas. *Journal of Crustacean Biology*, 1: 328-33; GORDON, G. (1985). A dive into the Ice Age. *Daily Mail* (London), 24 October.

97 *VALDECASAS, A.G. (1984). Morlockiidae new family of Remipedia (Crustacea) from Lanzarote (Canary Islands). *Eos*, 60: 329-33; PALMER, R. (1986). Ecology beneath the Bahama Banks. *New Scientist*, 110 (8 May): 44-8; PALMER, R. (1987). In the land of the lusca. *Natural History*, 96 (January): 42-7.

98 MITCHELL, A.W. (1981). *Operation Drake - Voyage of Discovery*. Severn House (London).

99 *RUSSELL, A.B. B. (1981). A spectacular new *Idea* from Celebes (Lepidoptera, Danaidae). *Systematic Entomology*, 6: 225-8.

100 MESSER, A.C. (1984). *Chalicodoma pluto*: the world's largest bee rediscovered living communally in termite nests (Hymenoptera: Megachilidae). *Journal of the Kansas Entomological Society*, 57: 165-8; SHUKER, K.P.N. (1991). *Extraordinary Animals Worldwide*. O.c.

101 *BECKER, K-H. (1975). *Basipodella harpacticola* n. gen., n. sp. *Helgoländer Wissenschaftliche Meeresunters*, 27: 96-100; *BRADFORD, J.M. & HEWITT, G.C. (1980). A new maxillopodan crustacean parasitic on a myodocopid ostracod. *Crustaceana*, 38: 67-72; BOXSHALL, G.A. & LINCOLN, R.J. (1983). Tantulocarida, a new class of Crustacea ectoparasitic on other crustaceans. *Journal of Crustacean Biology*, 3: 1-16.

102 LEWIN, R. (1983). New phylum discovered, named. *Science*, 222 (14 October): 149; *KRISTENSEN, R.M. (1983). Loricifera, a new phylum with Aschelminthes characters from the meiobenthos. *Zeitschrift für Zoologische Systematik*

und Evolutionsforschung, 21: 163- 80; KRISTENSEN, R.M. (1991). Chapter 9: Loricifera. In: HARRISON, F.W. & RUPPERT, E.E. (Eds.), *Microscopic Anatomy of Invertebrates, Volume 4: Aschelminthes*. Wiley-Liss, Inc (New York). pp. 351-75.

103 *HIGGINS, R.P. & KRISTENSEN, R.M. (1986). New Loricifera from southeastern United States coastal waters. *Smithsonian Contributions to Zoology*, No. 438: 1-70.

104 *KRISTENSEN, R.M. & SHIRAYAMA, Y. (1988). *Pliciloricus hadalis* (Pliciloricidae), a new loriciferan species collected from the Izu-Ogasawara Trench, Western Pacific. *Zoological Science*, 5: 875-881; KRISTENSEN, R.M. (1992). Personal communication, 11 February.

105 *BAKER, A.N., ROWE, F.W.E., & CLARK, H.E.S. (1986). A new class of Echinodermata from New Zealand. *Nature*, 321 (26 June): 862-4; ANON. (1986). Sea daisy, a star in a class of its own. *New Scientist*, 111 (3 July): 30.

106 *ROWE, F.W.E., BAKER, A.N., & CLARK, H.E.S. (1988). The morphology, development and taxonomic status of *Xyloplax...*, with the description of a new species. *Proceedings of the Royal Society of London (B)*, 233: 431-459.

107 *ROUX, M. (1985). Découverte d'un représentant actuel des crinoïdes pédonculés paléozoïques Inadunata (Echinodermes) dans l'étage bathyal de l'Ile de la Reunion (Océan Indien). *C.R.A.S.*, 301: 503-6.

108 ANON. (1988). A singular fly. *New Scientist*, 117 (14 January): 30.

109 ANON. (1990). She's got ants in her plants *New York Post* (New York), 16 October.

110 ANON. (1991). Bulldozers millipeded. *Express & Star* (Wolverhampton), 29 May.

111 DOUBLE, T. & DOUBLE, A. (1992). Here be giants. *BBC Wildlife*, 10 (May): 34-40; COLLARD, M. & YONOW, N. (1992). Looks familiar? *Ibid.*, 10 (November): 89.

112 ANON. (1961). New "living fossil" discovered. *The Times* (London), 21 December.

113 FELL, H.B. (1962). A surviving somasteroid from the eastern Pacific Ocean. *Science*, 136 (18 May): 633-6; FELL, H.B. (1962). A living somasteroid *Platasterias latiradiata* Gray. *University of Kansas Palaeontological Contributions; Echinodermata*, 6: 1-16; FELL, H.B. (1962). A living somasteroid. *Zoologicheskii Zhurnal*, 41: 1353-66.

114 MADSEN, F.J. (1966). The recent sea-star *Platasterias* and the fossil Somasteroidea. *Nature*, 209 (26 March): 1367.

115 BLAKE, D.B. (1967). Skeletal elements in asteroids. *Progr. Ann. Mtgs. of the Geological Society of America* (for 1967): 15-16; BLAKE, D.B. (1972). Sea star *Platasterias*: ossicle morphology and taxonomic position. *Science*, 176 (3 February): 306-7; BLAKE, D.B. (1972). Ossicle morphology of some recent asteroids and description of some west American fossil asteroids. *University of California Publications in Geological Science*, 104: 1-59.

INDEX